Models for the Perception of Speech and Visual Form

Models for the Perception of Speech and Visual Form

Proceedings of a Symposium

*Sponsored by the Data Sciences Laboratory
Air Force Cambridge Research Laboratories
Boston, Massachusetts
November 11–14, 1964*

Weiant Wathen-Dunn, Editor

The M.I.T. Press
Massachusetts Institute of Technology
Cambridge, Massachusetts, and London, England

PREFACE

Early in 1964 the Data Sciences Laboratory of the Air Force
Cambridge Research Laboratories undertook to sponsor a symposium
on models for the perception of speech and visual form. This decision
was based on the following premises: (a) models of these processes
were either very primitive or else totally lacking and (b) discussing
models in two different perceptual areas might not only clarify and re-
fine viable models but might also provide a cross-fertilization which
could yield insights not otherwise obtainable. The invitation to contribute papers stated the problem by saying: "In recent years considerable data regarding perceptual processes in speech and vision have
been gathered. Some of these conflict directly with established theories, while others are unrelated to any long-range central viewpoint.
It would appear that important principles of organization, needed in
the conceptual foundation of perception, are missing and that these
may be found in complex structured stimuli such as speech and visual
form. It seems appropriate, therefore, to focus new and old data
into meaningful models of the perceptual process so as to aid in re-
evaluating our present conceptual insights and in exploring new ones."

Accordingly, the announcement of the symposium outlined its
objectives as follows:

1. To state in an explicit form the prevailing models for the perception of speech and visual form and to encourage the submission
   of new models.
2. To examine the extent to which the hypotheses generated by
   these models are supported or refuted by experimental data in
   order to coalesce them into larger integrated viewpoints or force
   the confrontation of unreconcilable views.
3. To identify the areas in which our present models fail so that a
   more coherent set of experiments with long-range meaning can be
   undertaken.

Emphasis was to be placed on the thorough analysis of problems inherent in current models for the perception of structured stimuli, and
consequently models and experiments dealing with simple stimuli were
not of direct interest, except insofar as they illuminated the higher
problem.

In order to achieve these goals, a number of leading scientists, from both the United States and abroad, were invited to present papers, and an open invitation was extended to other authors to contribute papers. From those accepted in the latter category, most were selected for oral presentation, but some few were included in the program only for discussion. The proceedings contain all papers with the exception of six that have been withdrawn for one reason or another.

The symposium began with four sessions of invited papers which provided a framework for the contributed papers that followed. The latter were organized into six sessions, three on vision and three on speech. The format of the proceedings follows this session grouping with one exception, namely, that Professor Jakobson's banquet address, which deals with important differences between aural and visual perception, has been given the lead position. Interspersed at appropriate points are summary discussions and remarks voluntarily submitted by session chairmen. The size of the proceedings, quite aside from the difficulty of transcribing, editing, and condensing the huge amount of discussion material, has precluded the addition of other discussion summaries.

Credit for the conception of the symposium must be given to Mr. Harry Blum, and he, Dr. Philip Lieberman, Mr. John Mott-Smith, and myself formed the organizing committee. Our work was lightened to a very considerable degree by the able assistance of Mr. George Cushman, of Wentworth Institute, who acted as co-ordinator, and I wish to take this opportunity to express our appreciation of his efforts. To the authors, who made the core contribution, we are deeply indebted, and to them I would add my appreciation of their patience with the editorial process. Lastly, my secretary, Mrs. Jean Young, did yeoman service, and she was assisted in part by Mrs. Linda Wojas. To both I extend my thanks.

Bedford, Massachusetts   Weiant Wathen-Dunn
April 12, 1967

CONTENTS

BANQUET ADDRESS

ABOUT THE RELATION BETWEEN VISUAL AND AUDITORY SIGNS

Roman Jakobson
Samuel Hazzard Cross Professor
of Slavic Languages and Literature
and General Linguistics
Harvard University
Cambridge, Massachusetts, and
Institute Professor
Massachusetts Institute of Technology
Cambridge, Massachusetts

During these two days we have had some extremely interesting papers and discussions, and several points which were emphasized seem to me particularly important and productive. It was emphasized repeatedly in today's discussions that there is a great difference between the perception of speech sounds and of sounds which are not identified by the listener as constituents of speech, even though they be externally similar or even identical. The discussion of today about the relevance of a phonological, categorial approach to the perceptual discrimination of vowels and consonants has been indeed illuminating.

Another question, raised in the very interesting paper by Webster and Chaney, is that of the different reaction of the ears, and more exactly of the brain, to speech sounds as compared to all other sound stimuli. The authors of this paper state — and in so doing they are developing some very stimulating views expressed by Kimura in the Canadian Journal of Psychology three years ago — that the right ear has a more exact discrimination of speech sounds and the left ear a more exact discrimination of other sound stimuli. It becomes ever clearer that the problem of belonging to a system of signs, to a semiotic system, as Charles Peirce would say, is a very pertinent criterion. Today we heard a further discussion about different systems of signs and in particular about the extent to which problems of speech and music are similar, as well as about the divergencies between the two systems. It is impossible to analyze exhaustively a single system of signs without constant reference to the general problems of semiotics, and in the context of this new and rapidly developing science the

1

question of the relation between the various systems of signs is one of the fundamental and burning questions. We face the task of constructing an over-all model of sign production and sign perception and separate models for different types of signs.

To the same cycle of problems belongs the question of the relation between the perception of audible speech and reading, approached today in the brilliant paper by Liberman and Cooper and their co-workers. It was said — and this seems to me a very stimulating observation — that, if you were to present letters one at a time with the same speed as we hear the corresponding speech sounds, it would be quite impossible to perceive the message.

Now what I would like to touch upon is the structural and perceptual relation between visual and auditory signs. I returned to this problem after reading newspaper reports about Krushchev's recent declarations on modern art, his sharp and dictatorial protests against nonrepresentational, abstract painting. It was clear that he has really a violent aversion to this kind of picture, and the question inevitably arises in our mind, why do we meet so often this outraged reaction, this superstitious fear and inability to grasp and accept nonobjective painting? An official handbook has summarized this repugnant attitude: "We do not like abstract art for the simple reason that it takes us away from reality, from labor and beauty, from joy and sorrow, from the very throb of life into an illusory and spectral world, into the futility of the so-called self-expression." But why does the same tirade lose all sense when applied to musical art? How rarely in the entire history of the world has one angrily asked, "What facet of reality does Mozart's sonata such and such represent?" The question of mimesis, of imitation, of objective representation seems, however, to be natural and even compulsory for the great majority of human beings as soon as we enter into the field of painting or sculpture.

A young specialist in linguistics and poetics, M. Aronson, worked at the end of the 1920's in the Leningrad radio among those experimenters who tried to diversify and enrich the broadcast programs by complementing the words and music of the radio dramas with reproductions of natural sounds and diverse noises. These attempts proved, however, to be totally vain. People were not capable of discriminating various noises and assigning them to their sources. It remained unclear to the listeners whether they heard thunder, trains, or breakers. They knew only that it was noise and nothing

more. The conclusion drawn in Aronson's study from these very
interesting data was, however, inaccurate. He supposed that vision
plays a much greater role than audition. It is enough to recollect that
radio dealt with mere audition of speech and music. Thus the essence
of the problem lies not in degree of importance but in difference of
function between vision and audition.

I have mentioned one puzzling question, namely, why abstract painting
surprises and sometimes even provokes prohibitive measures and
obstructions against it. Another question which likewise cannot be
answered immediately but asks for a solution is that of the universality
of audible speech. All human beings except those with pathological
conditions speak. Speechlessness is a pathological state. On the other
hand, illiteracy is a widespread, in some ethnic groups even general,
social condition. Why is it that visual word messages are, so to say,
a superstructure, a "parasitic formation" upon the universal phonome-
non of oral speech? Why are all other forms of human communication
only secondary and optional? Either they are, as in the case of
writing, mere substitutes for oral communication or they are only
concomitant, subsidiary vehicles, like, for example, gestures or facial
expressions. These facts demand elucidation.

Then let us try to answer the questions raised. It is clear that
all the phonemena we have mentioned occur in both space and time. In
visual signs it is the spatial dimension which takes priority, whereas
the temporal dimension takes priority in auditory signs. Auditory
signs act in a time sequence. Every complex visual sign, for example,
every painting, presents a simultaneity of various components, whereas
the sequence appears to be the fundamental axis of speech. Of course,
one should not draw the frequently suggested but oversimplified conclusion that speech displays a purely linear character. It cannot be
considered a unidimensional chain in time. It is a successive chain
of phonemes, but phonemes are simultaneous bundles of concurrent
distinctive features, and language exhibits various other structural
properties which prohibit regarding speech as mere linearity. Nonetheless, the predominantly sequential character of speech is beyond
doubt, and this primacy of successivity must be analyzed.

What is the substantial difference between spatial and auditory
signs? We observe a strong and conspicuous tendency to reify visual
signs, to connect them with objects, to ascribe mimesis to such signs,
and to view them as elements of an "imitative art." Painters of all

times have splashed blotches or spots of ink or color and tried to
visualize them as faces, landscapes, or still life. How often broken
twigs, furrows in stones or other natural bends, crooks and patches
are taken for effigies of things or beings. This universal, innate
tendency explains why a naive spectator when looking at an abstract
painting subconsciously assumes it to be a kind of puzzle picture, and
then loses his temper when unable to discover what this work "is
supposed to represent" and concludes that "this is just a mess!"

What, on the other hand, is typical for sequential signs, especially
verbal and musical? They show us two essential features. First, both
music and language present a consistently hierarchized structure, and,
second, musical as well as verbal signs are resolvable into ultimate,
discrete, rigorously patterned components which, as such, have no
existence in nature but are built ad hoc. This is precisely the case
with the distinctive features in language, and it is likewise exact about
tones as members within any type of musical scale. The same idea was
clearly formulated by Thomas of Aquinas. When defining the characteristic traits presented by the phonic components of language, he stated
that they are significantia artificialiter. They act as significant units
in an artificial arrangement. Such a system of compulsory hierarchical structures does not exist in painting. There is no obligatory
superposition or stratification, as we find in language and in music.
When discussing problems of visual perception at a scientific meeting,
Walter Rosenblith, well acquainted with the linguistic investigation of
distinctive features, aptly observed: "What a pity that in our visual
experience we find no correlates to distinctive features. How much
easier it would be to dissect and describe the visual percepts." It is
not a fortuitous difference but a cardinal and specific property inherent in the temporal, sequential, auditory system of signs.

Cinema offers a very fruitful field for semiotic studies, and some
initial steps in this direction have been made by international research workers. In connection with our discussion of spatial and
temporal signs may I share with you my personal experience with
abstract films. Although I have belonged to the ardent adherents of
abstract painting from the time of the first Russian steps in this
direction (Kandinsky, Larionov, Malevich, Bajdin, Romanovich,
Rodchenko), I feel completely exhausted after 5 or 10 minutes of
watching such films, and I have heard similar testimonies from other
people. Yesterday Professor MacKay had a good expression — "visual

noise" — which renders perfectly my response to these stimuli. The
chasm between the intention of the artist and the reaction of an un-
sophisticated decoder to a nonrepresentational visual sequence is a
noteworthy psychological fact.

If we continue to discuss problems of simultaneity and successivity
we must refer to the instructive views on this matter expressed in the
modern literature about aphasia. Especially the Moscow expert in
language pathology, A. R. Luria, has insisted on the substantial difference between two basic types of disturbances which I have tentatively
termed "the simultaneity disorder" and "the successivity disorder."
Luria convincingly demonstrates the distinctive characteristics in the
topography of the cortex which correspond to these two kinds of
impairments. Together with the successivity disorders, simultaneity
disturbances also play a considerable role in the pathology of language.
When we say "simultaneity" we mean not only deficits in the copresence
of such concurrent components as the distinctive features bundled into
phonemes but also all the impairments affecting the so-called
paradigmatic axis of language, impairments in the choice of grammatical
or lexical forms which can occupy the same place in the sequence and
thus constitute a commutative set within our verbal pattern. The
whole field of grammatical transformations evidently belongs to the
same area.

In his new book on the highest functions of the brain, Luria shows
that it was wrong to connect all the disturbances in the visual perception of such objects as paintings solely with the so-called visual
centers in the back of the cortex. He discloses that its frontal premotor part is also responsible for certain distortions, and he has
analyzed the essence of these impairments. In our perception of a
painting, we first deploy step-by-step efforts to go over from certain
selected details from parts to the whole, and for the contemplator of
a painting the integration follows as a further phase, as a goal. Luria
observed that certain premotor impairments affect precisely this
process of passing from one stage to another of such preliminary perception, and he refers to I. M. Sechenov's pioneering studies of the
1870's. In connection with speech and similar activities, this great
neurologist and psychologist outlined two distinct and cardinal types
of synthesis, one sequential and the other simultaneous.

The problem of the two types of synthesis plays a very great role
in linguistics. Today we have heard allusions to this dyad in the

various papers about models of speech perception. The interrelation
of successivity and simultaneity in speech and language has been
vividly discussed by linguists of our century, but certain paramount
aspects of the same problem had been sagaciously approached already in the old Indic science of language. In the fifth century,
Bhartṛhari, the great master of Indic linguistic theory, distinguished
three stages in the speech event. The first is the conceptualization by
the speaker which implies no time sequence; the message as a whole
may be simultaneously present in the mind of the speaker. What
follows is the performance itself which, according to this scholar's
treatise, has two faces — production and audition. Both of these
activities are naturally sequential. This stage yields to the third one,
namely, the stage of comprehension, where the sequence appears to
be changed into a concurrence. The sequence must be seized and
experienced by the interpreter at one and the same time. This conception is akin to the modern psychological problem of "immediate
memory" astutely examined by George Miller, or in other terms the
"short-rate memory," as we heard it outlined today in this symposium.
At this stage the whole sequence, whether it be a word, a sentence,
or a group of sentences, emerges as a simultaneously present totality
which is decoded by means of "simultaneous synthesis."

These vital questions reappear again and again in world literature,
and similar principles have been applied repeatedly to verbal art. Two
centuries ago a fascinating discussion took place in Germany, where
the famous master and theoretician of literature, G. E. Lessing, tried
to fix a rigid boundary between verbal art and the fine arts. He taught
that painting is an art based on simultaneity (räumliches Nebenei-
nander), whereas poetry operates solely with time sequence (zeitliches
Nacheinander). Another remarkable German writer and thinker, J. G.
Herder, answered Lessing by saying that the idea of a mere literary
succession is fictitious, and an art based on mere Zeitfolge is
impossible. In order to comprehend and evaluate a poetic work, we
must have, according to Herder, a synchronic insight into its whole,
and he gives the Greek name energeia to such a simultaneous synthesis
which enables us to comprehend the entirety of a verbal flow.

It is clear that between visual, spatial signs, particularly painting,
and on the other hand verbal art and music, which deal primarily with
time, there are not only a number of significant differences but also
many common traits. Both these divergences and convergences must

be carefully taken into account, and whatever the import of the
simultaneous synthesis, nonetheless there exists a profound dissimilarity
between the spatial and temporal arts and between spatial and temporal
systems of signs in general. When the observer arrives at the
simultaneous synthesis of a contemplated painting, the painting as a
whole remains before his eyes, it is still present; but when the listener
reaches a synthesis of what he has heard, the phonemes have in fact
already vanished. They survive as mere reminiscences, and this
creates an essential difference between the two types of perception and
percepts.

At the end I would like to add that my remarks should by no means
be interpreted as a common front with the antagonists of abstract art.
The fact that it is a superstructure and does not follow the line of
least resistance with regard to our perceptual habits stands in no
contradiction to the legitimate and autonomous existence of nonrepresentational painting or sculpture and of representational bents
in music. The transmutative character of the abstract art which
forcefully infringes the border between music and fine arts cannot be
branded as decadent, perverse, or degenerate (entartet). From the
fact that writing is socially and territorially limited, whereas spoken
language is universal, one would hardly draw the conclusion that
literacy is harmful or futile. The same principle is to be applied to
nonobjective art. It is clear that both of these designs — written
language and abstract painting — are superstructures, secondary
phenomena, epiphenomena; but it is not an argument against their
prosperous development and diffusion, even if at some loss to oral
communication and tradition or to the strictly figurative arts.

Invited Papers

INVITED PAPERS I

The Perception Problem

Chairman: Weiant Wathen-Dunn
Data Sciences Laboratory
Air Force Cambridge Research Laboratories
Bedford, Massachusetts

DYNAMIC MODELING

J. C. R. Licklider
Thomas J. Watson Research Center
International Business Machines Corporation
Yorktown, New York

Introduction

It seems appropriate, at the beginning of this symposium, to discuss dynamic modeling even though dynamic modeling is only now in the process of being fashioned into a tool that can be used in research on the perception of speech and visual form. It seems appropriate because the field of research with which the symposium is concerned is in such a dynamic phase, moving forward rapidly with vigor and, indeed, force. As will be evident, I feel sure that dynamic modeling will play an important role, during the coming years, in research on speech and visual form. My purpose, therefore, is to describe the new tool and the way in which it appears to be developing and to relate the new tool to problems of perception.

By "dynamic modeling" I am referring to a meld of mathematical modeling, computer-program simulation, dynamic display, and on-line interaction between human modelers and computers. Mathematical models have been used in research and development for many years. Analogue computer models, which often combine mathematical models with dynamic display and man-machine interaction, are old, familiar friends. What is new — new within the last five or six years and only now coming into truly practical application — is the combining of dynamic display and close man-machine interaction with digital com-

11

puting and digital-computer program simulation. Whereas dynamic modeling with analogue computers was restricted mainly to processes describable by integrodifferential equations, dynamic modeling with the aid of digital computers has an almost unlimited domain.

For the study of perception, dynamic modeling with the aid of digital computers is particularly significant because the method is the only one that is capable of handling problems and processes of the complexity that is encountered at every hand in the psychophysiology of cognition. I do not say that dynamic modeling makes it easy to handle complexity of that order. I say only that it makes it possible. As I shall try to elucidate, dynamic modeling in the context of on-line interactive computing offers two great promises. The first of these is a method and means of feeling one's way into and through a complex problem or process, of making trials easy and errors tolerable, of accumulating gains both large and small until a successful representation of even a very complicated, dynamic situation has been achieved. The other great promise is to facilitate cooperation among members of a research community — even though the community may be geographically dispersed — and to provide a way for their individual contributions to interact rapidly and precisely with one another and, insofar as they are compatible, to fit together into a coherent, over-all theory. Those promises are rather far from being realized — the second one, particularly — but I think they are worth discussing at this time. Without them, the prospect of making coherent sense of the perception of speech and visual form might seem discouragingly bleak.

Inadequacy of Static Models

My own interest in digital computers and dynamic modeling stemmed directly from frustration with the tools and techniques that were available a few years ago to facilitate thinking about problems of auditory perception. It will help me explain my enthusiasm for dynamic modeling if you will let me try to recall some of the problems and some of the difficulties that arose in thinking about auditory perception.

Perhaps seven years ago, we were trying to understand — as, indeed, we still are now, but we are farther along the road — how speech is generated, how it is perceived, and how the circuit through generation and perception is closed. We thought we understood fairly well how the outer ear and middle ear work. We thought we understood their functioning qualitatively, though perhaps without great quantitative precision. Actually, except for a few specialists among us, we thought that not very much of great significance to hearing and understanding speech happens to the speech signal as it passes through the outer ear and the middle ear; merely a little frequency distortion and, when the signal is too strong, a nonlinear clamping down by the muscles of the middle ear. Thus we had in our minds a picture of the speech waveform as it passed through a few small spaces and structures and as it was transformed from acoustical to mechanical vibration and flowed into the complex, dynamic, but familiar structure of the inner ear.

From Békésy (1956, 1958; Békésy and Rosenblith, 1951), Zwislocki (1946), Fletcher (1953), and a few others, we had derived dynamic images of the cochlear canals, the cochlear partition, the Organs of Corti, and so on. More importantly, we had, in varying degrees, an understanding of the transformations carried out by the cochlear dynamics. We thought of the input to the cochlea as a time function (pressure varying with time) and of the cochlear output as a manifold of activity (displacement varying with distance along the cochlear partition from base to apex, as well as with time). Our thinking about the dynamics of the cochlea took place partly in moving images of traveling waves, partly in terms of stationary graphs, and partly in mathematical equations. In my own assessment of the situation, Flanagan's (1960, 1962) computer-program simulation of the cochlear process was quite important because, even though not connected to a dynamic display, it did serve as a bridge between an essentially mathematical description of the structure and a graphical, visible expression of behavior. Békésy's (1956, 1958) demonstration models were important to me, also, because they provided a bridge, fairly clear even though implicit, to a mathematical description of structure and, at the same time, a bridge of very clear dynamic display to visual perception.

Trying to move on from the cochlea into the neural processes under-lying perception, we ran into difficulties almost immediately. It was possible to add to our pictures of the cochlear process the stage in which the mechanical output of the cochlea is transformed into electrical or electrochemical excitation of neurons in the auditory nerve. Experiments by Békésy (1951, 1952), by Davis and his col-leagues (1950), and others were providing significant information about the transformation, but many of us could not — at that time, at least — develop a much clearer picture of what happened in the transformation,

from the time function of the displacement of the cochlear partition
to the time function of neural excitation, than that the function was
essentially nonlinear.

From the auditory nerve on into the brain, and from the auditory
cortex back into the lower auditory centers, our pictures and our
understanding of what went on in the auditory perception became vague
and also fragmentary. We knew quite a bit about speech as a physical
stimulus and something, thanks to such scientists as Jakobson, Fant,
and Halle (1965), about speech as a carrier of language. We hoped to
establish correlations between physical events, psychological events,
and neurophysiological events. There was, however, both too much
information and not enough information. There was no way to represent all the parts of the puzzle explicitly and to make them interact
together so that we could see whether we had any significant fraction
of the necessary data in our hands or heads.

One could set down a similar description of the situation then prevailing in the generation of speech. The articulatory movements were
understood, at least to some extent, and they could be visualized dynamically. It was understood, of course, that the articulatory movements are controlled by muscles, which in turn are activated by
messages from the nervous system. We could imagine processes,
back there in the brain some place, that dealt with events corresponding to phonemes — or "phonoids" as some of us called them in order
to avoid appropriating a term that had a more sharply defined meaning
in the field of language. We were almost helpless to relate those
merely imagined processes to our equally vague concepts of the
brain's dynamic representation of the world.

In thinking about those things, we were trying to hold in mind and
correlate extremely many and diverse elements of information. We
were trying to fit them together into coherent patterns, trying to find
internally consistent and contextually plausible mechanisms that
would serve as testable hypotheses. The trouble was that the situation
had become too complex to be handled with the available tools. Too
much was known about the physical acoustics of hearing, too much
about the neurophysiological processes of hearing, and too much about
auditory behavior — too much for us to hold all the parts in mind at
once. Even though we could not process all the information we had, it
was obvious that there was much information we did not have. Many
members of the research community continued, therefore, to conduct

experiments and to acquire new information. Others of us, believing that new information would not help much until we had improved tools for processing and digesting it, turned from further experimentation, and from continuation of the effort to understand simply by reading and thinking. Indeed, some of us may have, in the quest for new tools, traveled so far from the substantive territory of psychoacoustics as to raise doubt about the probability of return. However, it is better not to think of returning until one has successfully completed his quest. The question with which I am concerned here is: Are any promising tools being found?

The answer to that question that I urge upon you is affirmative. The basic tool is dynamic modeling. The context within which dynamic modeling presents itself, the context of interactive computing systems, is perhaps even more important than the basic tool, itself, because the context makes it possible to employ the tool and because the context carries with it a variety of companion tools that are useful in themselves and which produce, with dynamic modeling, a mutually facilitatory effect. Of these associated tools, the ones that I shall mention are on-line information retrieval and communication, through a teleprocessing network, with other workers in a field of research.

Dynamic Models

Whereas a static model has only one form, the static form, a dynamic model has two forms, a static and a dynamic. Ordinary mathematical models are static models. They are representations in symbols, usually written in pencil or ink on paper. They do not behave in any way. They do not "solve themselves." For any transformation to be made, for any solution to be achieved, information contained in the model must be read out of the static form and processed in some active processor, such as a mathematician's brain or a computing machine. A dynamic model, on the other hand, exists in its static form only while it is inactive. The dynamic model can be set into action, by one means or another, and when it is active, it does exhibit behavior and does "solve itself" in the sense of exhibiting the consequences that stem from the interplay between its initial or boundary conditions and its internal structure. In the past, some of the best examples of dynamic models were flying scale models of airplanes, wind-tunnel models of airplanes, testing-basin models of ships, and analogue-computer models.

During the last few years, digital-computer models (models expressed in the form of digital-computer programs) have risen, I think it is safe to say, to the first rank of importance in dynamic modeling. If there is a distinction to be made between digital-computer simulations and digital-computer dynamic models, I should like it to be based upon the emphasis, in the dynamic models, of dynamic display and of close interaction between the model and the modeler. There is nothing about the terms, as terms, that forces that distinction, any more than there is between the terms in the distinction between multiprogramming and time sharing. It is simply that dynamic modeling has come, or is coming, to have the connotations of display and interaction. By "dynamic display" I mean the kind of display that is provided by cathode-ray oscilloscopes. By "interaction between the modeler and the model" I imply that the modeler manipulates the model, varying its parameters or its basic structure and observing the effects thus produced, either in order to understand how the behavior stems from the structure or to explore the behavior, itself, over a wide range of structures and conditions.

The main reason for the ascendance of digital-computer program models, I think, is that digital computers are capable of handling an almost unrestricted range of problems, whereas other means of dynamic modeling are constrained to narrow classes of problems. Digital computers and their programs are capable, of course, of reproducing exactly the same behavior, over and over: they do not "drift." One can build up an increasingly complex structure by concentrating his attention now on one part, now on another, without worrying lest a part perfected earlier fall out of adjustment while he is paying attention to a new subroutine. Furthermore, of course, several or many people can cooperate to produce an exceedingly complex computer program. I shall not say that team or group programming has yet been reduced to an efficient procedure, or that complex computer programs are easy or inexpensive to produce, but I shall say that some progress is being made toward mastery and efficiency, and that computer programming is the only known way of producing testable representations of very complex situations or processes.

Flanagan's (1960, 1962) model of the cochlea is a good example of a computer-program simulation. It accepts as input computer-processible representations of simple or compound oscillations and produces, as output, representations of the displacement of the cochlear partition at closely spaced points between the base and the apex. However, it does not permit the modeler to watch traveling waves progress along the basilar membrane in the way he would if the waves appeared on the screen of an oscilloscope and moved before his eyes. I do not know of any simulation or model program in the area of hearing that does have that characteristic. I must go outside the field of hearing, therefore, for examples of dynamic modeling with the aid of computer programs.

The first dynamic models I ever saw were, I believe, those of Farley, Frishkopf, Clark, and Gilmore (1957), computer-program and oscilloscope-display models of the dynamic behavior of assemblies of schematized neurons of the kind discussed by Donald Hebb in his Organization of Behavior (1949). Looking at the arrays of "cell bodies" on the oscilloscope screen, one could see waves of discharge propagating in what appeared to be partly regular, partly haphazard patterns. Farley and Clark systematically varied the parameters of the assembly model and catalogued the observed behaviors. Those early investigations contain the essence of what I think is most important in dynamic modeling. It is, as mentioned earlier, that the model has both static and dynamic forms. Actually, the model exists in three domains: it exists in processible form within the memory of the computer; it exists in displayed form in a dynamic presentation device; and it exists in perceived form in the mind of the modeler. The role of the display, of course, is to connect the computer-processible form and the perceived form directly together and thereby to permit exploration by the modeler of the structure and the parameters of the model.

My own first involvement in the construction of dynamic models dealt with so simple a matter that one might hesitate to use the word "model." Even in a very simple application, however, one can sense the great power of the arrangement consisting of computer program, dynamic display, and facilities for intervention and control by the modeler. Several of us then at Bolt Beranek and Newman prepared computer programs to help students understand the relations between the symbolic and the graphical forms of simple mathematical equations. The equations were straight lines, parabolas, or cubics. They were stored in the computer memory as configurations of bits representing the equations as equations. They were displayed on the

oscilloscope screen, however, both symbolically, i.e., in the form of
letters and numerals, and graphically, in the form of straight lines or
curves against rectangular coordinates. Adjacent to the coordinate
frame was a system of scales and arrows. By pointing to the scales
with a light pen, the student could assign whatever values he liked to
the coefficients in the equations. Whenever he changed a coefficient,
both the symbolic and the graphical displays adjusted immediately to
the new value. Thus the student could perceive directly "what each
coefficient did" to the graph, and he could see how each change in the
graph appeared in terms of the coefficients. The equations were
perhaps too simple to be thought of as models, but this experience with
the idea impressed me greatly, and I think that it exhibited the essence
of a fundamental of dynamic modeling, as I am using that phrase.

Probably the most significant single step in the development of
techniques for dynamic modeling was Ivan Sutherland's doctoral
dissertation (1963), Sketchpad, worked out on the TX-2 computer of
the M. I. T. Lincoln Laboratory. Since Sketchpad is doubtless familar
to most of you, I shall not describe it in detail. Let me, however,
describe two if its many demonstrations that illustrate what can be
done with dynamic-modeling techniques in the domain of mechanical
linkages and structures.

Sketching with a light pen on the screen of the TX-2 computer,
Sutherland defined the structure of a mechanical linkage consisting of
pivots, crank arms, and coupling linkages. The structure, idealized
by the computer from Sutherland's hand-drawn sketch and displayed on
the oscilloscope screen as straight, even line segments, was just a
bit too complicated for the viewer to see exactly what would happen if
one of the cranks were turned. Sutherland "grasped" the end of the
crank with the light pen and turned the crank. The other members of
the linkage moved in response, respecting the constraints imposed
upon them by the structure, and at once one member collided with
another — and it was immediately clear what circumstances and what
characteristics of the structure caused the difficulty. Using the light
pen again, in conjunction with the erase button, Sutherland immediately
repaired the linkage system and tested it again. This time it
functioned flawlessly.

Calling for a new sheet of "paper," Sutherland then sketched a
simple bridge structure consisting of several boxes with crossbracing.
He drew a support under each end of the bridge and attached (sche-

matically) a weight to the bottom of the bridge at its center. The bridge
sagged under the load, and numbers appeared on the display — one
number for each line or member in the structure — indicating the value
of the tension or compression to which it was being subjected. Sutherland did not carry the demonstration to the extreme of causing the
bridge to break when the strength of a member was exceeded, but he
could have done that without much trouble.

During the years since the advent of Sketchpad, techniques of graphic
input to computers and graphic display by computers have been developed intensively for application in the new field of computer-aided
design. Most of the applications have been to design of mechanical
structures, vehicles, highways, and the like. Programs have been
prepared, for example by Bert Green[1] , by Lawrence Roberts (1963),
and by Timothy Johnson (1963), to display three-dimensional objects
as oblique drawings, as perspective drawings, and/or in plan view,
front view, and side view in the manner of an engineering drawing.
The techniques are not essentially restricted, however, to the modeling
of physical objects and structures. Indeed, their intellectual (as opposed to economic) power may be greater in dealing with abstractions,
for the techniques permit abstractions — permit the behavior of dynamic or kinematic abstractions — to register directly through perception, and people seem to grasp complex, dynamic things much more
readily when they see them happen than when they have to reconstruct
such processes mentally from a succession of messages that define,
but do not dynamically depict, the processes. Complex, abstract processes there is no way to see directly. Dynamic modeling may have
great value, therefore, in converting such abstractions to concrete
form through dynamic display.

In the field of perception, advocacy of dynamic modeling at this
time — or at any rate my enthusiasm in advocating it — has to be
explained, or justified, by saying (as I tried to say in the Introduction)
that the field so needs the new tool that one may talk about it in a
hortatory tone even before it has been tested and proved in significant
applications. In the field of computer-aided design, however, that is
no longer the situation. Important applications were undertaken almost
concurrently with the first laboratory demonstrations of the technique.

---

[1] Personal communication.

At the Fall Joint Computer Conference in San Francisco (September 1964), engineers of the General Motors Corporation (Jacks, 1964) unveiled a successful, significant application of computer-program simulation and display in the design of automobile bodies and related structures. The program was carried out with prototype equipment, and it is clear that there are many improvements in hardware and software to be made, but it is also clear that the fundamental concepts of the method are very powerful.

On-Line Modeling in a Time-Sharing Computer System

The fields with which we are concerned in this symposium are, of course, far too broad to be subsumed in any single model created by an individual, too broad to be understood by any single individual. The understanding of hearing and vision is an undertaking for a research community. It is, therefore, not enough to have techniques for the programming and display of models. It is necessary to have techniques that will support interaction among members of the research community with one another and with the models that they create, test, modify, publish, and criticize. Models of subprocesses have to be fitted together to make models of processes. Models cast in diverse forms have to be compared with one another. Models have to be brought into interaction with experimentation, with data reduction, and with processes of extrapolation and prediction. These considerations pose requirements for systems and techniques that go far beyond the present state of the art, but in the present art there are beginnings that hold out promise for the effective handling of the broader parts of the problem as well as of the focal element, dynamic modeling.

Since most of you are familiar with one or more of the recently developed computer time-sharing systems, I shall give only a brief sketch of the context within which it seems likely that dynamic modeling and interaction among research colleagues and their models will develop. The context is, essentially, a network of computer time-sharing systems. It seems likely that time-sharing systems will in due course be set up in most of the universities, government research laboratories, and other institutions within which research in our fields is conducted. It seems likely, also, that many of the time-sharing systems will be interconnected to form a network or networks. It will then be possible for most of the research workers in a field of science to communicate with one another through the computer network. That

way of communicating will have marked advantages over telephone
communication, mail, and publication, for two or more people with
common concerns can work together with their models and with their
data. They can substitute the running of a model for mere talk about
it.

The way of working just described is in one sense a distant dream
and in another sense a present reality. Some of our colleagues at
M. I. T., Carnegie Institute of Technology, Stanford University, and
perhaps a few other institutions already hold intergroup teletype con-
ferences. However, for overpowering economic reasons, they do not
transmit dynamic oscilloscope displays across the country. Indeed,
there is not nearly as much dynamic display on oscilloscope screens
as there is typing on paper in existing time-sharing systems. To
operate a complex, dynamic display by plotting and replotting every
individual point requires a large amount of calculation by a computer
and a large amount of transmission from the computer to the display.
One can simplify and economize by taking advantage of the spatial
and temporal redundancies in the displayed configurations. If
character-generating and function-generating devices are incorporated
into the console, the load on the central computer and on the transmission facilities is reduced. Important steps have already been taken
along that line, and the relevant technology is advancing rapidly, but
dynamic display makes, at the present time, a somewhat embarrassing
demand on the central processor of a time-sharing system, and the
cost of long-distance transmission of the signals required to maintain
dynamic displays is, at present, too great to permit widespread use.
That is to say, the techniques and the technology are not precisely
standing there crying for immediate application in our fields of study.
On the other hand, I think they will be ready — quite ready — before
our field, and others like it, will be ready to take full advantage of
them.[2] It is that consideration, basically, that leads me to discuss this
topic in the introduction to this symposium.

---

[2]Between the time of the symposium and the time of publication,
significant technical developments occurred. Storage display tubes and
small computers associated with consoles now offer promising solutions.

Field-Oriented Languages for Dynamic Modeling and Related Activities

The over-all task of preparing a complex, dynamic model is so great, so demanding of diverse skills, that dynamic modeling cannot become an effective way of working for the great majority of substantively oriented scientists and engineers until a considerable amount of tool-making has been done by computer-oriented scientists and engineers. I have mentioned briefly one or two of the things that need to be done in the display hardware area. Of greater direct concern to our group, however, are the things that have to be done in the software area — things that have to do with the preparation of the computer programs that constitute, or underlie, dynamic models. The main thing that has to be done in this area is to develop a modeling language in terms of which the substantively oriented scientist or engineer can describe what he has in mind and from which his statements can be converted automatically into an operable dynamic-model program.

Most of the work of constructing such a language, or such languages, is work for the computer programming specialist. Part of it, however, has to be the responsibility of people who understand deeply the areas of application. That is to say, the general-purpose parts of a dynamic modeling language can be constructed by computer programmers, but the part that defines the operations and vocabulary peculiar to a particular field of application has to be done by substantive experts working in close collaboration with computer programmers. Some substantively oriented scientists and engineers, therefore, are going to have to become closely acquainted and associated with computer software specialists and their field of activity before there will be truly effective and convenient tools for use in the various branches of science and engineering.

An Approach to the Development and Testing of Dynamic Modeling in Hearing and Vision

Being convinced that dynamic modeling is potentially of revolutionary significance for our fields, I should like, in closing this talk, to make a suggestion — a proposal of an approach that might accelerate the introduction of dynamic modeling in a practical way into the fields of hearing and vision. The proposal can be stated briefly as long as one does not go into detail about particulars. I shall not go into detail.

The idea is for five or six research workers in the field of hearing and/or five or six research workers in the field of vision to take two years off from their usual activities, one year in the near future and the other year somewhat later. The group would be invited, let us suppose, to work at one of the institutions at which there is, in existence now, a time-sharing computer system and a community of computer-oriented experts and also a community of substantively oriented scientists and engineers who are more or less familiar, as users, with the system. During the first year of work in that context, the project group would spend about half its time learning, as deeply as possible, the lore of on-line interactive computing. The other half of its time the group would spend in theoretical discussion of problems of mutual interest, plus perhaps some experimentation, and particularly in exploration of the problem of expressing ideas and hypotheses in computer-program form. By the end of the year, the members of the group would be creating and operating small models of various sorts, and there might even be some progress toward connecting several small models into an assembly that would present in a tangible way the problem of writing programs that are compatible with programs written by colleagues and documenting programs to facilitate communication of the ideas they embody. The first year would not, however, see the accomplishment of a theoretically significant system of dynamic models in vision or hearing. The significant product to be hoped for would be a series of working papers and a final report — or two final reports, one for vision and one for hearing — on the requirements, as seen by persons of longstanding expertness in the substantive fields and newly acquired sophistication in on-line computing, for a language to facilitate the creation, testing, and communication of dynamic models in hearing and/or vision.

The complementary part of the proposal now comes into the picture. It is that a small group of computer programming specialists design and implement a language for dynamic modeling, a language that would meet the requirements set forth by the substantive experts. That might be accomplished in one year. It might require two. In either case, it would involve a certain amount of consultation between the computer experts and the substantive experts, but the task would be mainly in the hands of the computer experts.

The proposal now goes back to the researchers in hearing and/or vision. They should work again in the context of a time-sharing computer system — or within more than one such context, if their own organizations have time-sharing systems by then — and try to prepare theoretically significant dynamic models. Their effort would test the language prepared for them. Doubtless there would have to be modifications. The computer programming experts would still be in the picture, and would make the improvements. The modelers would concentrate on small enough theoretical areas that models set up within them would be able to make contact with one another and to be organized together into a system of models. The models would be prepared in such a way that they would interact with experimental data — either being tested by confrontation with the data or adjusting automatically to come into accordance with it. The program of the second year of the vision/hearing group thus would consist of both theoretical and experimental activity, with dynamic models at the focus of it all. The scientific product of the second year might include published papers of the conventional type, but it would include, also, a new kind of scientific publication: the published dynamic model, a thoroughly tested and documented computer program designed to represent, and also to present dynamically, scientific or technical ideas too complex to be communicated effectively by static strings of characters or static graphs and diagrams.

References

Békésy, G. von. DC potentials and energy balance of the cochlear partition. J. acoust. Soc. Amer., 1951, 23, 576-582.

Békésy, G. von. DC resting potentials inside the cochlear partition. J. acoust. Soc. Amer., 1952, 24, 72-76.

Békésy, G. von. Simplified model to demonstrate the energy flow and formation of traveling waves similar to those found in the cochlea. Proc. nat. Acad. Sci., Wash., 1956, 42, 930-944.

Békésy, G. von. Pendulums, traveling waves, and the cochlea: Introduction and script for a motion picture. Laryngoscope, 1958, 68, 317-327.

Békésy, G. von, and Rosenblith, W. A. The mechanical properties of the ear. In S. S. Stevens (Ed.), Handbook of experimental psychology. New York: Wiley, 1951. Pp. 1076-1115.

Davis, H., Fernandes, C., and McAuliffe, D. R. The excitatory process in the cochlea. Proc. nat. Acad. Sci., Wash., 1950, 36, 580-587.

Farley, B. G., Frishkopf, L. S., Clark, W. A., Jr., and Gilmore, J. T., Jr. Computer techniques for the study of patterns in the electroencephalogram. M. I. T. Lincoln Lab. tech. Rep., 1957, No. 165.

Flanagan, J. L. Models for approximating basilar membrane displacement. Bell Syst. tech. J., 1960, 39, 1163-1191.

Flanagan, J. L. Models for approximating basilar membrane displacement — Part II. Effects of middle-ear transmission and some relations between subjective and physiological behavior. Bell Syst. tech. J., 1962, 41, 959-1009.

Fletcher, H. Speech and hearing in communication. New York: Van Nostrand, 1953.

Hebb, D. O. The organization of behavior. New York: Wiley, 1949.

Jacks, E. L. A laboratory for the study of graphical man-machine communication. Proc. AFIPS Fall joint Computer Conf., 1964, 26, 343-350.

Jakobson, R., Fant, C. G. M., and Halle, M. Preliminaries to speech analysis. (6th ed.) Cambridge: M. I. T. Press, 1965.

Johnson, T. E. Sketchpad III: A computer program for drawing in three dimensions. Proc. AFIPS Spring joint Computer Conf., 1963, 23, 347-353.

Roberts, L. G. Machine perception of three-dimensional solids. Lincoln Lab. tech. Rep., 1963, No. 315.

Sutherland, I. E. Sketchpad: A man-machine graphical communication system. Proc. AFIPS Spring joint Computer Conf., 1963, 23, 329-346.

Zwislocki, J. Mechanical frequency characteristics of the ear. Experientia, 1946, 2, 415-417.

WAYS OF LOOKING AT PERCEPTION

D. M. MacKay
Department of Communication
University of Keele
Keele, Staffordshire, England

I take my brief to be to "stir the pot," so to speak, in the hope that its various ingredients may be better brought into contact with one another in our minds. At the outset I should like to make a remark which I hope will not be thought to be provocative, but which may serve to keep us on our toes. The kinship of interest between designers of automata and theorists of perception has, I think we would all agree, led to a remarkably fruitful series of interactions; but there are subtle differences of emphasis between the two sides which have also, I think, tended toward a confounding of a distinction that is useful in thinking of the application of the study of perception to the problems of automation. I mean the distinction between perception as experience, as becoming aware of features of the world, and perception as observable behavior, as the manifestation of input-output coordination. Perception becomes a subject of scientific observation as a result of rather a long chain of reasoning which we tend to forget. A percept can be thought of as a current constraint on the organization of action by the perceiver. What I perceive becomes a datum for my calculation of any action or reaction to which its presence is relevant. The observable evidence of my having perceived it is usually, therefore, the correlation observed in my behavior between input and output, provided that I am suitably motivated to display this. (Anyone who experiments on perception knows that the real problem is to make sure that the subject is, in fact, motivated to display the coordination in which we are interested.)

Typical perceptual tasks are those of discrimination, classification, matching; and in each case the study is conducted by trying to ensure that the subject is motivated to perform an action whose form will reflect the form of the feature which we want him to perceive. Because such input-output correlations are often required for practical purposes, there is then a temptation to take any device which shows the appropriate correlation between input and output as ipso facto a possible explanatory model of perceptual processes in a living organism, so reducing the problem of perception to a problem of discriminative, classificatory public behavior, leaving out the awkward questions of motivation to action and the experience of the perceiving agent. I want to suggest that as the study of perception advances we will need to sharpen this distinction between perception and mere input-output coordination, because it will become more and more questionable which features of perception, particularly in the human case, are relevant and necessary in an automaton to do the kinds of jobs we might describe as "input-output coordination."

To see that this distinction is one of fact and not merely of linguistic convention, it is only necessary to remind ourselves of all the bodily processes which come into the category of input-output coordination (the matching of the diameter of the pupil to the intensity of light, for example) yet are unaccompanied by conscious perception. Similarly, there are many processes of an artificial kind which are discriminatory, classificatory, and so on, where it would seem to be a little perverse to speak of perception. A sieve, for example, will receive an input and will nicely classify it into categories according to size, but few of us would regard it as perceiving what it handles. Throughout the world there are in fact any number of more complex natural processes which can be regarded as classificatory, but which it would be very odd indeed to call perceptual. For example, wherever water dribbles from the end of a rain pipe or the edge of a rock and the wind is blowing, the heavier drops are deflected a short distance, and the smaller drops a greater distance. So here is "classification" going on — but who would be so animistic as to call it an instance of perception?

What I am suggesting, then, is that in our models the mere appearance of internal configurations which match or correspond 1 for 1 to features of the environment, though it may be a necessary feature of any model of perception, does not ipso facto guarantee that perceiving is going on in these models, nor that what is going on is in any sense an adequate model of what goes on in peoples' nervous systems when they perceive. In other words, we must take into account not only the physical correlate of classification, but also the correlate of action and the planning of action, and the part played by the percept in the planning of action. All of these would have to make their appearance in our model before we could even begin to advance it as a candidate for the explanation of perception.

The Organization of Action

Action may be defined as activity in view of ends. The familiar skeleton map of Figure 1 summarizes the essential features. An effector system E has a repertoire of activities within the field F. Information as to the current state of F is supplied via a receptor system R. The problem of the organization of action is to secure a running selection from the repertoire of E which is best calculated to achieve

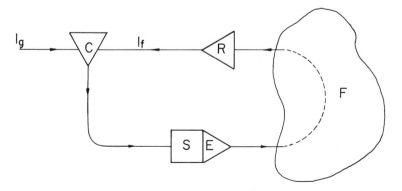

Fig. 1. Basic flow map for goal-directed activity.

current ends (goal-pursuit, norm-holding, threat-avoidance) on the
basis of current and past information. It is a dual problem, then, that
confronts us. We have, on the one hand, to secure within this system
an internal representation of the external world, the data on which
action is to be based. Secondly, and perhaps less often noticed, there
has to be some system concerned with the ordering of goal priorities
in situations of conflict between incompatible goals. In other words,
the organization of action has two aspects, the indicative and the
normative; the representation of what is the case, and the representation of what shall be pursued and in what order of priority.

Organization to Profit from Redundancy

In this context, then, we can think of perception as the organism's
adaptive response to redundancy in the pattern of demand and constraint imposed upon it by the field in which it is active. The field
is not purely random, but structured. The structure is responsible
for redundancy in the pattern of demand (actual or conditional) flowing
in upon the organism via its receptive system R.

The general outline of the scheme of Figure 1 is very familiar, but
it may serve to focus our ideas, and we may as well stick to the conventional example of the thermostat, because I do not think it leaves
out anything that matters for our purpose. Here E is a heater, R a
thermometer, sending an indication (I_f) of the temperature of the field
to an evaluator C, which compares it with an "indication of goal" (I_g).
In the simplest situation there is a continual selective operation by
the evaluator C upon the repertoire of E, calculated to minimize the
disparity between I_f and I_g. Suppose now that the pattern of demand
for selective action shows some regularity, due for example to the
alternation of day and night. Then, of course, the selective operation
upon E could in principle be partly prefabricated; and we could imagine incorporating an organizer (O) in the system (see Figure 2),
which replicates those components of the selective operation that are
predictable on the basis of this regularity (MacKay, 1951, 1956a, 1956b).
This organizer may in part act upon feedforward from the receptive
system (for example, a second thermometer outside the building,
registering ambient temperature); or it may simply abstract from the
output of the evaluator the regular features that become predictable;
but in either case this organizer, which prefabricates as much of the
selective operation as matches the regularity of the demand, in a

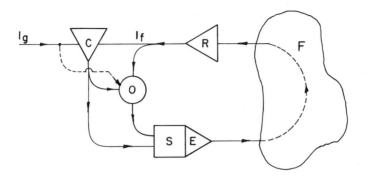

Fig. 2. Flow map with "feedforward".

sense represents internally the regular feature in the outside world
to which it is adaptive.

Indication of goal (I_g) is here supplied by an open terminal, so to
speak, and is normally set by the housewife. Now if the housewife
wants the system to respond as quickly as possible, she would not
necessarily do best by merely moving the indicator of I_g to the new
setting. She could usually do better by also precomputing the extent to
which the heater ought to be turned up or down, and setting it roughly
to match her demand, leaving the evaluator to make the fine adjustments. So we require for the purpose a feedforward from I_g into the
organizing system in addition to the feedback which comes by way of
the field and I_g, and any feedforward supplied by the thermometer
sampling the temperature of the outside environment. What I want to
point out is the importance of the proper balance of feedforward and
feedback in this continual process of adaptation to the redundant
features of the pattern of demand.

Meta-Organization

So far our system has been a slave. It depends on an outside source
for its goal-specification. Before we can begin to approximate to
autonomous cognitive agency, we must introduce a second system, MO,
whose function is to determine and order the priorities of the goals
to be pursued (Figure 3). We may term this the meta-organizing
system (MacKay, 1966). In the case of our thermostat (Figure 1) the
meta-organizing function would normally be exercised by the housewife, who might for example adjust the goal-temperature according to
her current activity, or her household's state of health, or the size

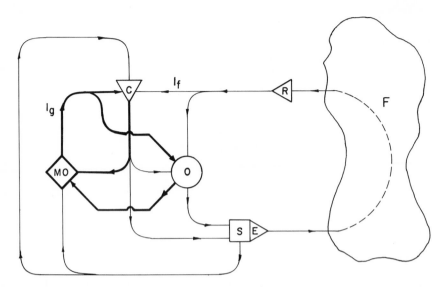

Fig. 3. Addition of "meta-organizing" system (heavy lines) to
evaluate and modify organizing activity.

of the fuel bill, and so forth; but it is not difficult to envisage a
mechanical system taking her place. Here, of course, the goal-adjust-
ment required is simple and one-dimensional, but the principle can
be extended to a goal-hierarchy of any complexity. In each case there
has to be a flow of information from the meta-organizer (MO) into the
evaluator, setting the criteria of evaluation. Again, for this to
function with greatest efficiency, we will want feedforward from the
meta-organizing system into the organizer. We also will require
feedback from the internal field of activity of the meta-organizing
system, analogous to the feedback from the external field of activity
to the organizing system. So we end up with a hierarchic organization,
in which the job of goal pursuit is organized by a system which treats
the internal organizing network as its field of action, receiving feedback from it and supplying feedforward as well as acting directly on
its goal-settings. Finally, of course, the meta-organizing system
must receive from the evaluator an indication of the effectiveness of
its current programming, i.e., the data which are relevant to a change
of goal priority. To take a simple example, an organism may be
pursuing some simple goal, say intake of food, when it receives some
indication of a threat. As a result the goal of eating is set aside in
favor of flight, the threat-avoidance program. This kind of goal-

switching process, and the computations behind it, count as meta-organizing activity.

One further point. As a result of the evaluator's stirring up the organizing system, the organizing system will set in motion events in the field of activity which will be reflected in the input to the evaluator. One way of evaluating the success of the program is then for the evaluator to compare key features of what is coming in with what was programmed to be produced by the effector system. For this we require an input to the evaluator from the output and/or the input to the appropriate effectors. This is analogous to what von Holst (1950) called the "efference copy": the copy of what is meant to be produced in the sensory input as a result of effector action. We shall have more to say of this later.

Development of the Organizing System

We have now sketched a network in which we can say that action occurs, calculated in view of a representation of the external world and of a hierarchic goal structure which the system itself generates and adapts in its meta-organizing system.

In concrete terms of what goes on in the nervous system, this raises many questions. First of all there is the question of the way the organizing system itself gets organized. Clearly it would be possible to prefabricate it; but to prefabricate the organizing system (the system which in effect, we remember, represents the regular features of the external world) would of course be to run into the danger of irremediable category blindness. Only predetermined categories could be taken into account by the system. If a new category became relevant which the designer had not thought of, the system would never grasp it, so to speak. So, although some prefabrication will obviously be useful in an organism living in our world, which has indeed many universal regularities, we would expect also to find some use for a more flexible approach. In addition to having some pre-fabricated general principles of organization, the organizing system should also be adaptive, able for example to assemble trial organizers, and later if necessary dismantle or set them aside according to the outcome of their use. This amounts to suggesting that within the organizing system there must be a region that we could call a "work-shop" (MacKay, 1959b); a region in which trial subroutines can be constructed and run, perhaps run ahead of time, and their outcomes then evaluated by the meta-organizing system, for potential usefulness in securing particular ends.

Secondly, there is the problem of keeping the whole system up-to-date; and here, at last, is where we make contact again with our topic of perception. What I am suggesting is that in the context of this skeleton model, we can define the correlate of perception as the activity of keeping up-to-date the organizing system that implicitly represents the external world, by an internal matching response to the current impact of the world upon the receptive system. Once again, perception as an updating activity may be carried on either (a) through the action of prefabricated filters which extract from the input the necessary clues to select the appropriate state of the internal organizing system, and/or (b) through a process of self-guided modification of the internal state of the organizing system to match the incoming data: e.g., by "backing off" the incoming data in such a way that an isomorphism is developed between the principles of generation of the internal back-off signal and the structure of the external percepta to which the internal state is a match (MacKay, 1951, 1956b).

I do not want now to go into detail. The purpose of this introduction has been to sketch the context in which the relative merits of (a) "filtering" and (b) "matching" (or as some Americans call it, "analysis by synthesis") can be rationally discussed — not, I would emphasize, as rivals, but as complementary principles to be adopted in different proportions. A bank of filters covering all possible features would of course offer the speediest way of keeping a system up-to-date; but to be comprehensive it must be extremely large and hence inefficiently employed. A self-matching mechanism, on the other hand, can be extremely compact, but it may be slow, and it is limited (by the number of its degrees of freedom) as to the number of features it can "track" at a time. (This, by the way, is also a notorious characteristic of human perception.)

Consider for example a system required to respond differentially to n different frequencies of input. On the filter principle a bank of n filters will be needed, with a response time only of the order of $1/\Delta f$ (Δf = bandwidth). On the "matching" principle we need only a single servo-operated sine wave generator plus comparator, the system hunting until it matches the incoming frequency. The economy of the second is obvious, but also its slowness and its limitation to one signal at a time. Our choice between the two would clearly depend on the size of n, and on the value we place on the different costs of equipment and time. The first could be important, in spite of the bulkiness or the multiplicity of the elements required, where relatively little prior information was available as to the nature and number of the features to be matched simultaneously; whereas conversely, where it is known that only one or two degrees of freedom will be needed, the second, self-matching process is likely to be more efficient. In the perception of speech, for example, where the ensemble of commands for generating speech is relatively limited, and the elements form a sequence ordered by few parameters, there may be more to be said for a self-molding adaptive, matching-response model than, for example, in the perception of shape. In most cases, however, (speech included) we might expect maximum efficiency to be derived from a combination of the two principles, using a number of self-matching generators guided by rough clues from filters.

Physiological Evidence

Most people will be familiar with the physiological evidence which has begun to temper speculation in this field, so on this I will be brief. It is now over five years since the physiologists Hubel and Wiesel (1963), Barlow and Hill (1963), and Lettvin and others (1959) began to discover in the visual system networks of cells which were selectively responsive to such features as the direction of a contour, motion of a contour, rate of change of brightness, curvature of contour, and things of that kind. More recently Evans and Whitfield (1964) and others have found somewhat analogous gradient detectors in the auditory system. So it is now pretty generally agreed that any perceptual model of the visual or auditory system had better assume the existence of banks of filters in the input to the organizing system, permitting a preliminary extraction of cues to which the internal organizing process has to match itself.

Psychological Evidence

Let me now refer to some striking psychological indications that seem to point in the same direction. The first concerns the adaptive response of the visual system to fields of near parallel lines. Figure 4, for example, has a high degree of contour-directional redundancy. After looking at it for a while and looking away, one sees a curious pattern of wavy circles. With Figure 5 on the other hand, one sees

Fig. 4. "Ray" pattern which evokes complementary images.

wavy radial streamers as an afterimage. A general description, then,
would be that after exposure to near-parallel lines in one direction,
the visual system seems to be hypersensitized to a direction roughly
orthogonal to the direction of the stimulus. This led (for once, in
advance of the physiological evidence) to the suggestion (MacKay,
1957) that in the visual system there might be networks specifically
sensitive to direction, and capable of adapting to direction in the kind
of way that our color-sensitive mechanisms tend to adapt to color, so
that complementary directions tend to be seen after exposure to a
given direction just as complementary colors tend to be seen after
exposure to a given color.

It turns out to be possible to reveal and study tendencies of this
sort continuously by using as a "neutral" test stimulus a random
succession of randomly patterned figures which we call "visual noise".
This can be generated electronically on a television tube (MacKay,
1957) or photographically with a cine film of random fields such as
photographs of sandpaper or distributions of confetti (Wilson, 1960).

Fig. 5. "Target" pattern.

When superimposed on Figures 4 and 5, the randomness largely disappears, the "noise" being seen as organized into a totally different
pattern, in the one case a kind of rotating rosette, and in the other a
set of radial streamers (MacKay, 1957, 1961). So here we have what
looks like good evidence that the visual system is indeed hypersensitive
to directions contrasting as strongly as possible with the directions
of contour that are present in excessively large numbers.

   Another related phenomenon recently discovered with the same tool
we call, for want of a better term, the "maggot" effect (Fiorentini and
MacKay, 1965). When each frame of a random noise sequence is
followed by a blank flash at a certain interval of the order of 25 msec,
then even without any superimposed line pattern, the "noise" takes on
a linear structure, as if the screen were filled with short maggotlike
objects (Figure 6). Tentatively our interpretation is that by this particular rhythm, namely a flash following each frame with a delay of the
order of 25 msec, we must be "presensitizing" certain elements in
the visual perceptual mechanism which are sensitive to contour, so

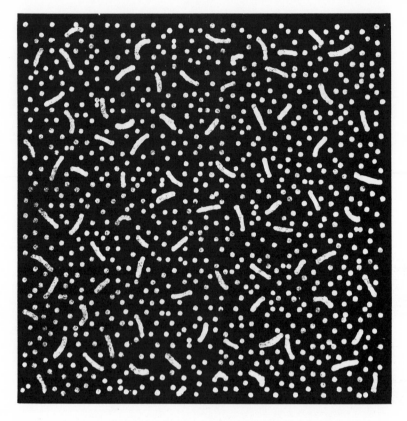

Fig. 6. An impression of the "maggot" effect.

that subjective contours are spuriously generated when none are
objectively present in the stimulus. We are still working on this one,
and finding interesting correlates in the evoked potentials (MacKay
and Fiorentini, 1966).

One other illustration will show the sort of data that are accumulating on this general topic of the visual pattern-filter mechanisms.
Figure 7 shows a "noise" pattern which is reasonably random. After
a few seconds' fixation of a particular point, subjects report spontaneously that the appearance of randomness diminishes, and may
even be replaced by a periodic structure. Displacing the fixation point
by a few degrees at once reveals the magnitude of the change that has
taken place (MacKay, 1964). Once again we are only beginning to
investigate this, but it looks like evidence of adaptation in yet another
filter mechanism, whose function is to signal or abstract inhomo-
geneities in distribution. We cannot blame this on ordinary adaptation

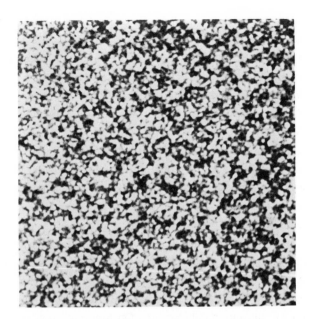

Fig. 7. A sample of "visual-noise."

to brightness, because the phenomenon is visible with all-or-none patterns, in which brightness adaptation presumably leaves the geometrical distribution unchanged in form. It may be significant that patterns like newsprint, which has, of course, a high degree of redundancy already, show this effect much less strongly.

To summarize thus far, what I am suggesting is that we should think of the modeling of perception, not in terms of an exclusive choice between filtering and internal adaptive matching by the internal replication of the input, but in terms of the interaction of both. The foregoing demonstrations would seem to indicate that perception is indeed a synthetic activity, but one guided by cues extracted by the filter mechanisms; what we see has many elements which come from the structure within rather than from the stimulus without.

The Problem of Perceptual Stability

If our image of the perceived world is implicitly embodied in our state of organization to cope with it, it may be expected to be naturally stable. The perception of change will be an updating response triggered only by a significant degree of mismatch between the incoming indications and the internal criteria of evaluation adopted in the light of the

action currently programmed. As a concrete illustration of the implications of this way of looking at perception, I should like to turn to the
problem of the stability of the perceived world in the face of transformations of the input caused by voluntary actions.

Take first the tactile case. Suppose it is dark and we are exploring
a surface with the palm of our hand. We use our arm muscles to move
our palm around the tactile world, thus giving rise to all manner of
rubbing sensations — sensations of relative motion between the surface
and the palm. But we do not in consequence perceive the object under
our palm as in motion. On the contrary, if the object under our palm
were, let us say, a trolley mounted on a rail so that as we moved our
palm the trolley followed, it would be the <u>absence</u> of motion signals
under those circumstances that would supply information that the
trolley was in motion. The motion signals generated by tactile exploration, then, do not have to be <u>canceled</u> or suppressed in any way
in order to prevent us from feeling that a stationary object is in
motion, when we run our hand over it. On the contrary, they are
<u>evaluated</u> as evidence of stability, in the light of criteria appropriate to
the fact that we have organized an exploratory movement.

In terms of Figure 3, we may say that the meta-organizing system
has set up as a goal the exploration of the object by palm movement.
Some kind of information flow from the effector to the evaluator is of
course necessary in any model if the evaluator is to interpret the incoming signals properly; but the point I want to make is that this
information need not have either the complexity or the accuracy that
would be required in order to <u>cancel</u> the incoming motion signals.
All it has to do is to attach the appropriate <u>significance</u> to them as
evidence for a static, stable representation of this object. We may
assume that some internal representation of my tactile world fills
out in detail as I explore: but unless I make contact with an actually
moving surface the motion signals generated by my exploration are
only confirmatory of the validity of my stationary world-model, and
not destructive of it.

Very briefly, I should like to suggest that the same logic seems to
apply to the much-discussed problem of the stability of the visual
world: that using my eye muscles to throw my retina around the
visual scene can be regarded as analogous to using my arm muscles
to throw my palm around the tactile world. It is true that there are
many differences, in proprioceptive inputs and so forth, between the two

cases; but there would seem to be no more reason to expect that the
visual motion signals generated by voluntary eye movement should be
canceled or suppressed, than the friction signals from the palm. What
is necessary, once again, is rather that the flow of information from
the eye-movement system should modify the criteria of evaluation of
these signals, so that they become indications of the stability of the
visual world rather than the contrary (MacKay, 1959a, 1962).

A number of simple demonstrations help, I think, to support this view
of the matter. If we close one eye and press very lightly on the open
eyelid at the corner, the visual world of course appears to move. The
impression of motion is irresistible. If we look closely, however, we
find that the region around the fixation point appears to move more
than the peripheral region; and in fact with very small movements we
may not feel that the periphery is moving at all, but only the region
around the fixation point. If we now do the same while viewing Figure
4, an interesting feature emerges. In addition to the displacement of
the center, we see a sort of "rubber-sheet" distension and contraction
of the field, perpendicular to the direction of motion (MacKay, 1960).
For example, if the image is displaced from left to right, the regions
at "3 o'clock" and "9 o'clock" seem to perform a fanwise expansion or
contraction. Suppose now that a vertical marker of some sort is introduced halfway along, say, the "3 o'clock" ray. At once the rubbery
expansion in its vicinity ceases, although in the symmetrical region
at 9 o'clock (without a marker) it is still present.

In each case what we see, I suggest, can be interpreted as the result
of a mismatch of the evaluatory criteria: but these anomalies illustrate
the thesis that our internal representation of the world is affected only
in proportion as there is information to justify a change. On this
principle, it is not surprising that when the visual image is displaced,
we normally see the central region, which stimulates an area rich in
detectors, as "moving" more than the periphery. Again, in the
absence of significant mismatch of a particular feature of the visual
representation, no change in that feature is perceived. We do not see
a displacement of Figure 4 as a whole, because the translation of a
contour along itself gives no information; but we do perceive expansion
corresponding to any change in separation of the contours. On the
other hand, given a marker in the orthogonal direction, we see displacement but no expansion.

Let me mention one further striking illustration. If a small steadily glowing lamp is viewed against a background lit stroboscopically at about five flashes per second, and the same eye-pressing experiment is repeated, a dramatic dissociation takes place (MacKay, 1958). With sufficiently gentle displacements, the lamp is seen to move, although the background remains stationary; yet the lamp is not seen to move relative to the background! Once again, the change perceived is the minimum justified by the optical evidence, however intellectually improbable or absurd that change may be.

A particular moral of these demonstrations for our present purpose is that whatever the principle on which our visual world is kept stable, it cannot be a matter of some global transformation of the incoming optical pattern of the sort familiar, for example, in a shipborne radar system. On board ship, to preserve a "true north" map on the radar screen, the incoming radar picture is subjected to a rotation which exactly cancels any rotation produced when the ship's head turns. There is a sensory gyro that signals the amount of ship-rotation to a "compensator," which "subtracts out" this rotation and so ensures the stability of the display. What I am suggesting is that we cannot plausibly use that kind of model for at least the more complicated effects of exploratory changes in the direction of our eyes, or indeed, of any of our sensory surfaces. Many experimental results under various pathological conditions and abnormal conditions, as with anaesthetized eye-muscles or stabilized retinal images, may indeed be qualitatively the same on either a "cancellation" or an "evaluation" model; but the quantitative accuracy required in the information channels is quite different (MacKay, 1959a, 1962). In our model (Figure 3), the information supplied from the effector system (whether derived from its input or output) need have an accuracy comparable only with the accuracy of the criterion of evaluation, which can be no greater than the accuracy of the effector system. In the radar case, on the other hand, the cancellation must be carried out with accuracy comparable with the resolving power of the receptive system if no instability is to be detected. In the case of the visual and tactile senses, such accuracies in the "efference copy" would seem to be physiologically improbable, if not unattainable; and in any case, on the view I have advanced, they are unnecessary.

The Distinction Between Perception and Sensorimotor Coordination

May I now return to the point made at the outset, that the discovery of a satisfactory model of coordination between sensory input and motor output may not necessarily settle the question of <u>perception</u> which is associated with it. Perception, in the sense of the subjective experience of the perceiver, is something that we have seen may even embody mutually incompatible components. In addition to the demonstrations I have mentioned, let me remind you of the familiar "waterfall illusion" for example. After watching a moving surface and looking away, one sees a stationary surface as <u>both</u> moving <u>and</u> yet not changing its position. Such mutually incompatible components in perception could not result in any coherent motor coordination. Hence the importance, as I see it, of keeping sharp and clear the distinction between modeling mechanisms of sensorimotor coordination, and finding models to explain perception as conscious experience. Many perplexing problems of the perceptual theorist may be bypassed if all we want to do is to design an automaton to make adequate use of sensory input.

Does this distinction help at all to clarify or give a sharper meaning to the old question of the neural <u>location</u> of perceptual activity as such? We are all inclined, I think rightly, to be wary of such questions, feeling that they may be as silly as to ask for the "location of triangularity" among the dots of a triangle. I want to suggest, however, that in the light of our operational model such an answer would be a little too short. In principle it is operationally meaningful to imagine ourselves gaining access to the flow-system of Figure 3, and blocking or clamping various channels so as to isolate particular sub-systems. It would then be possible to stimulate on each side of the isolating barrier, and discover which activity had a perceptual correlate according to the testimony of the subject. There is thus an operational meaning in asking where the neural activity takes place which is correlated with perception, as distinct from sensorimotor coordination. The suggestion that emerges from our model when one looks into it (MacKay 1956a, 1966), is that whereas much sensorimotor coordination is likely to be cortically mediated, the basic correlate of perception as such, of <u>consciousness</u> of the external world, would be activity evoked in the meta-organizing system by sensory stimulation: activity molded and elaborated by the activity of the (presumably cortical) organizing system that matches the sensory input "on behalf of" the meta-organizer. If then we venture to ask where in the nervous system are the minimum necessary elements for conscious awareness, it may well be that we will have to look not in the great massive market place of the cerebral cortex, where demands are met by subroutines matched to them, but rather in a much smaller normative meta-organizing system, perhaps (who knows?) in the limbic system, where the priorities and policies of the whole traffic are determined and kept up-to-date (MacKay, 1956a, 1966).

Conclusion

In relation to the main purpose of this conference, the point I would stress in summary is that in most of our artifacts the work of conscious, normative meta-organization is intended to be performed by somebody else. Normally we design our automata to subserve ultimate goals which are not autonomously determined: they are set by ourselves. Most of our automata need not, and normally should not, have any autonomous meta-organizing system; so they lack an essential feature of conscious agency. Hence the suggestion that not all features of models of human perception which try to do justice to the experienced aspects of it are necessarily relevant to the design of artifacts required to develop mere sensorimotor coordination. Conversely, there is no guarantee that the most effective solution of this design problem need have any claim on the attention of psychologists. In other words, oddly enough, automaton designers with an interest in the perception of speech and visual form might do well to ignore, in the first instance, those aspects of the psychological theory of perception that are primarily concerned with perceiving; for perceiving is something that their automata may not be required to do.

References

Barlow, H. B., and Hill, R. M. Evidence for a physiological explanation of the waterfall phenomenon and figural after-effects. Nature, 1963, 200, 1345-1347.

Evans, E. F., and Whitfield, I. C. Classification of unit responses in the auditory cortex of the unanaesthetized and unrestrained cat. J. Physiol., 1964, 171, 476-493.

Fiorentini, Adriana, and MacKay, D. M. Temporal factors in pattern vision. Quart. J. exp. Psychol., 1965, 17, 282-291.

Hubel, D. H., and Wiesel, T. N. Shape and arrangement of columns in cat's striate cortex. J. Physiol., 1963, 165, 559-567.

Lettvin, J. Y., Maturana, H. R., McCulloch, W. S., and Pitts, W. H. What the frog's eye tells the frog's brain. Proc. IRE, 1959, 47, 1940-1951.

MacKay, D. M. In search of basic symbols. In von Foerster (Ed.), Trans. 8th Conf. cybernetics, 1951. New York: Joseph Macy, Jr., Foundation, 1951.

MacKay, D. M. The epistemological problem for automata. In C. E. Shannon, and J. McCarthy (Ed.), Automata studies. Princeton: Princeton Univer. Press, 1956. Pp. 235-251. (a)

MacKay, D. M. Towards an information-flow model of human behavior. Brit. J. Psychol., 1956, 47, 30-43. (b)

MacKay, D. M. Moving visual images produced by regular stationary patterns. Nature, 1957, 180, 849-850.

MacKay, D. M. Perceptual stability of a stroboscopically lit visual field containing self-luminous objects. Nature, 1958, 181, 507-508.

MacKay, D. M. The stabilization of perception during voluntary activity. In Proceedings of the fifteenth international congress of psychology, 1957. Amsterdam: North-Holland, 1959. Pp. 284-285. (a)

MacKay, D. M. Operational aspects of intellect. In Nat. Phys. Lab. Sympos. No. 10, 1958, Mechanization of thought processes. London: HMSO., 1959. Pp. 37-52. (b)

MacKay, D. M. Modelling of large-scale nervous activity. In J. W. L. Beament (Ed.), Soc. exp. Biol. Sympos. No. 14, Models and analogues in biology. London: Cambridge Univer. Press, 1960. Pp. 192-198. (Amer. ed., New York: Academic Press, 1960.)

MacKay, D. M. Interactive processes in visual perception. In W. A. Rosenblith (Ed.), Sensory communication. New York: M.I.T. Press and Wiley, 1961. Pp. 339-355.

MacKay, D. M. Theoretical models of space perception. In C. A. Muses (Ed.), Aspects of the theory of artificial intelligence. New York: Plenum, 1962. Pp. 83-104.

MacKay, D. M. Dynamic distortions of perceived form. Nature, 1964, 203, 1097.

MacKay, D. M. Cerebral organization and the conscious control of action. In J. C. Eccles (Ed.), Brain and conscious experience. New York: Springer-Verlag, 1966. Pp. 422-445.

MacKay, D. M., and Fiorentini, Adriana. Evoked potentials correlated with a visual anomaly. Nature, 1966, 209, 787-789.

von Holst, E., and Mittelstaedt, H. Das Reafferenzprinzip. Naturwiss., 1950, 37, 464.

Wilson, J. P. The response of the visual system to spatially repetitive stimuli. Unpublished doctoral thesis, University of London, 1960.

INVITED PAPERS II

Visual Shape Perception I

Chairman: Harry Blum
Data Sciences Laboratory
Air Force Cambridge Research Laboratories
Bedford, Massachusetts

SUBJECTIVE STROBOSCOPY AND A MODEL OF VISUAL MOVEMENT DETECTORS

J. F. Schouten
Instituut voor Perceptie Onderzoek
Eindhoven, Netherlands

Visual Movement

The perception of movement corresponds only partly with the actual speed of objects in the field of view. First, apparent movement slows down during viewing. Secondly, a striking afterimage of movement is observed when the field of view is brought to a standstill. This applies equally to horizontal movement (train panorama effect) and to vertical movement (waterfall effect). It also applies equally to rotary movement (gramophone disc effect) and to contracting or expanding patterns (size effect). Thirdly, in Wertheimer's phi-phenomenon, two lights which are alternately switched on and off will seem to swing back and forth right across the dark gap between the lights.

The afterimages are confined to the area of the retina exposed to the moving object and to its immediate surroundings. This property provides a major argument against the hypothesis that the illusions of movement are caused by a persistence of the tracking movements of the eye.

In fact, the phenomenology of both the slowdown and the negative afterimage is adequately described by Gibson's (1937) principle of "adaptation with negative after-effect." Recently, Taylor (1963) carefully measured the decay of the negative afterimage of rotating irregular patterns.

Neurophysiological Background

Gibson's principle applies equally to movement, color, brightness, heat, etc. MacKay (1961a) ventured the idea that the visual system might incorporate "detectors of motion as such." Lettvin, Maturana, McCulloch, and Pitts (1959) discovered "moving-edge detectors," neurons specifically sensitive to movement in a particular direction, in the visual system of the frog. Similar neurons were discovered by Hubel and Wiesel (1959) in the visual system of the cat and by Barlow and Hill (1963) in that of the rabbit.

The existence of movement detectors in the human visual system is still a matter of inference.

A Model of Movement Detectors and Its Consequences

It seems inevitable to assume that a neuron, in order to react specifically to movement in a particular direction, __must__ obtain its information from at least two retinal receptors, R_1 and R_2, spaced some distance λ apart and characterized furthermore by a time constant τ (see Figure 1).

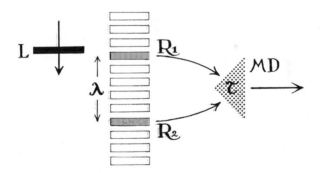

Fig. 1. Model of a movement detector. (Two retinal receptors R_1 and R_2, spaced λ apart, feed into the movement detector MD. The movement detector reacts if the light L first hits receptor R_1 and then, after or within a time τ, hits receptor R_2.)

The operational requirement of this unit would be that the neuron responds if and only if receptor R_1 is stimulated first and receptor R_2 at or within a time τ later. Then this simple space-time coincidence unit will act as a movement detector (MD). It will respond only to the component of movement in the direction of its two receptors and within a certain range of speeds determined by its λ and τ.

Let us assume that the human perception of movement takes place by virtue of such movement detectors. We do perceive movements in all directions anywhere in the field of view. Hence the visual system should have detectors of different orientations in each area of the retina.

This model elegantly accounts for the phi phenomenon since the movement detector will report movement when one light moves continuously from receptor R_1 to receptor R_2, but equally when one light strikes R_1 first and then another light strikes R_2. In fact one movement detector would be unable to distinguish between these two widely different stimulus patterns.

We perceive a wide variety of speeds. This could be explained by two different hypotheses. First, we can assume that all detectors respond universally to any speed. Then the measure of movement would be given by the number of detectors responding per second. Second, we can assume that the individual detectors respond specifically to particular speeds V. This would involve a range of either λ's or τ's or both for each area of the retina. In either case, however, the assumption of a finite spacing λ between the two receptors feeding into one movement detector leads us to an inevitable consequence.

Suppose a regular black-and-white striped pattern moves across the retina. If the spacing S between the stripes is large compared to the receptor spacing λ then the movement detectors will obtain faithful information on physical speed. If, however, S is of the order of magnitude of λ stroboscopic illusions should occur.

Such subjective stroboscopic illusions were demonstrated beautifully by Hassenstein and Reichardt (1956), by Reichardt and Varjú (1959), and by Götz (1964) for the facet eye of insects. When the insect follows a regularly striped pattern with spacing S, a reversal of the direction of flight was found when this spacing, in terms of angle, became of the order of the angle λ between adjoining facets (see Figure 2). This is readily understood in terms of the moiré pattern produced by two superposed regular gratings of almost identical spacing.

The unavoidable consequence drawn from our model of movement detectors thus boils down to stating that the visual perception of the vertebrate eye, as far as movement is concerned, should display certain characteristics of the insect's facet eye.

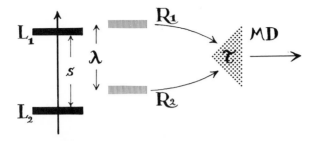

Fig. 2. Reversal of movement. (A regular pattern with a spacing S larger than the spacing λ between the receptors is moved in counterdirection across the retina. The stripe L_1 will hit receptor R_1 first. Then L_2 will strike R_2. Hence the movement detector will report a movement which is the reversal of the physical movement.)

Experimental Considerations

In order to put the expected stroboscopic illusion to a test the following considerations were made:

1. Unidirectional movement of parallel stripes was considered unfavorable since precautions would have to be taken against the natural tendency of tracking.

2. Perceptual cumulation over not too small an area around the fovea was expected to enhance the illusion.

3. Visual inacuity and the diameter of cumulation areas increase, in first approximation, linearly with the distance ψ from the fovea. It was guessed that the average receptor spacing λ might increase similarly with ψ. Hence the spacing S of the black-and-white pattern should also increase with ψ.

These considerations led to the choice of rotating discs with radial black-and-white sectors (see Figures 3 and 4). A set of 17 discs of 30-cm diameter was made in which the number of black-and-white sector-pairs ranged between n = 1 and n = 90. The characteristic constants of such rotating discs are given by the sector angle $\phi = \dfrac{360°}{n}$, which is independent of viewing distance and the frequency f at which sectors pass any point of the retina. This frequency f is given by f = ng if g is the turning rate of the disc.

Experiments

Though most of the phenomena to be described can be seen to some extent with all discs investigated, the most striking results were obtained with n = 18-60 sector-pairs.

Fig. 3. Sector discs and wedding cake cylinders. (Seven-
teen discs with n = 1-90 sector pairs were used. The cylinders
have 24 and 8 stripe pairs, respectively. When mounted on
a gramophone turntable [50 cps, 78 rpm] the stripe frequencies
are 31.2 and 10.4 cps, respectively. Changing the driving
frequency permits easy alteration and calibration of the stripe
frequency.)

When slowly rotating any disc in daylight, while fixating the center,
one clearly sees the slowdown in apparent movement. The same can
be said for the negative afterimage of movement, which often is still
perceptible after an hour or even longer.

For sector frequencies below f = 5 cps the pattern gains in contrast,
the black sectors becoming velvety black, the white ones shiningly
white. The edges have colored fringes and, though remaining rather
sharp, have a wavy appearance.

At f = 8-12 cps the first stroboscopic effect sets in (α-stroboscopy).
The pattern is still distinctly black and white. The disc partly seems
to come to a standstill while other sectors look as though they are
performing a hurdle race over the standing ones. Central fixation is
still necessary.

At f = 30-35 cps the distinctness of the pattern has all but dis-

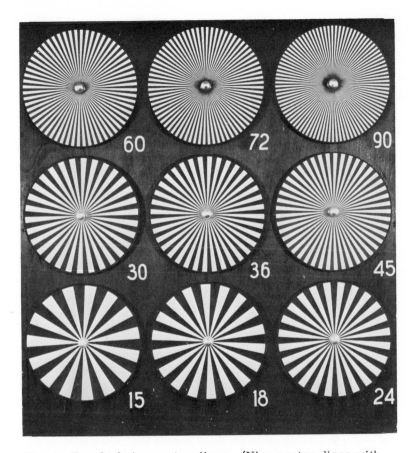

Fig. 4. Panel of nine sector discs. (Nine sector discs with
n = 15, 18, 24, 30, 36, 45, 60, 72, and 90 sector pairs are
mounted on a panel. The discs are coupled in such a way that
all sector frequencies are equal. Thus, e.g., the disc with
n = 90 sector pairs turns six times as slowly as the disc with
n = 15. With this panel it can be ascertained whether the
frequency f at which the reversal of movement [β -stroboscopy]
occurs is dependent on the number of sector pairs.)

appeared. At times a definite counterrotation[1] is seen of a grayish
striped pattern (β -stroboscopy), very similar to the normal stroboscopic pattern when viewing with ac lighting. Central fixation is
helpful but not necessary.

At f = 40-100 cps the disc appears almost uniform except that <u>at all</u>

---

[1]This effect was first demonstrated at a meeting of the Royal Netherlands Academy of Sciences on April 25, 1963.

sector frequencies a standing grayish pattern is seen (see Figure 5) in a quivery sort of standstill (γ-stroboscopy). This phenomenon is totally independent of fixation. At odd moments a part of the almost uniform disc is seen in a flash as a black-and-white zebra patch (Figure 5).

Fig. 5. Γ-stroboscopy and zebra patch. ([Drawing of the author's impression.] At sector frequencies f = 40-100 cps a grayish pattern of sectors is seen in quivery standstill [γ-stroboscopy]. At odd moments a clear black-and-white zebra patch is seen, the location of which on the disc is indicative of the direction and speed of the saccadic eye movement which causes it.)

Discussion

The heightened contrast at low turning rates is easily understood by considering that each sector runs in the wake of the negative after-image of its predecessor.

The reversal of rotation observed at f = 30-35 cps (β-stroboscopy) was the one we set out to demonstrate as a consequence of the hypothesis of the paired receptors R_1 and R_2. This reversal was clearly seen by many observers with discs covering a wide range of n = 15-90. Very much to our surprise, though, the required sector frequency

turned out to be about 30 to 35 cps for all discs. Moreover this
frequency is scarcely dependent, if at all, on illumination level up to
bright sunlight. This is the more surprising since the critical fusion
frequency is known to be strongly dependent upon illumination level.
The higher the level of illumination the more pronounced the effect of
reversal of rotation becomes.

The β-stroboscopy is thus determined by a universal time constant
$2\tau = 30$ msec $\pm$ 10%. Then, if the speed observed is determined by the
relation between λ and τ, the consequence is that the λ's cover a wide
range of values. Since the reversal is also seen in noncentral fixation,
proof is lacking as to whether we were right in guessing that the
average spacing increases with increasing distance from the fovea.
Yet, sectors with low n often show the reversal more pronouncedly in
peripheral rather than in central vision.

The partial standstill above f = 8-12 cps (α-stroboscopy) was not
predicted by our simple model. It provides a test, however, to any
more detailed assumptions regarding its properties.

The black-and-white zebra patches are evidently caused by saccadic
eye movements. If the eye makes a sudden jerk in a certain direction
with a certain speed, a particular part of the rotating disc will throw
a standing image on the retina. It is easily seen that the compass
direction on the disc correlates with the direction of the jerk and the
distance ψ from the center with the speed. Moreover the width of the
zebra patch in the direction of ψ should give some indication of the
duration of the jerk.

Thus the zebra patches provide an extremely simple and elegant way
of entoptically observing saccadic eye movements and even of obtaining their statistics in terms of rate, direction, speed, and, to some
extent, duration.

The γ-stroboscopy at frequencies above f = 40 cps, consisting in a
quivery sort of standstill independent of frequency, baffles us for an
explanation. As far as we can judge, it is either due to slight irregularities in rotation, or to the irregular movements of the eye which,
according to Ratliff and Riggs (1950), have an amplitude up to two
minutes of arc and frequencies between 30 and 70 cps.

We did find that similarly small movements of the field of view
(e.g., by looking through a vibrating mirror) or of the eye (by applying
a vibrator to the upper eyelid) cause a striking standstill, often of
surprising sharpness, if the vibrator frequency is in synchronism with

the sector frequency. Also the smallest shock to the eye, as caused
even by clenching one's teeth, is sufficient to see a momentary standstill. In both cases the evidence points strongly towards the assumption
that the standstill is caused by the moments of standstill of the image
on the retina. In both cases, be it irregular rotation or irregular eye
movements, the retina would obtain many glimpses a second of a
standing pattern which, since its phase would be different from glimpse
to glimpse, would lead to the observed quivery aspect of the standstill.
Even though we feel satisfied that irregular eye movements could explain the very phenomenon observed, we are not certain that minute
irregularities in disc rotation can be ruled out as a possible cause.

Other Phenomena

Of the many phenomena encountered, we particularly want to draw
attention to the three following ones.

The Fast Swirl. If, immediately after looking at a slowly rotating
disc, the eye is shifted towards a dark surface, a fast and fine-grained
countermovement is seen, lasting for no more than second or two.
This swirl is evidently identical with the one described by MacKay
(1961b) after looking at standing sector discs. MacKay's observations
on the swirl may be interpreted in terms of the aftereffects induced
in the motion detectors by the small erratic movements of the eye.

The swirl, as observed as a brief afterimage of a rotating disc, has
three curious features:

1. It is very fine-grained, possibly as fine as the resolving power of
   the eye.

2. The center rotates faster than the outside. It is not inconceivable
   that its angular speed across the retina is a constant which is
   vaguely estimated at some $20°-30°$ per sec. In any case the
   speed is far in excess of the initiating sector speed of say
   $5°-10°$ per sec.

3. This short-lived afterimage, though negative with respect to movement, is positive with respect to brightness. It is seen as a
   persisting sensation of brightness, preferably against a uniform
   dark background. The long-lived afterimage of movement,
   though also negative with respect to movement, is negative with
   respect to brightness in that it is visible when viewing details and
   contours of a luminant field of view but scarcely, if at all, in total
   darkness. Hence it relates to the sensitivity of the visual system.

Subjective Stroboscopy in Everyday Life. The author, after having become familiar with the stroboscopic illusions, had many occasions to observe them in everyday life. If, from a train which is gathering speed, one looks in sunlight at the sleepers (ties) of the neighbouring track while keeping fixation constant in relation to the window, the following phenomena are observed. Normally the sleepers are seen to run backward with respect to the train. At a sleeper rate of about 10 cps the sleepers seem partly to run along with the train (α-stroboscopy). If the sleeper rate reaches the value of about 30 cps they suddenly seem to run ahead of the train (β-stroboscopy).

Similar phenomena are observed in car driving with regular white stripes on the road or with black-and-white blocks on curbs or on tunnel walls. It is evident that these stroboscopic effects, if by chance striking a casual observer, may lead to dangerous distraction of attention.

Finally, it may be recalled that parallel striped designs of dress material often have a weird appearance. This is usually ascribed to astigmatism. We may now assume that it may be caused also by subjective stroboscopic illusions, arising if the striped pattern moves with appropriate speed across the field of view.

Mental Afterimages. The author, after intense occupation with the discs during the day before, often clearly "saw" the discs in dim light when waking up the next morning. The patterns were very clear, mostly in central fixation, often still, but at times rotating and without strict correlation with the number of sectors of the discs viewed the day before. It should be mentioned that normally the author is not subject to visual hallucinations and remembers having experienced them only a few times in his life. Therefore it is remarkable that the discs produce them so vividly and so repeatedly.

Conclusions

1. The idea is put forward that movement detectors in the visual system must operate by virtue of their connection to at least two retinal receptors. The detector model is then characterized by the spacing λ of the receptor pair and by a time constant τ.

2. This model offers an elegant neurophysiological explanation of the phi-phenomenon, since the movement detector will report movement either when a light passes continuously from its one receptor to the other or when a light strikes the first receptor first and a second light strikes the second receptor somewhat later.

3. The consequence of this model is that a stroboscopic illusion of reversed movement should occur, e.g., when the spacing of a moving periodic pattern is slightly larger than the receptor spacing λ.

4. This illusion of reversed motion (β-stroboscopy) was observed indeed. The most pronounced effect was found with turning discs having n = 18-60 sector pairs. The time constant τ was found to be a universal constant 2τ = 30 msec ± 10% (sector frequency f = 30-35 cps), scarcely dependent upon either pattern or brightness. Bright sunlight is most favorable for observing the illusion.

5. These findings strongly support MacKay's hypothesis that "detectors of motion as such" exist in the human visual system.

6. It may be assumed that the adaptive effects of subjective movement occur in the movement detectors proper or in their subsequent neurons.

7. An illusion of partial standstill (α-stroboscopy) was observed at sector frequencies above f = 8-12 cps. No explanation is put forward.

8. At sector frequencies above f = 40 cps black-and-white zebra patches are seen. These are evidently caused by the saccadic eye movements, which would provide an exceedingly simple way of obtaining the statistics of one's own eye movements with respect to rate, direction, speed, and possibly duration.

9. At sector frequencies f = 40-100 cps a grayish sector pattern in quivery standstill is observed (γ-stroboscopy). This pattern is probably due to minute and fast irregular eye movements, but could also be provoked by slight irregularities in the turning rate of the discs. In both cases the apparent standstill would be caused by the rapid summation of individual standstills.

10. A fast swirl in reversed movement is seen for a few seconds on a dark background as a short-lived afterimage of a slowly turning disc. This swirl seems identical with the one observed by MacKay with stationary discs. It is much more pronounced, though, and of unambiguous direction. This afterimage, though negative with respect to movement, is positive with respect to brightness. The suggestion seems reasonable that, when viewing a standing disc, the erratic eye movements produce similar afterimages, which would then be seen in either of two directions.

11. In general it seems highly promising to reconsider all known phenomena of perception of movement in terms of movement detectors. This applies particularly to the illusions of movement when looking at optical noise.

12. Most work on flicker phenomena was carried out with one light source only; hence with pure time flicker. The flicker fusion frequency is known to depend strongly on brightness. The phenomena described above are essentially a space-time flicker. The time constant $2 \tau = 30$ msec was found to be independent of brightness. It seems very promising to pay more attention to space-time flicker in general. This would also apply to the curious illusions of color when viewing the Benham disc.

References

Barlow, H. B., and Hill, R. M. Selective sensitivity to direction of motion in ganglion cells of the rabbit's retina. Science, 1963, 139, 412-414.

Gibson, J. J. Adaptation with negative after-effect. Psychol. Rev., 1937, 44, 221-244.

Götz, K. G. Optomotorische Untersuchung des visuellen Systems einiger Augenmutanten der Fruchtfliege Drosophila. Kybernetik, 1964, 2, 77-92.

Hassenstein, B., and Reichardt, W. Systemtheoretische Analyse der Zeit-, Reihenfolgen- und Vorzeichenauswertung bei der Bewegungsperzeption des Rüsselkäfers Chlorophanus. Z. Naturforsch., 1956, 11 b, 513.

Hubel, D. H., and Wiesel, T. N. Receptive fields in the cat's striate cortex. J. Physiol., 1959, 148, 574-591.

Lettvin, J. Y., Maturana, H. R., McCulloch, W. S., and Pitts, W. H. What the frog's eye tells the frog's brain. Proc. IRE, 1959, 47, 1940-1951.

MacKay, D. M. Interactive processes in visual perception. In W. A. Rosenblith (Ed.), Sensory communication. New York: M.I.T. Press and Wiley, 1961. Pp. 339-355. (a)

MacKay, D. M. Visual effects of non-redundant stimulation. Nature, 1961, 192, 739-740. (b)

Ratliff, F., and Riggs, L. A. Movements of the eye during fixation. J. exp. Psychol., 1950, 40, 687-701.

Reichardt, W., and Varjú, D. Uebertragungseigenschaften im Auswertesystem für das Bewegungssehen, Z. Naturforsch., 1959, 14 b, 674-689.

Taylor, M. M. Tracking the neutralization of seen rotary movement. Percept. mot. Skills, 1963, 16, 513-519.

CRITERIA FOR A TENABLE THEORY OF FORM PERCEPTION

Fred Attneave
Department of Psychology
University of Oregon
Eugene, Oregon

Everything I have to say to you is obvious. Some of it may even be found in elementary psychology texts. If I willingly take the risk of insulting you thus, it is because all of us have an extraordinary capacity for ignoring the obvious — particularly in our own fields.

The problem of how we identify objects — how we are able to tell cats from dogs, chairs from tables — is so obviously a fundamental one that we might expect anyone interested in perception to concern himself with it. Actually, however, interest in object identification is rather recent. Even those persons most concerned with form perception (specifically, the Gestalt psychologists) tended to ignore it. I know of only three serious attacks on the problem prior to 1950: those of Rashevsky (1938), Pitts and McCulloch (1947), and Hebb (1949).

More recently there has been a great upsurge of interest in the problem. Some of it comes from engineers who would like to build reading machines and similar devices. Some of it, on the other hand, is from psychologists who would like to know how real organisms function. A good many of these psychologists are employing computer simulation as a way of theorizing. It may be, indeed, that serious theory construction in this area has had to await the large-scale computer as a medium in which theories complicated enough to be realistic may be embodied. Even when a theory consists of simple postulates, its elaboration in a very large system may require a large-scale computer to determine what implications the postulates have. In any case, computer simulation rigorously enforces the first requirement of a true theory: that it be clear and explicit enough to have determinate implications.

A number of theories or systems of object identification have been proposed in recent years: we have n-tuple systems, pandemonium systems, template and part-template systems, and so on (see Hunt, 1962; and Uhr, 1963). My intention today is not to review or evaluate these, but rather to summarize, as clearly as I can, the problems with which any such system must cope if it is to be psychologically plausible.

Invariance of Response

It is now fairly well agreed that object identification is for the most
part a matter of form perception, at least at the human level. Form
may perhaps best be defined as a set of properties that are invariant
over certain transformations. Let us consider what these transformations are, keeping in mind that our concept of form will be no clearer
than our specification of them.

First, we would certainly say that form is invariant over several
transformations involving brightness and color. Within broad limits,
changing over-all illumination, or varying the "brightness" control on a
television receiver, does not change the perceived identity of objects.
Neither does change in the dispersion of brightnesses, as when the
"contrast" control of the television set is varied. We may wish to go
further and say that any transformation that preserves spatial discontinuities of intensity likewise preserves form, which would take
into account the formal equivalence of line drawings to the objects they
represent. Essentially, this would restrict visual form to properties
of "contours." Presumably contour may be generated by discontinuities in psychological properties of light other than brightness —
i.e., hue and saturation — though our empirical knowledge of the
behavior of real organisms in this area is surprisingly scanty. It
is a psychological fact that some kinds of discontinuity in "texture"
may generate contour (see, for example, the work of Julesz reported
in this symposium).

Second, we come to a group of spatial transformations that are,
up to a point, precisely definable. These may be characterized most
easily as the transformations of a projected (retinal) image that are
produced by moving a rigid body. There are six such dimensions of
movement: translations on each of three Cartesian axes, and rotation
about each of the three axes. (Note that translation on the z-axis
constitutes a size transformation of the retinal image.) Now, when the
rigid body under consideration is itself flat or two-dimensional, like
a blackboard drawing, these transformations show an appealing
mathematical tractability: i.e., one may build into a perceiving machine perfectly determinate mathematical principles enabling it to
give the same response to a form over the transformations. Unfortunately, this tractability is lost — or markedly impaired — when
we come to consider the rotation in depth (about x or y) of a solid

object, for the simple reason that there is no necessary or determinate mathematical relationship between the images of different sides
of the same object. The temptation is great — and I must confess to
having succumbed to it in the past — for the theorist to restrict himself
to what is essentially the reading-machine problem, the problem of
identifying flat shapes. The danger of this approach is, of course, that
the resulting theory is likely to be too elegant and simple, and un-
generalizable to solid objects. It is to Gibson's credit (1950) that he
has consistently tried to deal with surfaces and solid objects (though
he has not dealt with the problem of invariant identification), and I am
delighted to learn of the work that Roberts (1963) is now doing with
three-dimensional solids.

The remaining transformations that I wish to mention are messier
still: i.e., they are of indeterminate dimensionality, and difficult to
describe in precise terms. For this reason, however, they have been
neglected and therefore deserve major emphasis.

So far we have considered only rigid bodies, but many perceived
objects are by no means rigid: a book may be open or closed, an
animal may assume many postures, and so on. A tenable theory of
object identification must take into account corresponding transformations of the image. (Let me delay, for the moment, the question of
whether we are any longer talking about form at this point.)

It is evident, moreover, that different objects which are perceived as
more or less equivalent — i.e., placed in a common category — may
differ from one another in utterly arbitrary and nondescript ways.
Consider the class of objects called "chairs": it is difficult if not
impossible to find any visual properties, relational or otherwise, that
are common to all chairs but absent in nonchairs, and it is doubtful,
incidentally, that anyone would be inclined to say that all chairs have
the same form. If there is an essence of "chairhood," it must almost
certainly be looked for on the output rather than the input side of
the perceptual machinery.. Handwritten letters of the alphabet, with
which several people undertaking computer simulation have attempted
to deal, show similarly arbitrary variability. In limiting cases —
e.g., the common classification of upper- and lower-case characters —
it is clear that the response is to a disjunction of entirely different
sets of properties. Now, a system that can respond to arbitrary
disjunctions must be capable (aside from considerations of capacity)
of responding to nonarbitrary disjunctions, as in the case of the orderly

transformations that we started out considering. But how plausible is a system that takes no advantage of the lawfulness of orderly trans- formations? This is a theoretical issue of great importance.

Finally, let me mention invariance of identification over surrounds. Much has been made of the influence of context or surrounds on the perception of an object, but what is really striking is how little difference context makes. In the unlikely event that I return to my hotel room and find a small elephant standing inside, I shall not have any great difficulty identifying it as an elephant, despite the in- frequency with which I have encountered elephants in hotel rooms. The point is that a system which deals efficiently with an object hanging in a void may be swamped with noise when the object occurs in natural surroundings. Nearly all the systems with which I am familiar are in fact open to this criticism. Now, it is a definite possiblity that an object does hang in a void during the identification process, as a result of certain noise-suppression mechanisms. The emphasis of Gestalt psychologists on unit-formation, and the isolation of per- ceptual units from one another, bears directly on this problem. The grouping principles of Wertheimer (1923) refer, at least in part, to processes that may be involved in isolating objects, but psychologists interested in object identification have not always appreciated the relevance of such principles to their concerns.

In our survey of this somewhat formidable set of conditions under which object identification remains invariant, the concept of form has all but disappeared. Do we wish to say that visual form is entirely preserved in contour, or that other relationships, e.g., intensity ratios, also constitute formal properties of stimulation? Do frontal and profile views of a face have the same or different forms — or should they be regarded as different parts of the same form? Does the form of an animal change as it assumes various postures? Many questions of this sort can be asked, and the answers are entirely arbitrary. Form perception serves well enough as a name for the ball park in which we are playing, but we may as well accept the fact that form is an extremely ill-defined concept. This difficulty of definition is insubstantial and unimportant, however. What is important is that we understand, as clearly as possible, the facts of identification invariance that need accounting for.

Before proceeding, let me indicate one more such fact, or set of facts. I have perhaps suggested that identification is not impaired by certain transformations, when in actuality it is — most noticeably in cases involving fine discrimination. The difficulty of identifying an individual face, for example, is clearly increased by inverting it. An adequate theory must take into account decrements of this sort, and a system that works too well in such respects will not be realistic. Unfortunately, we do not know in much detail what the psychological facts are here. In the particular case of image rotation, experimental study is complicated by the varieties of rotational symmetry that an object may possess.

Some Further Problems of Identification

How may various properties of an image be abstracted, but still maintain association with one another? This question seems quite important to me, though it does not appear to bother anyone else (except possibly Boring, 1950, p. 93).

The issue may be spelled out at a fairly low level. Our heavy dependency on the information contained in contours leads to a belief that there must be mechanisms for contour abstraction. Some years ago Rashevsky (1938) suggested lateral inhibition as a means to this end, and we have subsequently learned that lateral inhibition is very much a reality in sensory systems. The output of a contour-abstracting net will of course be indifferent to a number of other sensory properties, and information about brightness, hue, etc., must presumably be tapped off at a lower level. We must nevertheless suppose that properties thus separated from one another remain in some sort of association, otherwise an observer confronted with a red circle and a green triangle would be confused about which shape had which color. This consideration is by no means irrelevant to the matter of identification, for identification is sometimes dependent upon joint states of color and shape (e.g., a purple object would probably never be called a tomato). The problem has a fairly obvious solution as long as we stay in a projection system, where representations of different properties might be somehow interleaved, but it becomes more puzzling when we have to consider representation in nonisomorphic systems. Even so, it may be most plausible to suppose that the representations of properties remain tagged with some kind of spatial coordinates.

Next I should like to comment on the relevance of the figure-ground distinction to identification. So many phenomena have at times been

discussed under the figure-ground rubric that one may question the
meaningfulness of the concept, but my point can be made in terms of a
very concrete situation. Take a circle and divide it down the middle
with some meaningless squiggle, as in Figure 1. Any drawing of this

Fig. 1. A nonsense drawing that
shows figure-ground reversal.

type can be perceived in either of two mutually exclusive ways. At a
given moment either the left side or the right is seen as a thing
(though not necessarily or typically as a familiar or identifiable
thing), and the two experiences are phenomenally quite different. A
long time ago Rubin (1915) showed that if one first sees such a display
in one way, and later sees it the other way, he is no more likely to
recognize it than if he had never seen it at all. Thus it seems quite
necessary to suppose that the perceptual system can generate two
entirely different descriptions or representations of the same contour,
and that these are in a competitive, flip-flop relationship to each
other. To the best of my knowledge and belief, no theory of identification to date has ever taken into account this extremely well-known
duality of process.[1] If one supposes that identification is to be based
on such component properties of contour as slopes and angles, it
should not matter which is the thing-side of the contour.

---

[1] In the discussion it was suggested that this statement was unjust to
Hebb, and it may be; certainly Hebb (1949) is cognizant of the figure-
ground dichotomy. I can understand that two cell-assemblies, or two
phase-sequences, might be mutually exclusive in this way, but why the
same contour should give rise to two such processes — especially when
little or no "meaning" is involved in either case — remains puzzling
to me.

This consideration makes me assign a much higher plausibility to diffusion or wave theories of perception than I otherwise would. Harry Blum (this volume) has not really convinced me that his theory can handle figure-ground reversal, but there seems to be at least a reasonable possibility that it might.

Perception as a Descriptive Process

It is evident that form perception involves a great deal more than the mere sorting of objects into gross classes. A realistic theory of identification must therefore be compatible with certain other functions, whether or not it undertakes to account for them in detail.

To say that perception is a set of processes by which the nervous system describes the world is a truism (i.e., the perceptual machinery can only represent or describe; it cannot otherwise internalize the world), but this way of viewing the matter may have considerable heuristic value. It invokes a linguistic analogy: in terms of the analogy we might say, without being too fanciful, that the identification problem is concerned only with the nouns in the nervous system's language, and ignores other parts of speech.

It is interesting to consider the degree to which this descriptive process is, in an operational sense, reversible. A good artist can view a complex scene and subsequently draw or paint it from memory. His reproduction will be neither complete nor altogether accurate, but it will clearly contain a great deal of the information that was once in his optic nerve. If we ask him, he will probably tell us that he retained an image or mental picture of the scene, and drew that.

Images have been out of fashion for some years, and I think it is about time for us to resume the study of them. They can tell us something about the nature of the perceptual process, though not in an uncomplicated way. It is a curious fact (at least I believe it is a fact) that one cannot have a universal image: imagine a dog, and you will find that it is a dog of some particular breed; its body will be oriented in some determinate direction, and probably it will have a determinate size and appear at a definite distance away from you. Better still, imagine a familiar melody, and you will find that you are thinking of it in some perfectly specific key, which you can determine (if you do not have absolute pitch) by going to the piano and searching for it, and which may or may not be the key in which you are accustomed to hearing it. The point of these examples is that an image seems inexorably to demand values on some (though not necessarily all) of the dimensions over which object identification is invariant; if these values are not contained in memory they will nevertheless be assigned in some arbitrary way. I should like very much to know what this means in terms of the system with which we are dealing.

A visual memory image may differ in important ways from its retinal precursor. A puzzle-picture like Figure 2 may or may not be "seen as" a familiar object. If it is not, the viewer will not have

Fig. 2. A puzzle picture of the Street-Gestalt type.

much success in attempting later to imagine or reproduce it. If it is, his subsequent image or reproduction will contain considerable information about the object but little or none about the individual patches of dark and light that made up the picture. Here it seems fairly clear that aspects of the input for which no descriptors are available, in the vocabulary of the system, or for which an excessively large number of descriptors would be required, are not stored. The memory image is more concrete than a gross object identification but more abstract than the retinal image; it seems to consist essentially of a set of lower-level descriptors on which object identification is based.

Now, we have every reason to believe that the optic nerve (not to mention other sensory channels) has a tremendously higher information capacity than does the perceptual machinery at higher levels. Thus a drastic simplification of the input must occur, and a major theoretical problem is to figure out exactly how it occurs. Speaking grossly, simplification may take the form either of throwing away information or of recoding it more compactly. The nervous system almost certainly does both, and in both processes (or in both aspects of the process,

depending upon how we conceptualize the system) the <u>lawfulness</u> or
regularity of the input assumes primary importance.

The perceptual system seems typically to discard information that
is not to some degree <u>coherent</u>. (See the recent and very interesting
work of Hake and his associates [1957] on coherence and coherence-
detection in perception.) Coherence is always identifiable with some
kind of lawfulness in the input: e.g., if two variables are highly correlated, certain of their joint states (those of high probability) are
coherent, others not. The regularity may be highly specific, and
clearly involve the past experience of the perceiver, as in the case of
associations among the parts of a familiar object. (Note the relevance
of this discussion to the matter of object isolation, and invariance over
surrounds, mentioned earlier.) On the other hand, and more importantly, it may consist in very general ecological principles, having
to do chiefly with the high incidence of homogeneity with respect to
such variables as brightness, texture, slope, value of angle, etc.

Exactly the same kinds of regularity have another aspect, however,
that of <u>redundancy</u>. This is the potentiality for economical description
that is inherent in any lawful situation; specifically, we are referring
to the possibilities that exist for recoding the information in afferent
nerves into a system of lesser capacity, without information loss.
How, and to what degree, does the perceptual machinery take advantage
of these possibilities?

A great deal of evidence indicates some sort of preference for
simple over complex ways of perceiving (i.e., describing) various
situations. Johansson's (1950) work on the perception of movement
provides some good examples of this tendency; so does the work of
Hochberg and McAlister (1953) on perception of depth and size.
Hochberg has shown most convincingly that the probability of perceiving a projection of a cube as two-dimensional versus three-dimensional
depends upon the simplicity or redundancy (number of lines of equal
length, number of angles of equal value, etc.) of the projection.

I suggested in 1954 (Attneave, 1954) that the perceptual system
achieves economical descriptions by abstracting features of high
informational value, e.g., contours at one level, and discontinuities of
slope, i.e., angles, at another. The evidence for contour abstraction
is good, as I have mentioned already, and Hochberg (1962) has found
that the eyes tend strongly to fixate on angles and other discontinuities.
Other evidence — the stabilized image study of Pritchard, Heron, and

Hebb (1960) and the electrophysiological work of Hubel and Wiesel (1962) — tends to support lines but not angles as basic perceptual elements or descriptors.

As an alternative hypothesis, consider the limiting case in which features are randomly sampled, without regard to their information content. If the input were sufficiently redundant, it could still be represented adequrtely (though not with optimal economy) in such a sample. Suppose iurther that a principle of like-facilitates-like applies generally to the system at some level, e.g., that descriptors of the same slope, the same hue, etc., are interconnected in such a way as to prime or facilitate one another. (It might be supposed that the facilitation is relative to some general background of lateral inhibition.) Such systems would have essentially the status of Hebb's (1949) cell-assemblies, though they might very well be innate. A like-facilitates-like principle might underlie various phenomena of completion or closure in perception, on the one hand (e.g., in tachistoscopic situations, and in the case of stabilized images), and in recall (memory images) on the other. A highly incomplete memory trace would tend to be completed at the time of recall in a more or less accurate manner, depending on the redundancy (homogeneity) of the original input. If this principle were operative, the representation of a lawful or regular stimulus-array would exhibit autofacilitative or "locking-in" properties consistent with Hake's concept of coherence, or with the older Gestalt concept of a strong or stable structure. Likewise, Hochberg's results with projections of cubes might be partially explained in terms of a dominance of those representations in which component descriptors facilitate one another.

I am not trying to present a theory, however. My present purpose is merely to point out that the issue of input regularity and economical description is one that a good theory must deal with.

Learning and Meaning

The dependence of perception on learning is so heavy, and probably takes so many forms, that I can do the matter no sort of justice within the limits of this talk. Since the hour is late, I shall mention only two problems that seem particularly prominent. First, in the case of object identification, by what process do class-criteria, and possibly class-boundaries, become established? Second, in the case of description more generally, by what mechanisms do stored traces affect the ongoing perceptual or descriptive process? This is the problem of "apperceptive mass," or "schemata." It has not attracted much hard theoretical effort; Oldfield (1954) has perhaps come closest to suggesting a definite model.

Finally, it is my firm belief that we cannot possibly develop a decent theory of perception without coming to grips with the problem of meaning. (The Transactionalists have been saying this, in effect, for a good many years. MacKay is clearly cognizant of the point; see his paper in this symposium.) Let me try to indicate what the problem is.

Suppose we have a system that identifies or categorizes objects, providing, by whatever means, a unique response for each of a number of object classes. (The system might at the same time provide unique responses constituting descriptors of various object properties, etc.) The nature of the unique response does not matter; suppose for convenience that it is the firing of a particular neuron: that there is one neuron uniquely responsive to dogs, another to chairs, and so on. Now, my question is: How do we know (or, rather, how does any other part of the system know) what any such unique response stands for? If there was a homunculus who could peek out through a hatch in the skull and determine what was making the unique neuron fire ("Ah! That must mean chair! ") the problem would be greatly simplified. Although I have argued elsewhere in favor of a neural homunculus (1960), I am altogether against allowing him to cheat in this manner. However, several theoretical systems have been proposed that allow object identification to be "learned" by means of some such independent, essentially extrasensory access to reality. This simplification is unrealistic in a way that may be very fundamental.

I leave you, then, with the question of how the nervous system is able to understand its own language. Or, to put it in a way that is possibly better: How is the nervous system able to devise a language that it can understand?

References

Attneave, F. Some informational aspects of visual perception. Psychol. Rev., 1954, 61, 183-193.

Attneave, F. In defense of homunculi. In W. A. Rosenblith (Ed.) Sensory communication. Cambridge: M.I.T. Press, 1960. Pp. 777-782.

Boring, E. G. History of experimental psychology. New York: Appleton-Century, 1950.

Gibson, J. J. The perception of the visual world. Boston: Houghton Mifflin, 1950.

Hake, H. W. Contributions of psychology to the study of pattern vision. USAF WADC tech. Rep., 1957, No. 57-621. (AD-142035)

Hebb, D. O. The organization of behavior. New York: Wiley, 1949.

Hochberg, J. The psychophysics of pictorial perception. Audio-Vis. Comm. Rev., 1962, 10, 22-54.

Hochberg, J. and McAlister, E. A quantitative approach to figural "goodness." J. exp. Psychol., 1953, 46, 361-364.

Hubel, D. and Wiesel, T. Receptive fields, binocular interaction and functional architecture in the cat's visual cortex. J. Physiol., 1962, 160, 106-154.

Hunt, E. B. Concept learning: An information processing problem. New York: Wiley, 1962.

Johansson, G. Configurations in event perception. Uppsala: Almquist & Wikesell, 1950.

Oldfield, R. C. Memory mechanisms and the theory of schemata. Brit. J. Psychol., 1954, 45, 14-23.

Pitts, W. and McCulloch, W. S. How we know universals. The perception of auditory and visual forms. Bull. Math. Biophys., 1947, 9, 127-147.

Pritchard, R. M., Heron, W., and Hebb, D. O. Visual perception approached by the method of stabilized images. Canad. J. Psychol., 1960, 14, 67-77.

Rashevsky, N. Mathematical biophysics. Chicago: Univer. Chicago Press, 1938.

Roberts, L. G. Machine perception of three-dimensional solids. Lincoln Lab. tech. Rep., 1963, No. 315.

Rubin, E. Synsoplevede Figurer. Copenhagen: Gyldendalske, 1915.

Uhr, L. "Pattern recognition" computers as models for form perception. Psychol. Bull., 1963, 60, 40-73.

Wertheimer, M. Untersuchungen zur Lehre von der Gestalt, II. Psychol. forsch., 1923, 4, 301-350.

INVITED PAPERS III

Speech Perception

Chairman: Philip Lieberman
Data Sciences Laboratory
Air Force Cambridge Research Laboratories
Bedford, Massachusetts

SOME OBSERVATIONS ON A MODEL FOR SPEECH PERCEPTION

A. M. Liberman [1] **, F. S. Cooper, Katherine S. Harris,**
P. F. MacNeilage, and M. Studdert-Kennedy [2]
Haskins Laboratories
New York, New York

Since this symposium is concerned with models, we should say at the outset that we do not have a model in the strict sense, though we are in search of one. What we do have are some notions about the general characteristics that a model of speech perception should have. We will try this morning to describe these notions and the facts that have led us to entertain them.

We should examine first certain facts that exist independently of any research on speech itself. Some of these facts emerge from an inquiry into the structure of language, others from a look at the limitations of the auditory system. Together, they define an important part of the job that a model of speech perception must do, and significantly constrain the assumptions it can use.

We begin, then, with some facts about linguistic structure. These have great generality in that they transcend any particular modality through which the message might come. They must be taken into account, that is, whether communication is by eye, by ear, or through

---

[1] Also at the University of Connecticut, Storrs, Connecticut.

[2] Also at Barnard College, New York, New York.

the skin. One might say of these facts, therefore, that they are somehow cognitive, but for our purposes we need only say that, being most
general, they have an obvious priority and we should consider them
first.

It is the more appropriate that we should begin with such general
considerations because this symposium is concerned with the perception of optical as well as acoustic signals, and we have in mind that
language is perceived, in literate people at least, by eye as well as by
ear. We will, in time, narrow our concern to the perception of spoken
language. In keeping with the purpose of this symposium, however,
and also in order to see our own problem of speech perception more
clearly, we will first consider what it is that must happen in all
linguistic perception, and then measure these requirements against
the abilities and shortcomings of the eye and ear.

Perception and Linguistic Structure

In studying the perception of language, we begin with the advantage
that there exists a reasonably good description of what is perceived.
We know that language is composed of segments arranged in
hierarchically ordered layers. We know, too, that the structure
formed by these segments and layers is described by two grammars:
one, the phonology, for the segments that are themselves empty of
meaning; and the other, comprising morphology and syntax, for the
segments to which meaning can be ascribed. Among the phonological
segments there are, at base, some 30 to 50 phonemes — themselves
composed of a smaller number of subphonemic features — from which
we proceed to a larger number of syllables, and then to units that may
be called phonological words. Beginning, in the other grammar, with
some thousands of morphemes, we move through a larger vocabulary
of words and a vast repertory of phrases to an infinity of sentences.

A consideration of this structure suggests several questions for a
model of speech perception. Is the model to deal with perception in
both grammars; that is, on both sides of the meaning barrier? Given
that we are on the one side or the other, is it, then, to explain the
perception of all the segments in each layer? And will it account for
the way the segments in one layer are organized for use at the next
higher one, or how the segments at one layer constrain, or operate
parallel with, those of another?

We can ignore these questions, but only if we assert that the

segments and layers are figments of a linguist's imagination or,
perhaps, linguistic abstractions that have no reality in perception.
And, indeed, we may at times be tempted to do just that. We will find,
for example, that the acoustic correlate of a given phoneme changes
considerably with different phonetic contexts, and we may accordingly
be moved to infer that the syllable, rather than the phoneme, is the
smallest segment of phonological perception. This would be unwise.
We have the greatest respect for the imagination of our linguist colleagues, but we cannot believe that they invented linguistic structure;
we hold, with them, that they only discovered it. No more can we
believe that this structure is not psychologically real and important.
There is evidence, both direct and indirect, that attests to the
psychological reality and importance of each one of the segments and
the subphonemic features, too. But there is not time to consider this
matter in detail. We will say only, then, that the model we seek must
deal with linguistic structure for the simple, and we think unassailable,
reason that linguistic structure is a description of what the listener
perceives.

We would like, of course, to understand the whole of linguistic
perception; that is, to answer all the questions we raised a moment
ago. Our ambition has realistic bounds, however, so we have chosen
to be concerned primarily with perception within the phonological
system. Still, we should be aware that other problems exist. We are
surely well advised to have in mind that a model of phonological perception will one day be married to a model for the perception of
morphology and syntax. We ought, therefore, to be concerned in
advance about their likely compatibility. At the very least, we should
be gratified if the two models grew up speaking the same meta-
language.

In this connection, we will get ahead of our story just long enough to
say about the model we seek that it contains a key assumption, namely,
that the sounds of speech are somehow perceived by reference to the
way we generate them. We have discussed this assumption and the
reasons for making it in a number of earlier papers (see Cooper,
Liberman, Harris, and Grubb, 1958; Liberman, 1957; Liberman,
Cooper, Harris, and MacNeilage, 1962; Liberman, Delattre, and
Cooper, 1952). An explicit model that embodies essentially this point
of view is described by K. N. Stevens (1960) and by Morris Halle and
Stevens (1962). They would recognize speech on the basis of

analysis by synthesis according to generative or articulatory rules.
Now, as Halle and Stevens (1959) pointed out in an earlier paper, such
a model is not too different from one that seems peculiarly appropriate
for perception at the higher levels of language too. This is hardly
a decisive consideration in the selection of a model for phonological
perception, but it is relevant, we think, and even interesting.

Requirements for Perception at the Phoneme Level.

Let us, now, take the shortest segment at the phonological level —
the phoneme — and consider the requirements that are imposed on its
perception by the nature of linguistic structure. There are two. The
first is that the phonemes must not lose their identity as they enter
into combinations with other phonemes. If this requirement is not
met, the system is not phonemic, in which case it is not linguistic.
Perception of the phoneme must also be independent of context in a
somewhat different and weaker sense: it is not enough to hear a
particular phoneme, say /t/, as something more or less like /t/ than
the last phoneme heard; rather, it must be heard as /t/ itself. This
is to say that we must identify absolutely, not merely discriminate.

The second requirement is one of speed. Since language is phonemic
we need only a few basic segments — not more than about 40, in
fact — to produce an infinite number of utterances. But we pay for
this economy, other things being equal, by the requirement that we
must transmit and receive a large number of these elements per unit
time. If we did not, communication would be slow. Worse yet, it
might even be impossible, for if one is to organize the phonemes into
units at a higher level, they must come in at a reasonably high rate.
Here we are limited by our span of apprehension or attention in time,
and if anyone doubts this, he need only have someone read to him
slowly, letter by painful letter.

In short, the language demands that the phonemes be absolutely
and rapidly identified. We shall, for convenience, use the word
"distinctive" to refer to stimuli that can be so identified. Let us
inquire now how the visual and auditory systems might meet this
requirement of distinctiveness.

Phoneme Perception in Relation to the Properties of the Eye and the Ear.

Keeping in mind that the problem is to get the phoneme strings from

one person's head into another's, consider first how this might be
done if we were dealing with computing machines rather than people.
The messages would be organized into word-length segments and then
transferred either in parallel or serially. Parallel transfers are
usually much faster, for obvious reasons, and we would suppose that
this would be true for humans, too.

The visual system appears to be organized on a parallel basis, so
one should anticipate no great difficulty in getting the phonemes through
the transmission link and into the recipient's head. We need only
devise a set of distinctive shapes, one for each phoneme, and set them
side by side. We could use one of the alphabets already available,
each of them highly distinctive, or we could invent a new one if for any
reason this seemed desirable. Because of the eye's ability to perceive in space, we can have a one-to-one relation between phoneme
and external signal, as we do with the alphabetic scheme we just described, and still encounter no real difficulty in perceiving word-
length sequences of these phoneme segments.

In the auditory case the problem is different and considerably
greater. To the extent that the input channel operates in the serial
mode, it is inherently slower than vision. Then, too, it is not all that
easy to get 40 highly identifiable signals, unless one is willing to use
up time in patterning the acoustic characters. And to do this is, of
course, self-defeating if our purpose is to communicate at high speed.
But let us assume that we have somehow overcome this difficulty and
succeeded in finding 40 or so highly identifiable acoustic signals that
are nevertheless of short duration — not appreciably longer, that is,
than the integration time of the ear. Consider now what happens when
we present these one after the other. At rates of 200 to 300 words per
minute — and we can perceive speech produced by time-compressing
machines at rates considerably above that — we should have something
between 10 and 20 of these signals per second. This is below the
threshold for pitch, but it is still so rapid that the signals would be hard
to discriminate, let alone identify and otherwise process.[3]

Perhaps the best way to see the ear's difficulty is to consider what
reading would be like if the eye were subject to limitations like those

---

[3] It was on the basis of such oversimplified assumptions about the
relation of sound segment to phoneme that R. H. Stetson (1951) was
led to conclude that the phoneme did not exist as a psychological
unit.

that beset the ear. The appropriate analogy would be with a reading situation in which the individual letters were flashed on and off, one at a time, in succession, and in the same place. But we labor the point and put ourselves in danger of being about to predict that people will never be able to perceive speech, or that our species will develop the ability to read and write before it learns to speak and listen.

At the very least, however, we should not be surprised to discover that speech is a uniquely distinctive set of acoustic signals. And we do discover precisely that. No other acoustic signals will work nearly so well. Some will object at this point that such a statement is true but trivial, having in mind, perhaps, that no one has ever really tried to develop an alternative acoustic system, or that it is, in any case, difficult to match the amount of practice we have all had in listening to speech. In general, such an objection is not well taken. Nonspeech ciphers on the phonemic structure of language have been developed and thoroughly tested, not only in the familiar case of Morse code but also in 50 years of research and development in the attempt to build reading machines for the blind. It is most instructive to review the results of that work, but we do not have time now (see Coffey, 1963; Cooper, 1950; Freiberger and Murphy, 1961). We can say only that nonspeech ciphers work very badly by comparison with speech.

We would like to be able to compare speech sounds more broadly with acoustic signals that are in no way tied to a linguistic system. Unfortunately, directly comparable data for the rate of processing nonspeech acoustic signals are not available (but see Pollack, 1952; Pollack and Ficks, 1954; Studdert-Kennedy, Liberman, and Rosov, 1963). We should consider, however, that in perceiving rapid speech, a listener processes information at rates of up to 50 bits per second. From such knowledge as we do have of the information-carrying capacities of nonspeech acoustic signals, such a rate appears to be very high indeed.

What, then, does the unique distinctiveness of speech sounds tell us about a model of speech perception? At the very least it suggests that there must be something special either about the properties of the signal or about the way we process it. Our own very strong tendency is to embrace both alternatives. Speech sounds have the interesting property that they are also produced by the person who perceives them. In this respect they are not truly unique, however, since we sometimes clap our hands, snap our fingers, tap our feet, and sneeze. Speech sounds are wholly unique in that they alone are produced by neuromuscular events that are at some point equivalent to the grammar of a language or, more specifically in this case, to the constituent units of phonology. This, in turn, creates the possibility for a special kind of perceptual processing: namely, that the acoustic signal is somehow decoded by reference to the manner in which these segments are produced. We said only that the possibility is created. We do believe, however, that people take advantage of this possibility, and that if they did not, speech would be far less distinctive than it is.

So much, then, for the problems and facts that exist independently of research on speech perception itself. Let us turn now to that research.

Acoustic Cues for Phoneme Perception: A Complex Code.

A finding which turns up over and over again in a variety of different, yet related forms is that there is a complex relation between perceived language and the acoustic signal which conveys it. More specifically, the acoustic signal is quite commonly not invariant with respect to the phoneme as perceived. We should not be surprised by this since we have just seen what difficulties would plague any attempt to get language past the auditory bottleneck by any simple and obvious means. But we must examine the nature of the complexity and explore its implications.

In the structure of language the phonemes are discrete segments. In the acoustic stream of speech they are not. And, indeed, we could not expect them to be, given what we know about the temporal resolving power of the ear and the number of pulses per second we should hear if the phonemes were acoustically discrete. Of course, the acoustic cues for the phonemes are there. We know what they are and where they are, and we can, moreover, manipulate them so as to change the perception on a phoneme-by-phoneme basis. But the cues for the phonemes do not lie along the time axis like so many beads on a string. Rather, they are overlapped and, more generally, encoded into units of approximately syllabic size. This is why one cannot synthesize speech from prerecorded segments of phonemic dimensions (see Harris, 1953; Liberman, Ingemann, Lisker, Delattre, and Cooper, 1959; Peterson, Wang, and Sivertsen, 1958). And in the reverse process of machine recognition, this is why the engineer finds it so difficult to segment speech into the phonemic constituents we humans perceive.

The encoding of phoneme strings into syllabic units reduces significantly the number of discrete acoustic segments (per unit time) the listener must hear. In this sense it helps to account for the rapid transmission of information through an auditory channel ill equipped to pass the serially ordered segments of language. But if this encoding solves one problem, it poses another, for we must now explain how the phonemes are recovered from the encrypted signals. In our view, a suitable decoding mechanism would be specialized to use information about the manner in which the phonemes were encoded in the first place. How the encoding first occurred will be considered shortly.

The rather complex encoding of the phonemes shows in other ways, too. Thus, we have in earlier papers commented on examples of a situation in which phonemic cues for different consonants are acoustically the same before different vowels. We have also described the converse examples in which cues for the same consonant are very different before different vowels.[4] The cases that we have particularly emphasized in this connection are, the by now, fairly familiar ones that deal with the burst cue in the perception of /pi/, /ka/, /pu/ and the transition shift from /ga/ to /gɔ/ (see Delattre, Liberman, and Cooper, 1955; Liberman, 1957; Liberman et al., 1952; Liberman, Delattre, Cooper, and Gerstman, 1954). It should be understood, however, that these are not isolated examples. Thus, with transitions that all begin at exactly the same point on the frequency scale, one can, before different vowels, produce all three stops /b,d,g/ (see Delattre et al., 1955). Conversely, one can, in the case of many consonants produce the same phoneme perception (before different vowels) with transitions that begin at frequencies that are, by any psychophysical standards, enormously different. If one chooses to define the acoustic cue differently — for example, as the direction and extent of the transition rather than its starting frequency — exactly comparable difficulties arise.

---

[4] In these cases we should distinguish two kinds of invariance lack. The one kind — and this is the kind we are particularly interested in here — includes all cases in which very different acoustic shapes lead to essentially indistinguishable perceptions. In the other kind, different acoustic shapes lead to discriminably different perceptions which are nevertheless classed as members of the same phoneme. An example of the latter kind is found with the vowels, where intraphonemic variations are easily heard (see Fry, Abramson, Eimas, and Liberman, 1962).

Indeed, the search for acoustic cues that would show a reasonable degree of invariance with respect to perception has had a long and largely unrewarding history, especially in the case of the consonants. The initial disappointments came in failing to find — a few cases excepted — component parts of the acoustic stream that were superimposable for occurrences of the same phoneme in different environments. These would, of course, have qualified as invariant cues in the simplest and strictest sense. Next best would have been such derived cues as the starting frequencies, or the direction and extent, of the formant transitions. Though these would not, by their nature, have met the strict test of superimposability, we could nevertheless, with some satisfaction, have defined them as the acoustic cues. As we have seen, however, we do not find invariance even when we define the cue in this rather lax way. To unify, at least to some extent, the great variety of acoustic shapes that in different environments produce the same phoneme perception, we had, in the case of the stop and nasal consonants, to discover the "locus" — the frequency to which the transitions point (see Delattre et al., 1955). Although the locus is here a very convenient concept around which to organize many otherwise diverse acoustic facts, it is in no sense available to the listener as part of the acoustic signal. Nor can it be made an actual part of that signal without grossly upsetting and changing the perception.[5]

Now the loci are more nearly invariant with respect to the perception than are the actual acoustic signals. And in this connection it is of more than incidental interest that the locus incorporates an essentially articulatory transformation (see Stevens and House, 1956). We would suppose that even better approximations to invariance with perception might be had by getting closer to the essential operations underlying articulation. We shall have more to say of these later.

The point to be made now is that for many of the important consonants there is no way to define the acoustic cues so as to have, except in a small number of phonetic contexts, an invariance between acoustic cue and phoneme perception. We cannot here list, or even

---

[5] If, with synthetic speech, one carries the transition all the way to the /d/ locus, for example, thus converting an imaginary extrapolation of the acoustic cue into a true part of it, a listener will hear /d/ in only a very few vowel contexts; in all others he will hear /b/ or /g/, as in the example given earlier in the text and referenced in Delattre et al. (1955).

classify, all the examples. We can only say that they are dramatic and numerous — so numerous, indeed, as to make this lack of invariance seem almost the rule rather than the exception.

From Phoneme to Acoustic Cue and Back: Encoding and Decoding.

The complex relation between acoustic cue and phoneme perception reflects, as we have already said, the encoding of acoustic signals into units of approximately syllabic length. In considering how these signals are perceived, we have at least two choices. As we have already implied, one is to reject the phoneme and begin with the syllable — to assert, that is, that /ga/ differs from /ba/ only holistically and not just in the first segment. Similarly, we should have to assert that /ga/ differs from /g/ holistically and not just in the second segment. But such assertions are, as we have already said, plainly contrary to fact. Besides, they lead us to assumptions that are uneconomical and in-elegant: Our model would have to perceive, at base, the thousands of syllables instead of the many fewer phonemes.

An alternative interpretation is that the listener manages somehow to recover the phoneme. To see how he might do this, we should consider how the signals became complexly encoded in the first place. We shall assume — indeed, we think we must assume — that somewhere in the speaker's central nervous system there exist signals which stand in a one-to-one relation to the phonemes of the languages. In the act of speaking, these signals, arranged of course in some temporal pattern, flow outward from the central nervous system and eventuate as commands to the articulatory muscles. At this level the relation to phonemic structure is conceivably still quite simple, that is, we can, perhaps, find a close correspondence to the phoneme by inquiring which muscles are commanded to contract, when, and how forcibly. (Just how close or remote this correspondence is will have to be con-sidered later.) The next steps, of course, are the transformation of these motor commands into a shape, or sequence of changing shapes, of the articulatory tract, and then into sounds. Now it is possible that in some instances the relation between the activation of a muscle and the resulting sound is simple, direct, and independent of neighboring movements, but this is surely rare. Given that the unit commands can and surely do overlap in time, and given all the interactions and constraints inherent in the anatomy and physiology of the vocal tract, we should expect to get the kind of scrambling that we do, in fact,

find — that is, a loss of segmentability and the frequent existence of
a complex relation between acoustic cue and intended phoneme (see
Cooper et al., 1958; Lisker, Cooper, and Liberman, 1962).

Thus, the complexities we find in the acoustic signals were not
always there. Accordingly, we can, perhaps, recover a simple relation
to the language by getting back on the other side of the successive
transformations by which the message was converted from neural
signal to sound. We should remind ourselves here that the perceiver
is also a speaker, and that he must, therefore, possess all the
mechanisms for putting the segments through the successive recodings
that result eventually in the acoustic signal. We wonder, then, whether
it is necessary, or desirable, or even reasonable to endow him with an
entirely different set of mechanisms for decoding that signal. We
would prefer to assume that he has but one mechanism, one center, if
you will, with some kind of link between sensory and motor areas.

At all events the kinds of data we mentioned a moment ago suggest
that perception may be more closely related to articulation than to the
acoustic signal. We should like to consider one more type of evidence
for that generalization: this is an example which relates in a special
way, we think, to the distinctiveness of speech, and which contributes,
also, to the development of our thesis.

Categorical Perception of Some Acoustic Cues

We have found in speech perception a number of cases in which a
continuously varied acoustic signal tends to be perceived categorically.
In these cases the articulation is also categorical, which is, of course,
the point. A specific example, and one of several we might choose,
concerns the perceived distinction between the words "slit" and "split".
Bastian, Eimas, and Liberman (1961) found first that a powerful and
sufficient acoustic cue for this distinction is simply the duration of an
interval of silence between the /s/ friction and the vocalic portion of
the syllable. They subsequently found, as others had found previously
in work with other consonant cues, that perception of this cue is
categorical in the sense that subjects tend to hear test stimuli, each
with a different duration of silent interval, either as /slɪt/ or /splɪt/:
Given equal physical differences between successive acoustic signals,
the listener discriminates very poorly within the range of a single
phoneme, then experiences what amounts to a quantal jump in perception at the phoneme boundary (see Bastian et al., 1961). In order

to find out whether the articulation was also categorical, these investigators had the subjects attempt to mimic the experimental stimuli
with their various durations of silent interval. Acoustic and electromyographic records of the subject's responses indicated that articulation was as categorical as the perception — that is, the subject either
closed his lips to articulate /splIt/ or he kept them open to produce
/slIt/. There were no partial closures in response to stimuli near
the center of the acoustic continuum (see Harris, Bastian, and Liberman,
1961).

Here, then, is a situation in which the acoustic variation is continuous, articulation is categorical, and perception — following
articulation but not the acoustic signal — is also categorical. There
are other instances of this, in the perception of /b,d,g/ (Eimas, 1963;
Griffith, 1958; Liberman, Harris, Hoffman, and Griffith, 1957), /d,t/
(Liberman, Harris, Kinney and Lane, 1961), and /ræ bId-ræ pId/
(Liberman, Harris, Eimas, Lisker, and Bastian, 1961), for example,
though /slIt-splIt/ is the only case of categorical perception so far
studied in which mimicry has been carefully measured and precise
data on articulation have been obtained.

In this connection, we should say that in the perception of stress,
which is, perhaps, not so categorical as the cases we just listed,
Peter Ladefoged has found that the perception bears a simpler
relation to the activity of respiratory muscles than to the properties
of the acoustic signal. From this fact he concludes that in perceiving
stress the listener is, in effect, perceiving the behavior that normally
produces it (Ladefoged, Draper, and Whitteridge, 1958).

The Perception of Speech and Nonspeech

If it is true that listeners hear speech in terms of the way they produce it, then speech signals and nonspeech signals must somehow be
processed differently. We turn now to the evidence which suggests in
one way or another that this may, in fact, be so. Consider again
the case of /slIt, splIt/ and recall that discrimination of equal physical
differences in the acoustic cue was considerably better at the phoneme
boundary than in the middle of the phoneme range. What happens when
we ask subjects to discriminate essentially the same acoustic
variable, namely, the duration of a silent interval between a patch of
noise and a complex tone, but in a nonspeech pattern? The answer
is that there is then no peak in the discrimination curve but only the

monotonic kind of function one most commonly finds in the perception
of one-dimensional variations of a stimulus (Bastian et al., 1961).
Essentially this same kind of experiment has been carried out for
several other consonant distinctions, and the same kind of result has
been obtained (see Liberman et al., 1961; Liberman et al., 1961).

Such results suggest that the discrimination peaks and the distinctiveness they provide are not inherent in the acoustic signal.
Moreover, they would seem to indicate that experience with the acoustic
variable, qua acoustic variable, is not enough. Learning to discriminate
durations of silence of the magnitude that distinguish /slIt/ from /splIt/
did not generalize to the perception of that variable in a nonspeech
context; the discrimination peaks occurred only when those physical
differences were in a signal that was itself heard as speech. One
can interpret this, ad hoc, as pointing to some kind of perceptual
interaction, or — and this is our preference — as indicating that the
peak occurs only when the signal, being heard as a speech sound,
somehow engages the special speech processing system. In our view,
a prominent feature of that system is a reference to articulation.

These results are reinforced by other evidence which suggests that
there is in perception no continuum between speech and nonspeech. In
one relevant experiment, House, Stevens, Sandel, and Arnold (1962)
produced various degrees of acoustic approximations to speech. Perceptually, there seemed to be no approximation. Their signals were
heard as speech or they were not. If they were heard as speech, they
were highly distinctive in the sense that they were easily learned in
a paired-associate learning task. Those stimuli that were not heard
as speech were not in this sense distinctive.

The many impressions one gets from everyday work with speech
synthesis also support the notion that there is no gradual approximation
to speech and, similarly, no gradual approximation to the distinctiveness of speech sounds. One seems either to be in the speech perception system or out of it.

It may also be relevant in this connection to consider the recent
evidence that speech and nonspeech are perceived on different sides
of the brain (Broadbent and Gregory, 1964; Kimura, 1961a; Kimura,
1961b; Kimura, 1964; Milner, 1962). These results do not tell us
anything about the nature of the perceptual processes in either case,
but the fact that speech and nonspeech are so clearly dealt with in
different places lends some support to the notion that they are dealt
with in different ways.

Earlier we referred to two problems one might expect to encounter in trying to get the phoneme strings through the auditory channel. One was in connection with the temporal resolving power of the ear and the low-ceiling set thereby on the rate at which discrete events can be heard. The other had to do with the difficulty of finding 40 acoustic signals that are highly identifiable though of short duration. We have already had occasion to remark how the encoding (and subsequent decoding) of the phonemes into the acoustic signal (and out of it) increases the rate at which strings of phonemes can be perceived. Now we should make explicit how this encoding-decoding might improve identifiability. As has been implicit in the discussion so far, a code based on a reference to the articulatory system should enable the listener to take advantage of the relative independence of some parts of that system. Given the existence of subsystems and the number of different muscle groups involved, we can suppose that the motor commands, and feedback associated with their activation might be more highly discrete and identifiable than the corresponding acoustic cues. This should be especially so when different phonemes involve different muscles rather than related muscles in different degree.

Continuous Perception of Some Acoustic Cues.

We have spoken of the complex relation between acoustic signal and perception. We should emphasize now that the relation is not always complex. Recall the case of /slIt, splIt/. There, acoustic variation was continuous, while articulation and perception were discontinuous. The articulatory situation for the vowels is quite different in that the speaker can presumably vary his articulation continuously. It is of some interest, then, that the perception of the vowels is different from that of the categorically articulated consonants in that vowel perception is more like that of most continuously varied signals: There are no quantal jumps in perception — that is, no substantial increases in discrimination at the phoneme boundaries — and the listener can discriminate many more stimuli than he can identify (see Fry et al., 1962). Here, then, is a situation in which acoustic signal, articulation, and perception tend to be in step: they all vary more or less continuously. There is, therefore, no basis on which we can say that a reference to articulation does or does not mediate the perception of these signals. We might conclude that we should not assume such mediation if we do not have to; alternatively, we might feel happier about keeping the whole speech perception system of one kind.

One Model or Two

It is, of course, possible that more than one mechanism is involved in speech perception. We have considered, for example, a duplex theory in which some phonemes would be perceived on an analysis-by-synthesis basis, but others would be processed straight through; that is, in terms of their acoustic properties alone and without any reference to the means by which they are generated. Others, for instance Chistovitch (1962) and Ladefoged (1959), have entertained similar notions. If, then, duplexity — I guess I should not say duplicity — is a real possibility, we are interested in the kinds of experiments that might help us choose between the possibilities. More generally we are, of course, even more interested in how the difference between the two classes of phonemes can be characterized, whether we are driven to duplexity or not. Is it simply a question of categorical versus continuous articulation? Or is it, as K. N. Stevens has suggested to us, a matter of whether or not the important acoustic cue results from rapid movement of the articulators?[6] These questions can be answered by carrying out further research similar to that we have already described, but on a broader variety of phoneme classes.

However the question of mechanism is resolved, we will be left with the important observed differences between various classes of phonemes: the stops, for example, tend to be perceived categorically, whereas for the vowels and certain other phonemes, perception is very nearly continuous. We should guess that these differences would have important implications for distinctiveness — that the categorically perceived stops would be more accurately and quickly identified than the continuously perceived vowels. We might also expect to find that phonemes with different degrees of distinctiveness would have different linguistic roles, or that they would, at least, carry different functional loads. There is not much that can be said about these guesses at the present time except that it will surely be possible to collect the relevant facts.

Invariance and Motor Commands

Having just considered the vowels in which there is a direct relation

---

[6] Personal communication

between acoustic signal and phoneme perception, we ought now to return to cases, which we made so much of earlier, in which the relation is not so direct. The particular point about these latter cases, as you will perhaps recall, is that an invariance is presumed to exist at some articulatory level. Our point, in effect, was that the speech message is processed through successive recodings and, indeed, circulates in a closed loop as we monitor our own acoustic output. At some point in this loop, there is a recoding which corresponds in discreteness of units and regularity of structure to our perception of the message, or more precisely, to the phonological constituents of the message. The argument, then, was that this correspondence almost certainly occurs at the level of the events in the central nervous system that initiate the process of which the speech sounds are an outcome. It is surely possible, perhaps likely, that the correspondence might still be very well preserved right down to the level of the motor commands that actuate the articulatory organs.

In any case, that possibility has the virtue of being empirically testable, and by taking electromyographic records we have for some time been trying to test it. Of course, the electromyogram actually measures the muscle potential that accompanies contraction. Such potentials are closely related to the neural commands that actuate the muscle, however, so we are able to make inferences about the motor commands. Unfortunately, the methods we use for the purpose of finding the EMG correlates of speech are not nearly so flexible or convenient as the methods now available for uncovering the acoustic correlates. Therefore we cannot, after only two or three years of research, make statements that are firm and general. We have some data, however, and they warrant the following tentative conclusions (Harris, 1963; Harris, Schvey, and Lysaught, 1962; MacNeilage, 1963; 1964).

When we deal with temporally overlapping phonemes that are articulated by different groups of muscles — such as /f/ and /t/, for example — we can find an invariant EMG tracing for each phoneme, regardless of the context in which the phoneme occurs.[7] We should

---

[7] It is not, of course, to be expected that all the muscles that are active during the articulation of a given phoneme will show a close and invariant correspondence between the EMG signal and that phoneme, nor in fact do they; the strongest assumption would be that some particular muscle (or closely related set of muscles) would show such highly correlated behavior. The experimental problem is then to search the plausible locations for EMG signals that are diagnostic in this sense. We have found several instances of such signals, all in situations of temporal but nonspatial phoneme overlap (see Harris, 1963; Harris et al., 1962; MacNeilage, 1963; 1964).

keep in mind that such invariance is most commonly not to be found
in the acoustic signal.

For temporally overlapping articulatory gestures involving more-
or-less adjacent muscles that control the same structure — such as
/t/ and /i/, for example — it is, for obvious reasons, more difficult
to discover what is going on. In several cases we think we have found
evidence that some parts of the gesture may be reorganized when the
phoneme appears in different contexts. Even in these cases, however,
there appears to be a common core of EMG activity that remains
invariant.

We have several times said that while the language is segmented at
the phoneme level, the acoustic signal is not. This is to say that there
are no marks in the acoustic signal by which one can determine where
one phoneme ends and another begins. In a strict sense, this holds
also for the EMG signals but with a difference: the separate pen
traces from different muscles give information about independent
dimensions of the articulation to a far greater extent than do the component parts (e.g., the formants) of a sound spectrogram. Hence, the
onsets and offsets of EMG activity on the several traces represent
a kind of segmentation, dimension by dimension, of the articulatory
event. We see, then, that in this important sense, too, the motor
commands bear a simpler relation to the perceived phonemes than
does the acoustic signal.

We say again that all of this is necessarily very tentative. As things
stand, however, we are encouraged to believe that the EMG correlates
of the phoneme will prove to be invariant in some significant sense.
At all events, we very much hope that this will be so, not in the
interests of a motor theory broadly conceived, since it is always
possible to push the assumed invariance farther upstream, but simply
because the motor commands are about as far upstream as we are
likely to go experimentally. If we find invariance there, we shall have
the solid basis for a simple description of the phonological structure
of the language. Surely we can all agree that such invariance, or lack
of it, is an essential consideration in the development of a model of
phonological production. We think it is essential, too, for a model of
phonological perception, for, as we have said, our strong inclination
is to assume that phonemes are perceived by reference to the way
they are produced. In this view, production and perception are two
aspects of the same process. If that general concept is also useful

for a perceptual model at the level of morphology and syntax, then at some future time it may be easier to produce a unified model that explains speech in the most general case.

Acknowledgments

The research described in this paper was supported in part by the National Science Foundation under Grant G23633, the National Institute of Dental Research under Grant DE-01774, and the Research and Development Division of the Prosthetic and Sensory Aids Service, Veterans Administration under Contract V1005M-12353. This paper was written while one of the authors, A. M. Liberman, was a Fellow at the Center for Advanced Study in the Behavioral Sciences and also a Research Fellow, National Institutes of Health.

References

Bastian, J., Eimas, P., and Liberman, A. M. Identification and discrimination of a phonemic contrast induced by silent interval. J. acoust. Soc. Am., 1961, 33, 842. (Abstract)

Broadbent, D. E., and Gregory, M. Accuracy of recognition for speech presented to the right and left ears. Quart. J. exp. Psychol., 1964, 16, 359-360.

Chistovich, L. A. Continuous recognition of speech by man. Mashinnyi Perevod i Prikladnaia Lingvistika (Machine Transl. and Appl. Ling.), 1962(7), 3-44.

Coffey, J. L. The development and evaluation of the Battelle aural reading device. In L. L. Clark (Ed.), Proceedings of the international congress of technology and blindness. Vol. 1. (2nd ed.) New York: American Foundation for the Blind, 1963. Pp. 343-360.

Cooper, F. S. Research on reading machines for the blind. In P. A. Zahl (Ed.), Blindness: Modern approaches to the unseen environment. Princeton: Princeton Univer. Press, 1950. Pp. 512-543.

Cooper, F. S., Liberman, A. M., Harris, K. S., and Grubb, P. M. Some input-output relations observed in experiments on the perception of speech. In Proceedings of the second international congress of cybernetics, 1958. Namur, Belgium: Association Internationale Cybernetique, 1960. Pp. 930-941.

Delattre, P. C., Liberman, A. M., and Cooper, F. S. Acoustic loci and transitional cues for consonants. J. acoust. Soc. Am., 1955, 27, 769-773.

Eimas, P. The relation between identification and discrimination along speech and non-speech continua. Language and Speech, 1963, 6, 206-217.

Freiberger, H., and Murphy, E. F. Reading machines for the blind. IRE Trans. Hum. Fact. Eng., 1961, HFE-2, 8-19.

Fry, D., Abramson, A. S., Eimas, P., and Liberman, A. M. The identification and discrimination of synthetic vowels. Language and Speech, 1962, 5, 171-189.

Griffith, B. A study of the relation between phoneme labeling and discriminability in the perception of synthetic stop consonants. Unpublished doctoral dissertation, University of Connecticut, 1958.

Halle, M., and Stevens, K. N. Analysis by synthesis. In W. Wathen-Dunn and L. E. Woods (Ed.), Proceedings of the seminar on speech compression and processing. Vol. 2. AFCRC-TR-59-198, USAF Camb. Res. Ctr., 1959. Paper D7.

Halle, M., and Stevens, K. N. Speech recognition: A model and a program for research. IRE Trans. Info. Theory, 1962, IT-8, 155-159.

Harris, C. M. A study of the building blocks of speech. J. acoust. Soc. Amer., 1953, 25, 962-969.

Harris, K. S. Behavior of the tongue in the production of some alveolar consonants. J. acoust. Soc. Amer., 1963, 35, 784. (Abstract).

Harris, K., Bastian, J., and Liberman, A. M. Mimicry and the perception of a phonemic contrast induced by silent interval: Electromyographic and acoustic measures. J. acoust. Soc. Amer., 1961, 33, 842. (Abstract)

Harris, K. S., Schvey, M. M., and Lysaught, G. F. Component gestures in the production of oral and nasal labial stops. J. acoust. Soc. Amer., 1962, 34, 743. (Abstract)

House, A., Stevens, K. N., Sandel, T., and Arnold, J. On the learning of speechlike vocabularies. J. verb. Learn. verb. Behav., 1962, 1, 133-143.

Kimura, D. Some effects of temporal-lobe damage on auditory perception. Canad. J. Psychol., 1961, 15, 156-165. (a)

Kimura, D. Cerebral dominance and the perception of verbal stimuli. Canad. J. Psychol., 1961, 15, 166-171. (b)

Kimura, D. Left-right differences in the perception of melodies. Quart. J. exp. Psychol., 1964, 16, 355-358.

Ladefoged, P. The perception of speech. In Nat. Phys. Lab. Sympos. No. 10, 1958, Mechanization of thought processes. London: HMSO., 1959.

Ladefoged, P., Draper, M., and Whitteridge, D. Syllables and stress. Phonetica, 1958, 3, 1-14.

Liberman, A. M. Some results of research on speech perception. J. acoust. Soc. Amer., 1957, 29, 117-123.

Liberman, A. M., Cooper, F. S., Harris, K. S., and MacNeilage, P. F. A motor theory of speech perception. In Proceedings of the speech communication seminar. Vol. 2. Stockholm: Royal Institute of Technology, 1962.

Liberman, A. M., Delattre, P. C., and Cooper, F. S. The role of selected stimulus-variables in the perception of the unvoiced stop consonants. Amer. J. Psychol., 1952, 65, 497-516.

Liberman, A. M., Delattre, P., Cooper, F. S., and Gerstman, L. The role of consonant-vowel transitions in the perception of the stop and nasal consonants. Psychol. Monographs, 1954, 68 (8, Whole No. 379) 1-13.

Liberman, A. M., Harris, K., Eimas, P., Lisker, L., and Bastian, J. An effect of learning on speech perception: The discrimination of durations of silence with and without phonemic significance. Language and Speech, 1961, 4, 175-195.

Liberman, A. M., Harris, K., Hoffman, H., and Griffith, B. The discrimination of speech sounds within and across phoneme boundaries. J. exp. Psychol., 1957, 54, 358-368.

Liberman, A. M., Harris, K., Kinney, J., and Lane, H. The discrimination of relative onset-time of the components of certain speech and non-speech patterns. J. exp. Psychol., 1961, 61, 379-388.

Liberman, A. M., Ingemann, F., Lisker, L., Delattre, P., and Cooper, F. S. Minimal rules for speech synthesis. J. acoust. Soc. Amer., 1959, 31, 1490-1499.

Lisker, L., Cooper, F. S., and Liberman, A. M. The uses of experiment in language description. Word, 1962, 18, 82-106.

MacNeilage, P. F. Electromyographic and acoustic study of the production of certain final clusters. J. acoust. Soc. Amer., 1963, 35, 461-463.

MacNeilage, P. F. Electromyographic study of the coarticulation of vowels and consonants. J. acoust. Soc. Amer., 1964, 36, 1989. (Abstract)

Milner, B. Laterality effects in audition. In V. B. Mountcastle (Ed.), Interhemispheric relations and cerebral dominance. Baltimore: Johns Hopkins Press, 1962. Pp. 177-195.

Peterson, G., Wang, W., and Sivertsen, E. Segmentation techniques in speech synthesis. J. acoust. Soc. Amer., 1958, 30, 739-742.

Pollack, I. The information of elementary auditory displays. J. acoust. Soc. Amer., 1952, 24, 745-749.

Pollack, I., and Ficks, L. Information of elementary multidimensional auditory displays. J. acoust. Soc. Amer., 1954, 26, 155-158.

Stetson, R. H. Motor phonetics. (2nd ed.) Amsterdam: North-Holland, 1951.

Stevens, K. N. Toward a model for speech recognition. J. acoust. Soc. Amer., 1960, 32, 47-55.

Stevens, K. N., and House, A. S. Studies of formant transitions using a vocal tract analog. J. acoust. Soc. Amer., 1956, 28, 578-585.

Studdert-Kennedy, M., Liberman, A. M., and Rosov, R. J. Rate of information transmission for one-, two-, and three-dimensional acoustic stimuli. J. acoust. Soc. Amer., 1963, 35, 808. (Abstract)

REMARKS ON ANALYSIS BY SYNTHESIS AND DISTINCTIVE FEATURES

Kenneth N. Stevens
Department of Electrical Engineering
Massachusetts Institute of Technology
Cambridge, Massachusetts

Morris Halle
Department of Modern Languages
Massachusetts Institute of Technology
Cambridge, Massachusetts

> "Lastly, I am to take notice, that there is so great a Communication and correspondency between the Nerves of the Ear, and those of the Larynx, that whensoever any sound agitates the Brain, there flow immediately spirits towards the Muscles of the Larynx, which duely dispose them to form a sound altogether like that, which was just now striking the Brain. And although I well conceive, that there needs some time to facilitate those motions of the Muscles of the Throat, so that the Sounds, which excite the Brain the first time, cannot be easily expressed by the Throat, yet notwithstanding I doe as well conceive, that by virtue of repeating them it will come to pass, that the Brain, which thereby is often shaken in the same places, sends such a plenty of spirits through the nerves, that are inserted in the Muscles of the Throat, that at length they easily move all the cartilages, which serve for that action, as 'tis requisite they should be moved to form Sounds like those, that have shaken the Brain."

> (de Cordemoy, G. A philosophicall discourse concerning speech. London: J. Martin, 1668.)

Some years ago we proposed a model of speech perception that we called "analysis by synthesis" (Halle and Stevens, 1959; Halle and Stevens, 1962; Stevens, 1960). This model postulated that the perception of speech involves the internal synthesis of patterns according to certain rules and a matching of these internally generated patterns against the pattern under analysis. We suggested, moreover, that the generative rules utilized in the perception of speech were in large measure identical with those utilized in speech production, and that fundamental to both processes was an abstract representation of the speech events.[1] The aim of the present paper is to explore certain aspects of our model in greater detail than in earlier papers with the hope that we might initiate discussion that might lead toward a deeper understanding of the perception of speech.

------

[1] It should be evident that our model is similar to that discussed sometime ago by Professor D. M. MacKay (1951) which he has subsequently refined in later papers, including the presentation at this symposium. The ideas underlying analysis by synthesis have a much longer history, however, going back to rationalist theories of perception.

The Role of Segments and Features in Speech Production

We begin by reviewing some of the evidence in favor of the view that an abstract representation of the speech event and a set of appropriate generative rules are involved in the process of speech production. Let us consider first the purely physiological aspect of speech production and examine from this point of view the English utterances spy, sty, and sky. It is immediately obvious that these three utterances resemble one another in certain striking respects; in fact, the sequences of gestures that are required to produce these words are all but identical. First a narrow constriction is created by the tongue immediately be-hind the teeth, through which air is blown from the lungs without exciting the vocal cords. This is followed by complete blocking of the vocal tract, causing an interruption of the air flow and a simultaneous buildup of pressure behind the point of closure, the vocal cords re-maining inactive all this time. Next, the blockage is released suddenly, and more or less simultaneously with the release the vocal cords begin to vibrate; the vocal tract, which previously had been blocked, is then made to assume a relatively unconstricted open shape. At the beginning of this opening phase the tongue is far back in the mouth, narrowing the top part of the pharynx; then the tongue is moved forward and upward towards the roof of the mouth where it remains to the end of the gesture. The differences between the three utterances are due solely to the differences in the placement of the blockage: in spy the blockage is at the lips, in sty it is just behind the teeth, and in sky it is back in the mouth in the rear of the soft palate.

The preceding, seemingly quite naturalistic description of the vocal-tract behavior, however, suggests a quantization of the gestures which is not always directly observable. In our description we have talked about features of the vocal-tract gesture such as the degree of narrowing, location of the narrowing, and vibration of the vocal cords as if these were entirely independent of one another. We have also imposed a temporal segmentation on the gesture by describing it in terms of features that are ordered with respect to each other in a sequence. In sum, our description has proceeded as if the events we described consisted of temporally delimited segments which are com-plexes of features.

The foregoing is, of course, the traditional manner of describing speech, and originally it was believed to be an accurate statement of what could be observed directly. Since the first X-ray motion pictures

of speech were produced some 30 years ago, however, serious questions have been raised with regard to the correctness of this belief.
It has become quite obvious by now that in the actual speech events
the discreteness of the segments and of the features is blurred or
totally obliterated, so that it is frequently impossible to isolate the
segments and features in the actual event. We are thus faced with the
difficulty that, though on the one hand speech can be described in very
satisfactory fashion in terms of segments and features, the latter do
not seem to be directly present in the observable speech event.

We believe that there is a fairly straightforward resolution of this
difficulty; namely, to recognize explicitly that characterizations of
speech in terms of segments and features are not more or less
naturalistic records of particular physical events but are rather
abstract representations of classes of events. The features and segments which appear in the abstract representation are related in an
explicit manner to different overt attributes of the speech event; this
relationship need not, however, be one-to-one nor need it necessarily
preserve the discreteness of the features and the segments. We may
regard the segments and features of the abstract representation as
instructions for particular types of behavior of the speech-generating
mechanism. When these instructions are executed, the interaction
between different physiological structures, each possessing its own
sluggish response characteristics, will naturally produce a quasi-
continuous gesture in which the discrete instructions initiating the
gesture are no longer always discernible as distinct components.

The actual practice of phoneticians conforms quite precisely to the
view just proposed that the phonetic transcription is an abstract
representation of instructions to the vocal tract. It is explicit already
in A. M. Bell's Visible Speech (1867), and accounts for the constant
recurrence in phonetic studies of remarks such as the following taken
from P. Ladefoged's recent study of West African languages (1964)
[our underlining — KS/MH]: "But although instrumental techniques
were used extensively in the course of this study, I would like to
stress that an equally important part of the work consisted of simply
observing and imitating informants. As a result of an experimental
approach, I was often able to select the most appropriate out of a
number of conflicting hypotheses about the way in which a particular
sound was made; and occasionally instrumental data revealed a new
articulatory possibility which I had not thought of before. Nevertheless,

I am still sure that 'instrumental phonetics is, strictly speaking, not phonetics at all. It is only a help. . . . The final arbiter in all phonetic questions is the trained ear of the practical phonetician.' (Sweet, 1911.) For those of us who are not as skilled as Sweet, instrumental phonetics may be a very powerful aid and of great use in providing objective records on the basis of which we may verify or amend our subjective impressions. But even the most extensive array of instruments can never be a substitute for the linguist's accurate observation and imitation of an informant."

Evidence concerning the nature of the abstract framework of segments and features that underlies the generation of speech is based not only on observations of the behavior of the vocal mechanism and on auditory impressions of speech sounds but also on observations of the way the segments and features play a role in other aspects of language (Halle, 1964; Jakobson, Fant, and Halle, 1952). It is a well-known fact that every language possesses specific constraints on the sequence of segments that can constitute a well-formed utterance. The most natural framework for characterizing these constraints is provided by the same set of features as those characterizing the motor behavior. Thus, for instance, there is in English a restriction on the appearance of nasals before stops: we get /m/ before /p/ or /b/; /n/ before /t/ or /d/; and /ŋ/ before /k/ or /g/. For example, trump, rombic, hint, hinder, think, finger are English words, but sequences such as thimk, trunp, or tringt are simply not English. It is all but self-evident that the nasal must be identical with the following stop consonant in the features of diffuseness and gravity (traditionally referred to as the point of articulation); but this characterization involves in an essential way features that are correlated with specific articulatory properties of speech.

Another area where features play an obvious role is in the determining of the phonetic shape of grammatical elements (morphemes) in different contexts. Thus, for instance, the past tense suffix of English regular verbs is (a) /id/ if the verb ends in /t/ or /d/; (b) /t/ if the verb ends in any voiceless segment except /t/; and (c) /d/ if the verb ends in any voiced segment except /d/. We note that in (b) and (c) the choice between the voiced /d/ or the voiceless /t/ as the past tense signal depends on the presence of the same feature in the last segment of the verb stem. This again is an instance where a higher level regularity can be accounted for in a natural fashion in terms of the feature framework utilized for characterizing the vocal-tract behavior.

Examples of the preceding type are so numerous and widespread
that there can be little doubt that features and segments are the
(abstract) entities that underlie the entire phonology of every language,
and not only its lowest stage, the vocal-tract gestures. The discovery
of important regularities on the more abstract levels of the phonology
of a language will, therefore, be taken as prima-facie evidence of the
existence of a given feature. In fact, it is reasonable to suggest that
a feature that plays a role in the phonology of a language must also
have plausible articulatory and acoustic correlates, although our
lack of knowledge of the physiological processes of speech may prevent such correlates from being immediately evident to us. Indeed,
examination of the phonology may well provide indirect evidence that
can lead to a better understanding of the organization and control of
speech gestures.

As a case in point, we may cite the feature diffuse in vowels, which
in the framework that we have adopted replaces in part the traditional
phonetic feature of tongue height. As will be recalled, the traditional
phonetic frameworks distinguish at least three degrees of tongue
height: high, middle, and low. Instead, in the feature system that we
have adopted here, we distinguish diffuse (high) vowels such as /i/
and /u/, from the rest which are nondiffuse. The latter are sub-
categorized into compact such as /a/ or /ɔ/ and noncompact such as
/o/ or /e/.

A particularly good example of the utilization of the feature diffuse-
nondiffuse is provided by modern standard Russian where, in unstressed position, nondiffuse vowels coalesce into /a/ after "hard"
(nonpalatalized) consonants, and into /i/ after "soft" (palatalized or
palatal) consonants. The diffuse vowels /i/ and /u/ on the other hand,
remain distinct in unstressed as well as in stressed position. Since
stress in Russian may fall on different vowels of a word in different
grammatical forms, the variations in position of stress are paralleled
also by variations in vowel quality, as indicated in the following
examples:

	after "hard" consonants	
/v'al/ (nom.sg.)	/val'ɨ/ (nom.pl.)	"wave"
/v'ɔl/ (nom.sg.)	/val'ɨ/ (nom.pl.)	"ox"
/e/ appears only after "soft" consonants		

after "soft" consonants

/vz̦'al/ (masc.sg.)	/vz̦il'a/ (fem.sg.)	"took"
/v̦'ol/ (masc.sg.)	/v̦il'a/ (fem.sg.)	"led"
/sț'en/ (gen.pl.)	/sțin'a/ (nom.sg.)	"wall"

But no change in vowel quality is observed in

| /bl̦'ul/ (masc.sg.) | /bl̦ul'a/ (fem.sg.) | "observed" |
| /p̦'il/ (masc.sg.) | /p̦il'a/ (fem.sg.) | "drank" |

From the point of view of articulation, this feature is correlated with
a maximally narrow (for vowels) constriction being placed in the front
part of the buccal cavity. (It is this placement which ensures the
production of a maximally low first formant — the well-known
acoustical correlate of this feature.) At first sight such an articulatory
correlate lacks the immediate appeal and plausibility of such other
universally recognized features as nasality, voicing, or labialization.
There seems to be no single anatomical structure which can be said
to be in control of the execution of this feature. In producing diffuse
vowels we can make a constriction either with the lips or with the
forward part of the tongue, and it is by no means obvious why these
two different organs should form a single functional unit. Cineradio-
graphic data show, however, that a constriction of this type must be
accompanied by a raised mandible. It is entirely possible, then, that
such a gesture provides a single articulatory correlate of the feature
diffuse. An alternative argument might be that the lips and forward
part of the tongue are involved in one of the basic types of instinctive
behavior in all mammals — sucking. We find it, therefore, not hard
to believe that the formation of a constriction in the forward portion
of the buccal cavity should constitute a single functional control unit
in the process of speech production.

Our view of the speech-production process, therefore, may be
summarized as follows. The speaker of a language has stored in his
memory an abstract representation of lexical items of the language.
These representations consist of segments which themselves are
complexes of features. The representations can, therefore, be
pictured as abstract two-dimensional matrices in which the columns
represent the strings of segments and the rows different features.
The syntactic component of the language establishes the order in which
different lexical items appear in the sentence as well as the relationship between the items in the string. The string of matrices is then
operated on by a set of rules which transform the matrices into sets

of instructions for vocal-tract behavior. Ultimately the execution of
these instructions produces the acoustical signal. While these instructions bear a close relationship to the articulatory behavior they
elicit and to the acoustical properties of the utterances produced by
it, there is no implication that the acoustic output must be necessarily
decomposable into sequences of discrete segments or that instructions
or features are directly recoverable from the signal. We are asserting
that the acoustical output is a joint function of the abstract representation, the rules of the language and the dynamics of the vocal tract,
but we do not mean to imply that this is a linear function of the segments in the abstract representation; nor is there any reason to
suppose that it must be so. As a result it cannot be expected that the
underlying representation should in all cases be recoverable from the
signal by simple techniques of signal analysis.

The Role of Segments and Features in Speech Perception

We should like to suggest that in speech perception the acoustic
signal is decoded into an abstract representation identical to that
already described, i.e., a representation in terms of segments and
features. Furthermore, we would like to argue that in decoding an
input signal into such a representation, the listener brings to bear
the same phonological rules as those used in generating the signal
from the abstract representation.

That such a representation plays a role in speech perception is
strongly suggested by the fact that normal speakers of a language
understand without apparent difficulty utterances in a fairly wide range
of dialects. This obvious fact would be quite inexplicable if we
assumed that utterances are identified solely by means of direct
classification of successive segments of the acoustical signal or by
comparison of the input signal against an inventory of stored patterns,
for the dialectal differences that do not inhibit comprehension are
precisely differences in the inventory of the sounds. If, on the other
hand, we assume that dialectal differences in the sounds are due to
the fact that a given abstract representation of a speech event is
actualized in accordance with different phonological rules, then the
performance of the normal speakers becomes at once understandable.
Having listened to a relatively small sample of utterances in a dialect
different from his own, the speaker of a language is evidently able to
determine the modifications of a few phonological rules of the dialect

as compared with those in his own dialect. He is then able to utilize
these rules to identify correctly combinations of elements or words
he has never heard before in that dialect.

Consider, for example, the case of one of our children who says
/sɪŋg/ instead of /sɪŋ/. Such an error is not uncommon among 4 to
6-year-olds; it is also quite interesting from a theoretical point of
view. Observe first that the child could not possibly be mimicking
anyone in its environments since no one in its surroundings speaks
English with this sort of an accent (which is characteristic, however,
of certain partially foreign milieus of our bigger cities). Since
imitation has to be excluded for lack of a model, we must look for
another explanation. We should like to propose that the child does not
primarily mimic its parents but rather tries to establish the rules
that govern the speech of its parents and utilizes these rules to construct utterances of its own. Since the child is new at it, he will
occasionally fail to establish a rule correctly or he may overlook a
rule altogether. He will then produce utterances that are at variance
with those of his parents.

Viewed in this light the pronunciation of /sɪŋg/ for /sɪŋ/ is no
longer an inexplicable curiosity. As observed above, the nasal /ŋ/ has
a peculiar distribution in English. It occurs on the one hand, before
/g/ or /k/ (e.g., finger, Lincoln), where it is the only admissible nasal
consonant; and, on the other hand, it is found in word final position
but never at the beginning of the word. The facts just listed can most
economically be described by saying that mature speakers of English
obey the following two rules, which incidentally have to be applied in
the order indicated:

1. A nasal consonant assimilates the place of articulation of the
   following stop consonant.
2. Final /g/ is deleted in word final position following a nasal
   consonant.

The child who utters /sɪŋg/ is evidently using the first of these rules
but does not invoke the final rule. Likewise, when he listens to and
identifies the word he must again be invoking these rules and be decoding the sound into the abstract representation /s + ɪ + nasal + g/ for
in English every word final velar nasal must derive from a sequence
of /nasal + g/.

An example that is, perhaps, more striking is the case, described by
J. Applegate (1961), of the "secret language" spontaneously created by

some children in Cambridge, Massachusetts. The difference between
the grammar of this "language" and standard English consisted of two
ordered rules: (a) in a word containing several identical stop consonants, all but the first of these is replaced by a glottal stop; and
(b) all continuants are replaced by the cognate stops. As a result of
these two rules, we find in the language of the children the following
deviations from standard English:

/baʔiy/	Bobby	/dəd/	does
/diʔ/	did	/takt/	talks
/dayʔ/	died	/teykt/	takes
/peyʔr/	paper	/dayd/	dies
/keyʔ/	cake	/payp/	fife

It is evident that these children are using the same abstract representation for these words as their peers, since they understand both
standard English and their secret language. In generating and in
perceiving utterances in the secret language, they simply impose a
slight modification on the rules of standard English.

Models of Speech Production and Perception

In order to render our remarks more concrete, we have attempted
to schematize the processes involved in speech production and perception in terms of block diagrams. A representation of the speech
production system is shown in Figure 1. The abstract representation
of an utterance in matrix form is denoted by the symbol P at the left.
As we have observed, a set of rules operates on this representation
to yield instructions to the vocal mechanism, which are designated by
V. These instructions cause appropriate activity in the articulatory
mechanism, which generates the output sound S. We assume that
included in the vocal system are the various auditory, tactile, and
other feedback paths; the operation of the vocal mechanism may, of
course, be very much dependent upon these feedback paths.

It is important to emphasize that in the model of Figure 1 we do not
equate the instructions V with movements of the articulatory structures. Rather, we regard the patterns V to be actualized in the form
of appropriate sequences of motor commands only after certain motor
skills have been acquired. Thus, for example, a given set of instructions V that occur in an utterance of a certain language may
require that the talker actualize a series of gestures with the tongue
and lips, but he may not in fact be able to realize the proper sequence

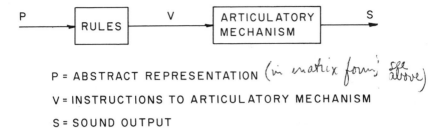

P = ABSTRACT REPRESENTATION (in matrix form; see above)

V = INSTRUCTIONS TO ARTICULATORY MECHANISM

S = SOUND OUTPUT

Fig. 1. Model of the speech-generating process, showing the transformations from the abstract discrete representation P to the articulatory instructions V to the sound S.

of movements, and consequently may speak the language with an accent. One can make an analogy with a person who observes a tennis game and then tries to play with no further practice. Obviously when he attempts to transform his observations into motor commands he cannot perform as well as a skilled player, even though he is generally aware of what is involved.

We now add to the model the capability of perceiving speech as well as generating it, as shown in Figure 2. Thus an input sound S' is processed by the auditory mechanism to yield auditory patterns, which we designate by A. The transformation that the auditory mechanism applies to S' is not understood in detail. At one time it was thought that the auditory system had the properties of a bank of filters, and that the auditory patterns A were much like the patterns produced by

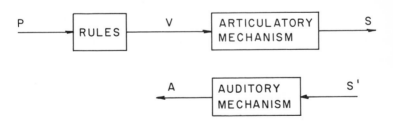

A = AUDITORY PATTERNS

Fig. 2. Model of the articulatory mechanism and of the speech-generating process.

a sound spectrograph. However, recent neurophysiological studies on sensory systems of lower animals — studies like those of Lettvin, Maturana, McCulloch, and Pitts (1959) on the visual system of the frog, and of Frishkopf and Goldstein (1963) on the frog's auditory system — suggest that fairly complex processing takes place fairly near the periphery. We would expect, therefore, that the auditory patterns A constitute a much more radical transformation of the input than a simple frequency analysis of the type performed by a sound spectrograph.

It is evident, furthermore, that these auditory patterns have close ties with articulatory activity, since we can produce an articulatory movement with instructions V and observe the consequences at the level of A.[2] A listener can also observe the utterances of others who are using the same phonological rules. Knowing the P → V transformations that the talker is using, he can make some estimate of the V → A transformation between the instructions V of the talker and his own auditory patterns A. The attraction of the suggestion that there is a close correspondence between A- and V-patterns resides in the fact that the abstract features of P would then be related in a direct way not only to the articulatory instructions V but also to the auditory patterns A. In this view, therefore, speech would be anchored equally in the motor and in the auditory system of man.

Consideration of the general model up to this point indicates that we all carry around with us (a) the abstract representation of the entities of our language; (b) the rules that operate on features or groups of features in this abstract representation to yield instructions to the articulatory mechanism; and (c) a description in some form of the transformation between articulatory instructions and auditory patterns. This latter transformation is presumably independent of language and depends only on the physiological and anatomical characteristics of the auditory and articulatory mechanisms.

We have already argued that speech perception involves decoding of the signal into an abstract representation P that is identical with that used by the talker. The question that remains therefore, is: What is the process whereby the auditory patterns A corresponding to an utterance are converted into the abstract representation P? We have

---

[2] F. A. Hayek (1963) has discussed in more general terms instances in which "correspondence (is) established between movement patterns which are perceived through different sense modalities." [p. 326]. He postulates that "the recognition of a correspondence between patterns made up of different sensory elements presupposes a mechanism of sensory pattern transfer, that is, a mechanism for the transfer of the capacity to discern an abstract order or arrangement from one field to another." [p. 327]

given examples to suggest that a direct segmentation and classification
of segments at the level of A cannot yield the representation P, and
that somehow the phonological rules that are used in speech production
must be employed by the listener in the decoding operation. We
propose the analysis-by-synthesis model as a possible description of
this decoding from A to P.

The principal features of this model are shown in Figure 3. We
observe outside the large dashed box the components and levels we
have already discussed: the abstract representation P, the phonological rules, the patterns V that give rise to motor commands, and
the auditory patterns A. We have included also a short-time memory
in which these auditory patterns can be stored. We postulate first
that the auditory patterns that result from an acoustic speech signal
at the ears undergo some preliminary analysis, and as a consequence
of this preliminary analysis, together with contextual information
derived from analysis of adjacent portions of the signal, an hypothesis
is made in a control component concerning the abstract representation
of the utterance. This hypothesized sequence of units, which we have
labeled P_{trial}, is then operated on by the phonological rules (the
same ones that are used in the generation of speech) to yield a
pattern V_{trial}. During speech production, this pattern would
normally give rise to motor commands that would lead to articulatory
activity and sound generation. During speech perception, however,
this path is inhibited, and instead an equivalent auditory pattern
A_{trial} is derived from V_{trial}, as indicated by the shaded box in
the figure. This computed auditory pattern is compared with the
pattern under analysis. If there is agreement between the two patterns, then the trial sequence of elements was correct and this
sequence is read out for processing at higher levels. If there is a
difference between the patterns, the control component takes note
of this error and assembles a new trial sequence of units. This process continues until the trial abstract representation gives a match
at the comparator, in which case the correct output sequence is
established as P.

Since we have recognized that the output of the auditory mechanism
may already be in a form that is closely related to the features of
the abstract representation, it may frequently, or indeed usually,
happen that the initial trial for P is the correct result. When contextual information supplements that provided by the direct analysis,

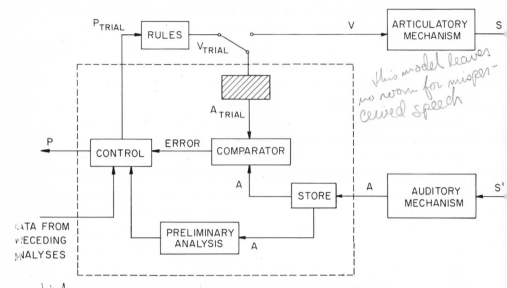

this model leaves no room for misperceived speech

Fig. 3. Model for the speech-generating and speech-percep-
tion process. (The dashed line encloses components of a
hypothetical analysis-by-synthesis scheme for speech
perception. The shaded component indicates the capability
of the model for effecting transformations between articulatory instructions and auditory patterns.)

then the probability of obtaining a correct guess on the first trial is
further enhanced. In spite of the fact that a correct output sequence
may frequently be obtainable even before a matching is attempted, we
would suggest that the matching process is always employed as a
check. That is, we suggest that normal speech perception can proceed
only through active participation of the listener — he makes hypotheses
on the basis of direct analysis and contextual information and he then
verifies these hypotheses through an internal replication and matching
procedure, though we expect that the criteria employed in the matching
operation may not always be very stringent.

We should emphasize that Figure 3 represents a model of the perception of speech and is not, of course, a model of auditory perception in general.[3] It is a particular mode of perception that is, so to
speak, "switched in" whenever a listener attempts to understand a
speech signal that reaches his ears. Since the output P of the speech

---

[3] Although, as D. M. MacKay suggests in his paper at this symposium,
it may well be that all types of perception involve an internal replication and matching process of the type discussed here.

perception model is in terms of segments and features it is categorial; indeed, when a listener is operating in the speech perception mode we suggest that he is always performing a categorization of the input. This tendency of a listener to categorize linguistic stimuli has been demonstrated in a number of studies (see Liberman, Cooper, Harris, and MacNeilage, 1962, and references cited therein). For example, Liberman, Harris, Hoffman, and Griffith (1957) showed that a series of consonant-vowel syllables in which the starting frequencies of the second formant for the initial stop consonant are arranged along a continuum are perceived not as a continuously changing sequence of sounds but rather as a series of syllables whose initial consonants change in a stepwise fashion from /b/ to /d/ to /g/. (However, in a similar series of experiments with isolated vowel stimuli characterized by formant frequencies spaced along a continuum, perception tended to be continuous rather than categorial [Stevens, Öhman, Studdert-Kennedy, and Liberman, 1964].) It would appear that in an experimental situation in which these isolated vowels are the stimuli, the listener utilizes a nonspeech mode of perception in which categorial responses are not required.)

Fundamental to the proposed model of speech perception is the requirement that in order to understand the speech of a talker a listener must know the phonological rules that the talker is using to transform the abstract representation in articulatory instructions. It must be emphasized that knowing these rules is not equivalent to being able to generate speech in the language or dialect used by the talker. One does not need to possess in detail the motor skills that are required to transform V-patterns into sound in order to understand the utterances of the talker. In the model of Figure 3 these motor skills are considered to be part of the articulatory mechanism, and thus are not directly involved in speech perception. Thus the learning of a new language is in large measure acquisition of the phonological rules (and, of course, the lexicon, and syntactic, and semantic rules) and not acquisition of certain motor skills. Such skills are required only if one wishes to speak the language with perfect native accent. Effective command of a language often falls far short of this aim.

Acknowledgment

This work was supported in part by the Joint Services Electronics Program under Contract DA36-039-AMC-03200(E); in part by the

National Science Foundation (Grant GP-2495, the National Institutes of
Health (Grants MH-04737-04 and NB-04332-02), the National Aeronautics
and Space Administration (Grant NsG-496), and in part by the U.S. Air
Force Cambridge Research Laboratories, Office of Aerospace Research, under Contract AF19(628)-3325.

References

Applegate, J. Phonological rules of a subdialect of English. Word,
1961, 17, 186-193.

Bell, A. M. Visible speech: The science of universal alphabetics.
London: Simpkin, Marshall, 1867.

Frishkopf, L. S., and Goldstein, M. H., Jr. Responses to acoustic
stimuli from single units in the eighth nerve of the bullfrog. J.
acoust. Soc. Amer., 1963, 35, 1219-1228.

Halle, M. On the bases of phonology. In J. A. Fodor and J. J. Katz
(Eds.), The structure of language: Readings in the philosophy of
language. Englewood Cliffs, N. J.: Prentice-Hall, 1964.
Pp. 324-333.

Halle, M., and Stevens, K. N. Analysis by synthesis. In W. Wathen-
Dunn and L. E. Woods (Eds.), Proceedings of the seminar on speech
compression and processing, Vol. 2. AFCRC-TR-59-198, USAF
Camb. Res. Ctr., 1959. Paper D7.

Halle, M., and Stevens, K. N. Speech recognition: A model and a
program for research. IRE Trans. PGIT, 1962, IT-8, 155-159.

Hayek, F. A. Rules, perception, and intelligibility. Proc. Brit.
Acad., 1963, 47, 321-344.

Jakobson, R., Fant, C. G. M., and Halle, M. Preliminaries to speech
analysis. M.I.T. Acoust. Lab. tech. Rep., 1952, No. 13.
(Cambridge: M.I.T. Press, 1965.)

Ladefoged, P. A phonetic study of West African languages.
Cambridge: Cambridge Univer. Press, 1964. P. xviii.

Lettvin, J. Y., Maturana, H. R., McCulloch, W. S., and Pitts, W. H.
What the frog's eye tells the frog's brain. Proc. IRE, 1959, 47,
1940-1959.

Liberman, A. M., Cooper, F. S., Harris, K. S., and MacNeilage,
P. F. A motor theory of speech perception. Proceedings of the
speech communication seminar. Vol. 2. Stockholm: Royal Inst.
Tech., 1962.

Liberman, A. M., Harris, K. S., Hoffman, H. S., and Griffith, B. C.
The discrimination of speech sounds within and across phoneme
boundaries. J. exp. Psychol., 1957, 54, 358-368.

MacKay, D. M. Mindlike behaviour in artifacts. Brit. J. Phil. Sci.,
1951, 2, 105-121.

Stevens, K. N. Toward a model for speech recognition. J. acoust.
Soc. Amer., 1960, 32, 47-55.

Stevens, K. N., Öhman, S. E. G., Studdert-Kennedy, M., and Liberman,
A. M. Crosslinguistic study of vowel discrimination. J. acoust.
Soc. Amer., 1964, 36, 1989. (Abstract)

Sweet, H. Phonetics. In Encyclopedia Britannica. Vol. 21. (11th ed.)
Cambridge: Cambridge Univer. Press, 1911.

PASSIVE VERSUS ACTIVE RECOGNITION MODELS
OR
IS YOUR HOMUNCULUS REALLY NECESSARY?

John Morton and Donald E. Broadbent
Applied Psychology Research Unit
Medical Research Council
Cambridge, England

MacKay (1956) has described two fundamentally different ways for automata to transform incoming "sensory" information and so recognize universals. The first of these involves a "generalising filter" and the second a "comparator." The difference between the two types may be summed up as "passive" versus "active."

The Halle-Stevens (1962) model for speech recognition involves a comparison of the input spectrum with some internally generated signals, and an error signal fed back to the generator for the next stage of the analysis-by-synthesis. The Haskins model (Liberman, 1957; Liberman, Cooper, Harris, and MacNeilage, 1962), " A motor theory of speech perception," appears to be similar in principle, if one takes the step of translating into a flow diagram statements such as "the speech sounds are perceived by reference to the articulatory movements that produce them" or "articulatory movements and their sensory feedback (or, more likely, the corresponding neurological processes) become part of the perceiving process, mediating between the acoustic stimulus and its ultimate perception."

These two active models appear to differ in one respect. In order to compare two signals meaningfully, it is essential that the signals, or neural pattern, should be at the same level. In the Halle-Stevens model the comparison is at the neuroacoustic level. A generator produces a trial phoneme sequence which is converted into a comparison spectrum presumably via the corresponding motor commands. In the Haskins model, on the other hand, it would appear that the comparison takes place on the neuroarticulatory level. Presumably then, the input spectrum would have to be converted from its neuroequivalent to a neuroarticulatory form for the comparison. As Fant (1963) has remarked,"...if the auditory analysis in the hearing process has proceeded so far as to allow the proposed articulatory matching, the decoding could proceed without an articulatory reference." He then proceeds to indicate ways in which this might be accomplished.

We have probably oversimplified and have possibly misinterpreted the Haskins statements. However, we have objections to active models of speech perception in general.

These are first, that the evidence quoted in their favor is not really inconsistent with a passive explanation, and second, that an alternative passive model is of greater generality (Morton, 1964b; Morton, 1964c). Such a model, illustrated in Figure 1, has as its central feature a "dictionary" of "units" or "logogens" which correspond to words. (The dictionary is useful for other, e.g., semantic,[1] reasons, and a "word"

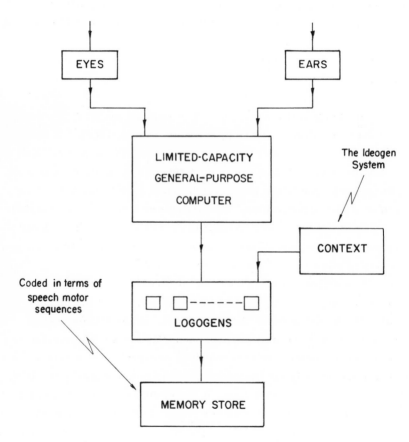

Fig. 1. Alternative passive model of speech recognition.

---

[1] Though it should not be thought that the logogen is the place where the meaning of a word is looked up. We have now abandoned the term "dictionary" to avoid confusion. One of us (Morton) is preparing a paper, "Rules concerning morphemes and words," which treats this more fully.

can be defined behaviorally.) When the activation in a logogen exceeds
a critical level it fires, and the corresponding word is available as a
response; that is, a representation of the appropriate motor sequence
is stored in the Immediate Memory. This sequence would operate with
or without sensory information, for the same response is available if we
free associate to "chair," complete the sentence "He put the plate on
the __ ," see the object, read the word "table" or hear it spoken. A
relevant sensory input would be coded in terms of "cues," the presence
of which would increase the level of activation in certain logogens. In
reading, the cues would be length, shape, etc., and in listening to speech
one could use the output from the Halle-Stevens Preliminary Analysis,
which would utilize the Haskins acoustic-articulatory rules.

It is irrelevant to the essence of the present theory whether the
information fed to the logogens is coded in terms of acoustic, articulatory or, for example, distinctive feature variables, or any combination
of these, continuous or discontinuous.

In the presence of a context, which may be a word, or a sentence,
or even nonverbal, certain logogens are activated differentially either
by direct connections with other logogens or via higher-order nodes
which will be referred to later. Since the logogens are conceived of as
having the properties of signal detection units, the difference between
a generation situation and a recognition situation could be merely
a criterion lowering in the former case to compensate for the absence
of external inputs to the system. In a recognition situation, the effect
of the activation due to the context is that less sensory information
is necessary to make certain logogens fire. Thus high probability
words can be recognized with lower exposure times, or with a lower
S/N ratio.

Such a system has the additional advantage that if I see or hear a
single word in isolation the recognition procedure differs from that
in context only in the amount of sensory information necessary to fire
a logogen. With any active theory it would seem to be necessary
either to generate all possible words (subject perhaps to limitations of
length) or to have error signals fed back from the first match of such
sophistication that all necessary deductions may be made as to the
correct response. We feel, without a formal demonstration, that a
system capable of generating such an error signal would also be
capable of decoding the original neuroacoustic signal directly. In addition, the word-frequency-threshold relationship would present

difficulties for the latter of the active alternatives.[2] In a passive
model this relationship is accounted for by postulating in any logogen
a residual level of activation which is related to the freouency of
firing of the logogen; not an outrageous postulate in a cryptoneurological
theory. Miller (1964) has pointed out that the efficiency of an active
model is critically dependent on the quality of the initial guess, and
that if this guess is not close the listener will be unable to keep pace
with rapid conversational speech. We would submit that even when
such a breakdown is due to a failure of "guessing," it need not be a
failure at the perceptual level (as most people understand the term)
but at some higher level. The failure is to understand, not to perceive;
the guess is at the idea level, not the word level. If words are missed
it is eoually feasible that the cause is the overoccupation with further
higher-order processing of the limited capacity channel, the general-
purpose computer, some short-term memory functions or attention
(the terms used depending on one's taste). Everyone has surely been
in the position of following every word of a speaker but understanding
nothing. It has been suggested elsewhere (Morton 1964a) that the
effects of redundancy on the perception of words may be traced back
to higher-order units than words, where difficulties with the number of
possible seouences arise as Miller, Galanter, and Pribram (1960) have
remarked. Such higher-order units, called "thought units" in the
previous paper, renamed "ideogens," may be few enough in number to
allow the statistical properties of the language to accumulate. Connections between ideogens, and higher-order nodes can be regarded
as concerned with predicting and understanding, and at such levels
we have no objections to an active network for, as MacKay (1956)
concluded, "...an automaton designed on statistical principles, which
can evolve an internal organizing routine to respond adaptively to
regularities of its sensory input, is capable in principle of developing
its own symbols for concepts of any order of abstraction, including
metalinguistic concepts, without prior instruction."

  We suggest that the necessary statistics can be kept within reason
only for the smallest units (for those conditional acoustic relationships
between adjacent phonemes, so convincingly demonstrated by the
Haskins work must be taken account of) and for units at a higher level

---

[2] A recent paper (Broadbent, 1966) has shown these difficulties to be
major ones.

of abstraction than words; we doubt whether this can be done either for
strings of phonemes (Halle and Stevens, 1962) or words.

In recognizing continuous speech, or in reading, one sees the process
of prediction as a flow of information from the logogens upwards
to give the context, and back down again to activate differentially the
predicted words. In such a system it may be necessary to fire only
the logogens corresponding to the kernel words, with some other system
taking care of syntactic information in both recognition and generation.
In our view the only cases in which an internal generator and comparator may operate as the sensory input would be (a) where the
universals were underlearned [though Fant (1963) has questioned even
this], (b) where great precision was required (as in phonetic transcription or many psychological experiments), or (c) where no response was
available, e.g., with a low S/N level or high information content.

It is also worth noting that under such conditions there is a tendency
to subvocalize or even vocalize not only in listening to speech but also
in reading, where the input can hardly be matched actively. We cannot
legitimately conclude therefore from such an observation that such
activity is a part of the perceptual or recognition process, and it may
equally well be a consequence of perception. Indeed, since subjectively
it seems that the words most often vocalized are those with a large
amount of semantic information, we may speculate as to whether
subvocalization is not a form of amplification for the benefit of
higher-order functions.

The passive model as presented has a place in it for other constructs
which relate to other forms of behavior (Morton, 1964c). A limited-
capacity channel with properties which Broadbent (1958) has described
may be introduced between the primary sensory functions and the dictionary and the different properties of short- and more long-term memory
(Broadbent, 1963) accounted for. In the model, material in short-
term memory is coded in terms of articulation patterns. Conrad (1962)
showed a correlation between errors in memory for visually presented
letters and errors in hearing the letters spoken in noise. We would
suggest that the former errors are due to errors in transcription of
the articulatory code. Thus the alternative model covers phenomena,
such as the word-frequency effect or reading, which lie outside the
scope of the motor theory.

What of the evidence in favor of a motor theory? It has been
criticized by Lane (1963) on methodological grounds, and he has also

shown similar results using nonspeech continua. On the present view
all these results show the efficiency of speech effector coding in
memory, which can apply equally to visual and auditory, speech and
nonspeech stimuli, given the experience and training.

It has, for instance, often been noted that students of a foreign
language have difficulty in discriminating between certain pairs of
words until they have been taught to make the difference by articulatory
prescription. The explanation of this phenomenon in terms of an active
recognition network would be that the listener must be able to generate
in order to match. We would submit that an equally valid explanation
may be formulated for a passive system in that in order to discriminate
between two stimuli it is necessary to have two different responses
available, and until the vital articulatory distinction is available there
can be no distinction between the two words. This does not of course
necessarily mean that the listener cannot hear the difference between
the two words spoken in juxtaposition, but here no discriminating
response is required. The Haskins results seem entirely analogous
to Brown and Lenneberg's findings with color perception (1954), yet
a motor theory of visual color perception is not thought necessary.

To be fair we must add that the evidence quoted against a generative
theory is not watertight. Roman Jakobson has already pointed out
this morning that he can understand phonemic distinctions in some
dialects which he cannot produce, and that children can understand
before they can speak. Such observations are however not fatal for an
active theory. It is possible to argue that internal discriminative
responses are in a coded form which is used in the comparator system;
usually this representation can be decoded to activate the speech
mechanism; in certain cases, and for children, this final step cannot
be taken. The comparator could still function though.

Yesterday, Attneave drew a box to represent the mechanism for
form recognition with two outputs labeled "table" and "chair." He then
posed the problem of how a signal on these outputs could mean something. It may mean that the appropriate logogen is activated. This,
of course, does not solve the problem; it merely takes it off Attneave's
desk and puts it onto ours.

Finally we might note that Halle-Stevens (1962) remark that in their
system only a rough analysis may be necessary at the neuroacoustic
level, with any ambiguities resolved later on the basis of constraints
at the morphological, syntactic, and semantic levels. Perhaps when

we get down to details, the models will not be so far apart.

We are not vindictive; we have nothing personally against any individual homunculus, (e.g., Stevens' reference to "the active participation of the listener"); we merely believe that most of them are being given more work than is strictly necessary.

Point from the Discussion

In reply to a question from Phil Lieberman, we agree that in listening, especially to dialects, matching filters in some Primary Auditory Analysis system must be adjusted actively before we can proceed fully in the passive mode. The situation represents one of the special conditions in which we accept that a Generative System may be necessary, and it is significant that when listening to a strange dialect we often fail to perceive the first few words.

MacKay pointed out that the model is essentially a classifying system and that we know that bodily processes go on which in effect classify stimuli and indeed evoke responses without our perceiving anything. Where then, he asked, does perception live in the model? We do not think it necessary to locate "perception"; it seems sufficient to say under what conditions a subject reports "I perceived the word." In our system this would occur when a word was available as a response with a simultaneous signal to the effect that a certain amount of sensory information contributed to this event. The subject's statement may have any degree of confidence and the response need not be correct; i.e., the perception may be illusory. The difference between our model and MacKay's "raindrop model" (see his paper in this symposium) as classifiers is not that the human "perceives" but that our model can develop "its own symbols for concepts of any order of abstraction..." (see the foregoing); and this depends upon the nature of the system following the classifying system.

Al Liberman criticized the work of Lane (1963), indicating that he thought Lane's evidence to be totally inadequate. In addition, he hoped the model did not begin at the level of the word, pointing out the psychological difficulties one encounters if one enters the linguistic system at that level or even the morpheme level in reading or writing; as, for example, with logographic writing which is far more difficult than an alphabetic system. We would regard the difficulties with the logographic system to be rooted in the lack of correspondence between the two stimulus modes and between the response modes. With an

alphabetic system there is a high letter-phoneme correspondence which
greatly simplifies learning, and preliminary work in England on the
Initial Teaching Alphabet shows that where the spoken and written
forms are in a one-to-one correspondence, the learning process is
often accelerated.

References:

Broadbent, D. E. Perception and communication. London: Pergamon,
1958.

Broadbent, D. E. Flow of information within the organism. J. verb.
Learn. verb. Behav., 1963, 2, 34-39.

Broadbent, D. E. Response bias and perceptual defence. Psychol.
Rev., 1966, in press.

Brown, R. W., and Lenneberg, E. H. A study in language and
cognition. J. abnorm. soc. Psychol., 1954, 49, 454-462.

Conrad, R. An association between memory errors and errors due
to acoustic masking of speech. Nature, 1962, 193, 1314-1315.

Fant, G. Comments by G. Fant to Paper D3 A motor theory of
speech perception. In Proceedings of the speech communication
seminar Vol. 3. Stockholm: Royal Institute of Technology, 1963.

Halle, M., and Stevens, K. Speech recognition: A model and a
program for research. IRE Trans. Info. Theory, 1962, IT-8,
155-159.

Lane, H. The motor theory of speech perception: A critical
review. In Prog. Rept. No. 4, Cont. OE-3-14-013, Experimental
analysis of the control of speech production and perception. Ann
Arbor: Behav. Anal. Lab., Univer. Mich., 1963. (Reprint,
Psychol. Rev., 1965, 72, 275-309.)

Liberman, A. M. Some results of research on speech perception.
J. acoust. Soc. Amer., 1957, 29, 117-123.

Liberman, A. M., Cooper, F. S., Harris, K. S., and MacNeilage, P. F.
A motor theory of speech perception. Proceedings of the
speech communication seminar. Vol. 2. Stockholm: Royal
Institute of Technology, 1962.

MacKay, D. M. The epistemological problem for automata. In
C. E. Shannon and J. McCarthy (Eds.), Automata studies. Princeton: Princeton Univer. Press, 1956. Pp. 235-251.

Miller, G. A. The psycholinguists. Encounter, 1964, 23(1), 29-37.

Miller, G. A., Galanter, E., and Pribram, K. H. Plans and the
structure of behavior. New York: Holt, 1960.

Morton, J. A model for continuous language behavior. Language
and Speech, 1964, 7, 40-70. (a)

Morton, J. A preliminary functional model for language behavior.
Int. Audiology, 1964, 3, 216-225. (b)

Morton, J. The effects of context on the visual duration threshold
for words. Brit. J. Psychol., 1964, 55, 165-180. (c)

AUDITORY PATTERNS OF SPEECH

Gunnar Fant
Speech Transmission Laboratory
Royal Institute of Technology (KTH)
Stockholm, Sweden

Introduction

Any attempt to propose a model for the perception of speech is deemed to become highly speculative in character and the present contribution is no exception. Neurophysiologists (Penfield and Roberts, 1959) have detailed information on the topology of the brain but not so much to contribute concerning the mapping of the information processing in successive stages of the auditory system. The purpose of the present paper is merely to stimulate discussions on these processes.

The current trend in speech research (Cooper, 1964) is to analyze speech spectra and other acoustic data in terms of speech production parameters and specifically in terms of a set of hypothetical motor commands controlling the articulatory and phonatory activity in speech. This has proved to be a very fruitful approach providing valuable organizational principles in dealing with the speech substance (Fant, 1962; Lindblom, 1963; Öhman, 1964). Some investigators have gone one step further and hypothesize that the brain utilizes the same principles for the decoding of speech. Typical examples of such "motor theories" of speech perception are those of Liberman (Cooper, 1964; Liberman, 1957; Liberman, Cooper, Harris, and MacNeilage, 1963) and Chistovich (Chistovich, Klaas, and Kuzmin, 1962). Their common element is that a primary stage of auditory signal analysis is followed by a stage of articulatory recoding before identification of words takes place. In one variant of the theory proposed by Liberman et al. (1963) the role of the speech motor functions is limited to the establishment of identification criteria during the process of language learning.

In my opinion the evidence brought forward in support of motor theories of speech perception is not conclusive. This does not imply that I consider the "motor" theory improbable, merely that all of the arguments brought forward in support of the motor theory would equally well fit into "non-motor" or "sensory" theories by which the decoding proceeds without the active mediation of speech motor centers.

I am pessimistic about the possibilities of proving whether the "motor theory" is right or wrong, and I feel that this may not be an essential problem either. Of greater importance is the search for the acoustic cues and features that underlie the decoding, whether it is a direct "sensory" process or a process with reference to the listener's articulatory functions. In this connection I should like to emphasize the basic idea of Jakobson, Fant, and Halle (1952) on the existence of distinctive features on both the articulatory, acoustic, and perceptual domains which is retained in the model of speech perception I am proposing. I am speaking up for an intensified search for "auditory patterns" in the sense of physiological mappings of speech wave patterns in the auditory system.

Our means of gaining direct information is limited, and we have to rely largely on psychoacoustic experiments in order to widen our understanding of auditory processing of speech stimuli. Experiments on the perception of speechlike stimuli which resemble real speech to within various degrees of approximation provide one way of gaining such information.

Models of Speech Perception

The fallacy of models of speech perception is that they tend to reflect technical principles of speech wave analysis, rather than physiological principles. The block diagram in Figure 1 is intended as a basis for discussing very gross functional principles only and is not

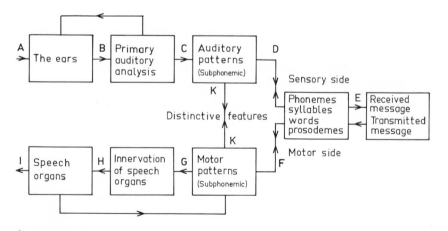

Fig. 1. Hypothetical model of brain functions in speech perception and production.

a physiological map of the brain. The organizing principle I have followed is that the motor and sensory functions become more and more involved as we proceed from the peripheral to the central stages. The final destination to the right of the model is the concept of the message which would comprise brain centers common to the receiving and transmitting functions of language.

The sound pattern of a word probably occupies a center separate from the articulatory patterning of the same word although closely connected. I cite Penfield and Roberts (1959, p. 247): "It was pointed out in Chapter X that there are definite differences in the types of aphasia produced by lesions in different portions of the speech cortex. In some cases there is more involvement of the sensory side of speech, and in others, more of the motor elements. Thus, there is what clinicians have called motor aphasia in which speaking is severely involved while understanding of speech is relatively, and comparatively, intact. There is also sensory aphasia in which the reverse is true. This strongly suggests that the motor units for words and phrases are separated somehow, spatially, from the sensory units. But it is also clear that they are both located in the general region of the cortico-thalamic speech areas of the left side, where they are closely inter-related in function."

On the phonemic and subphonemic level I have introduced a block of auditory patterns, CD, in the sensory branch which has its counterpart in a block, GF, of articulations and phonations on the motor branch. A connection between these two blocks indicates the possibility of the participation of motor functions in speech perception either actively, whereby decoding proceeds along the path ABCKFE, or passively in the form of a secondary activity KGHI originating from the block CD while the decoding proceeds directly in the path ABCDE.

The active mediation of the motor pattern block GF in speech perception corresponds to the theories of Liberman et al. (1963) and to that of Chistovich et al. (1962), whereas the passive action of the motor block would allow for a pure "sensory" decoding and still conform with any experimental evidence concerning mimicking or shadowing. The latter view is a consequence of the general theory of distinctive features, i.e., that they exist on the perceptual stage as well as on the stages of speech production and the speech wave. My attitude here is basically colored by a faith in the distinctiveness of the speech wave characteristics which we have acquired by being exposed to language in the first place and by reference to our own speech only in the second place.

My model conforms to that of Halle and Stevens presented at this symposium in so far as it includes stages of distinctive features both on the sensory and the motor side. However, I am somewhat skeptical about the principle of analysis-by-synthesis as applied to the level of phoneme identification.

Analysis-by-synthesis (Stevens, 1960) involves a process of specifying an unknown sign in terms of a best match selection from a standard inventory. In addition to this best match concept, analysis-by-synthesis implies a generation of standard patterns by means of a parametric synthesis process, e.g., a categorization and a quantization within each category. Thus there is no need for a storage of all the possible patterns to be compared with the incoming signal. This economy principle is valuable in technical applications, but it can be doubted whether the principle of efficiency is essential in brain mechanics.

In Halle and Stevens' view the generation of internal patterns is controlled by motor commands which are automatically translated to auditory distinctive patterns of the dimension of distinctive features. This is an elegant model and I would not exclude it. My guess, however, would be that incoming auditory signals are submitted to some kind of direct encoding into distinctive auditory features. Some phonemes, e.g., [s], are probably recognized immediately without a prior decomposition into sound features. The same could be true of some syllables and words. It does not seem improbable to anticipate parallel detection pathways so the both direct detection and recognition via features would occur.

Although I am somewhat skeptical about analysis-by-synthesis on the feature and phoneme level I find this principle of decoding with active engagement of motor functions more probable to exist on a higher level of message reception. I have in mind the principles whereby linguistic and conceptual constraints are utilized by the receiver.

An evident connection between sensory and motor parts of the system, at least at the word level and higher, is wnat we call the "running prediction." This "updating" as MacKay calls it involves the running synthesis of the most probable continuation of the message and checking against incoming flow on the sensory side, i.e., along the loop DEFD. This is the mechanism by which we normally make up for losses of whole words or parts of sentences under conditions of incomplete speech or severe distortion including insufficiencies in the auditory system.

What we do not know is how far down toward the peripheral end such prediction and correction normally take place. If it is active down to the distinctive feature level we have a process which represents one of the possible modes of operation of a "motor theory" of phonemic perception and much in the same line as the "analysis-by-synthesis" principle, except that the selection of synthesis parameters is no longer a search among equally likely alternatives and combinations. My guess is that we have means of direct sensory decoding of speech and that the prediction and correction via impulses from the motor system mainly add accuracy in making up for communication deficiences. In connected speech this prediction is probably indispensable for decoding at a normal speaking rate. At least it ensures that the listener hears what he expects to hear. But this is not the same as stating that one hears only what one can say.

In a contribution (Fant, 1963) to the Proceedings of the Speech Communication Seminar in Stockholm, 1962, I gave a rather detailed account for my view on the motor theory of speech perception as proposed by Liberman et al (1962). Summarizing I find the evidence not very conclusive. Liberman pays very little attention to manner features, and his observations with respect to place features can be interpreted differently. I do not share Liberman's pessimism in defining unique speech wave correlates of phonetic categories.

Liberman's observations on the relatively high discriminability of consonant parameter variations in the regions of phonemic boundaries can be explained from a "non-motor" point of view as an increased probability that a unit of variation along the stimulus scale will be associated with a change in the linguistic response. Subjects listen for phonemes even if they are told to listen in for sound qualities. According to Liberman they associate with their own articulation. In my view, subjects are conditioned by their experience as listeners in speech communication more than by their own speech. Liberman has not been able to disprove that speech-wave characteristics and basic auditory sensations are categorical without reference to articulation.

The experimental evidence put forward by Chistovich et al. (1962) in favor of a motor theory of speech perception is of considerable interest.

Their techniques involve shadowing experiments. A subject receives speech through headphones and is asked to repeat with a minimum of time delay. A set of mixed articulatory and acoustic records of his speech is made on a multichannel oscillograph. The speech material consists of nonsense syllables of the type vowel [a] plus consonant plus vowel [a] where the consonant is one of p, t, b, d, m, n, f, s, v, z.

Observed time delays were of the order of 100 to 150 msec. Consonant reproduction was initiated before the main part of the consonant was received by the subject. The reproduction frequently started with errors or double articulations which were resolved and corrected as more and more of the nonsense words entered the auditory system of the listener. Corrections required additional time delay.

I cite a part of Chistovich's conclusions: "The observed articulatory dynamics during fast reproduction and especially the fact that articulation is initiated before all of the information concerning the phoneme has reached the listener is not compatible with the idea that in the listener's brain there is first of all a process of phoneme classification and that the subject's articulation is merely a consequence of the particular phoneme selection. On the contrary, there is reason to believe the articulation during minimum delay reproduction reflects not the result of the identification processes in the brain but rather the very mechanisms of these processes, i.e., the running synthesis of consonantal articulation on the basis of the information bearing cues extracted from the external signal."

This interpretation apparently comes close to the views held by Liberman et al. and the "analysis-by-synthesis" model of Halle and Stevens.

The results of Chistovich et al. and their interpretations are also compatible with my own views, provided the distinctive feature analysis on the sensory side is postulated. I would therefore interpret the mimicking experiments such that the distinctive sound features are first recognized and then translated to the equivalent motor patterns causing innervation of the speech organs, i.e., the process would involve the pathway ABCKGHI of Figure 1. When the subject attempts to reproduce speech in spite of incomplete information, the unavoidable errors are corrected by updating the motor pattern block with the status of the auditory pattern block. From Chistovich's point of view, however, the delay needed to correct errors conforms with the theory that a correct articulatory representation must precede the final decoding. I appear principally to depart from defenders of a motor theory of speech perception in that I could consider the activity setup in the motor pattern block not as a requirement for identification but rather as a side effect.

The observation of the subjects' mimicking during listening need not imply that the underlying motor activity is necessary for identification, but one could all the same with Chistovich refer to this activity as "reflecting" the mechanism of identification.

Distinctive Features

My view on the theory of distinctive features is not orthodox in any way. The system to whose development I have contributed (Jakobson et al., 1952) I do not regard as a unique solution. Whether features always should be binary or if some of them should be allowed to be structured as a choice of three or four is quite unessential. Even more important, the set of features best suited for the metalinguistic sake of creating a minimal redundant descriptive system need not reflect dimensions of auditory analysis more than to a limited extent.

The basic foundation of distinctive features is the categorization inherent in the limited modes of phonatory and articulatory expression that man is equipped with. Most of these categories are binary in nature, e.g., various manners of articulation voiced/unvoiced, nasal/nonnasal, continuant/interrupted, etc. The economy of distinctive feature encoding arises from the power of one single distinction to separate several pairs of phonemes, e.g., [g] differs from [k], in the same way, as [d] differs from [t], and [b] from [p], and [v] from [f], and [z] from [s]. The cues and thus the detailed instructions to be given to an automatic feature analyzer are not the same for each pair. Modification with respect to the specific context is necessary. There are good reasons for stating that the relation of [p] to [t], or [b] to [d], or [f] to [s], or [v] to [z] has an element in common with the relation of [m] to [n] and even of [u] to [i] in a very general sense.

However, the labial/dental distinction among stops and fricatives is only in part similar to that among nasals and only in a very abstract sense similar to the acoustic distinction between back and front vowels. The common element of low versus high frequency pertains to second formant locus as well as spectral center of gravity, but this is a very diluted statement, and many other cues come into the picture depending on the particular class where this distinction is applied. I do not

anticipate a separate brain box responsible for the decision of grave/
acute irrespective of main category. Vowels and consonants are too
different.

Distinctive feature analysis applied to speech does not require an
initial stage of segmentation in terms of sharply time limited portions
of the speech wave (Fant, 1962). Some features appear and fade out
gradually, and the tendency of segmental structuring to be observed in
spectrograms is such that one phoneme is often characterized by cues
from several adjacent segments and that one segment may carry some
information on the identity of two or more successive phonemes.

The voiced/voiceless and nasal/nonnasal distinctions typically
affect several successive spectrographic segments, the relative
importance of each segment being dependent on the particular context.
The distinction between [g] and [k] , or [d] and [t], or [b] and [p] is
that of an earlier onset of voicing after the explosion and also a
greater amount of voicing in the previous stopgap. If the stopgap is
devoiced, its duration is relatively shorter for the voiced phoneme, at
least when expressed as a ratio to the previous length of the vowel.
Voiced phonemes simply display a relatively greater amount of voicing
in the sound substance within as much as two connected syllables.

The realization of the nasal/nonnasal distinction is quite similar.
Vowels preceding and also following a nasal, orally closed segment are
in part nasalized. Mártony has shown that nasalization as a cue of a
nasal consonant is more important in context with open vowels than in
context with closed vowels. How nasalization affects several segments
may be seen from Figure 2, exemplifying phonemes [d] , [l], and [n] in

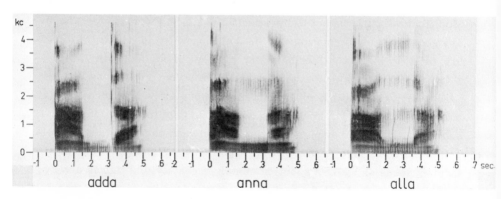

Fig. 2. Intervocalic [d], [n], and [l], combined with short vowel
[a]. Swedish male subject (B. L.).

intervocalic position. Nasalization is seen by the presence of the
voice bar in the entire word and comparable in intensity to the first
formant. The high F1-locus is an additional cue which has not been
observed very much. Nasalization also affects the F2-locus of [n],
which is lower than that of [d] and [l] in the context of vowel [a]. It is,
of course, quite feasible to differentiate these voiced dentals by means
of two out of three possible binary features, nasal/nonnasal, lateral/
nonlateral, interrupted/noninterrupted, although in perception they
might be recognized immediately as three separate individuals, once
the voiced, continuant, nonfricative properties are recognized.

   If we want to describe one of these features, it is not sufficient to
cut out the segment traditionally ascribed to the consonant and observe
it. We can, of course, observe some general differences in terms of
such segments, but if we gate out a single one of them, e.g., the [l]
segment defined by oral central closure and lateral opening and listen
to it, we will not hear an [l] but a vowel. It is the contrast with adjacent sound segments that accounts for the specific [l] quality.

   The role of temporal contrasts in consonant perception has already
been stressed by the Finnish phonetician, Pipping (1922). He said
that all consonants carry a noise element. In fricatives it is inherent
in the continuant noise, in nasal stops and laterals it is contained in
the temporal contrast between a louder element and a weaker element
and basically a contrast between sound segments with different excitation patterns along the basilar membrane. The sudden transition
has the effect of a step excitation of the peripheral receptors which
in turn is associated with a specific auditory quality (Halle, Hughes,
and Radley, 1957).

   It is a basic principle in human sensory functions that we are
especially sensitive to variations of stimuli in place and time. We
should pay more attention to this principle if we want to approach the
problem of basic dimensions of perceived sound patterns and thus
approach a dynamical theory of speech perception.

   There has been an overemphasis on second formant transitions and
more generally on F-pattern (F1, F2, F3) specifications as acoustic
correlates to place features of consonants. We could for a change view
the spectrum through the constraints of a cochlear model rather than
by means of a conventional spectrum analyzer, with the understanding,
though, that such a model represents only an extremely peripheral
aspect of the frequency-place analysis.

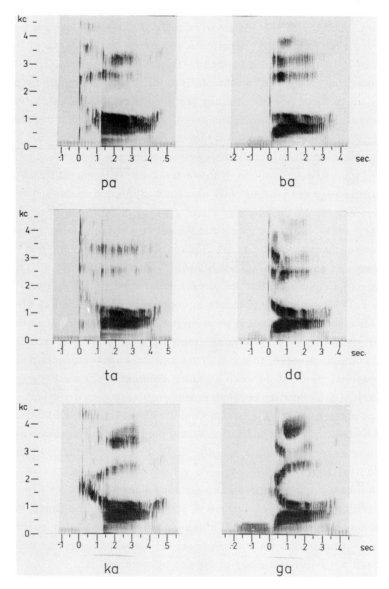

Fig. 3a. Stop consonants plus vowel [a]. Swedish male subject (B. L.).

Experiments with synthetic speech of various degrees of approximation and experiments with selectively distorted human speech (Öhman,
1962; 1966) can provide some evidence. This is in the line of the
early research at Haskins Laboratories. We want to know more about

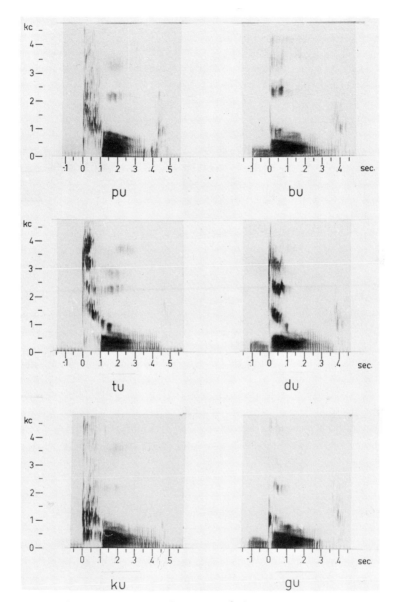

Fig. 3b. Stop consonants plus vowel [u]. Swedish male
subject (B. L.).

the relative importance of formants and to what extent vowels may be
substituted by a two-formant stimulus (Liberman, Cooper, and Gerstman, 1952) of equal phonemic value. One aspect of the latter problem
has been taken up by Fujimura in his paper presented at this symposium.

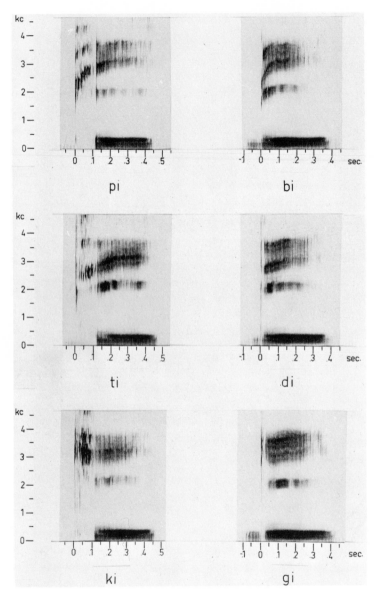

Fig. 3c. Stop consonants plus vowel [i]. Swedish male
subject (B. L.).

A related problem is to integrate segmental (from segment of
articulatory narrowing) and transitional cues concerning the place of
articulation of consonants. The ambiguity of the acoustic structure of
palatals when described in terms of a second formant locus, as

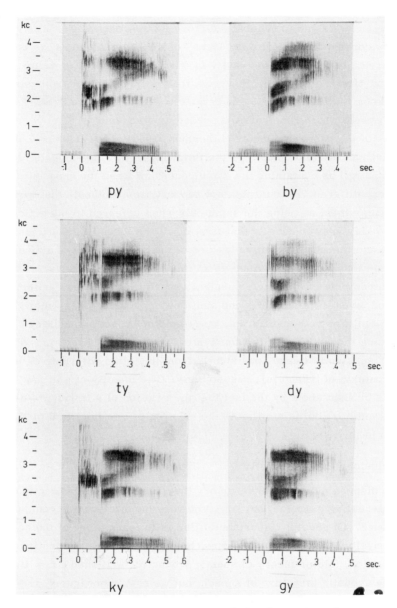

Fig. 3d. Stop consonants plus vowel [y]. Swedish male
subject (B. L.).

discussed by Liberman (1957), could be resolved (Fant, 1960) by
stating that the spectral energy in the consonantal segment and in the
first part of the transition is relatively concentrated and found close
to the perceptive mean of the second and upper formants with the

understanding that this mean is influenced considerably by F3 and F4 in front vowels and in general the more F2 approaches F3. The vocal cavity correspondence of this "locus" of the spectral energy is the resonance frequency of the cavity in front of the palatal or velar constriction (Fant, 1960). However, the validity of this hypothesis should be tested. Figure 3 shows spectrograms of some Swedish stops plus vowels which illustrate the preceding discussion.

One of the basic arguments (Liberman, 1957) of the Haskins Laboratory school of motor theory is the following: "How do subjects identify [gu] and [gi] as containing the same consonant when the apparent formant loci are different? Would this not support the hypothesis that we recognize them as being the same only when referred to the articulation?" My answer here is that first of all the locus is insufficient as a cue and that the distinctive feature of the palatal place of articulation among stops has to be defined as an integrated value of several cues which combine into a single spectral aspect as mentioned earlier. Second, even if the acoustic and auditory impression of [g] in [gi] and [g] in [gu] was rather different, this would not upset an auditory decoding theory. The only requirement is that both [gi]and [gu] shall differ substantially and consistently from any other alternatives in the contexts of [i] and [u], respectively. The identity of g in [gu] and [gi] is brought about by the fact that the relation of g in [gu], to d in [du], and b in [bu] is similar to the relation of g in [gi], to d in [di], and b in [bi].

Conclusion

To discuss motor versus sensory theories of speech perception is an interesting exercise, but it will be very hard to provide conclusive evidence. Of greater importance I find is to learn more of the acoustic and physiological structure of speech and what cues are effective in perception. Motor theory of speech production will shed a new light on the acoustic structure of speech, but we should not ignore perceptional patterning simply by a reference back to production.

References

Chistovich, L. A., Klaas, I. A., and Kuzmin, I. I. The process of speech sound discrimination. Voprosy psikhologii (Psychol. Prob.), 1962(6), 26-39. [Trans. Emmanuel College Res. Lang. Center, E-T-R-63-10, AF19(604)-8505, AFCRL, OAR, 1963].

Cooper, F. S. Instrumental methods for research in phonetics. Paper read at Fifth International Congress of Phonetic Sciences, Münster. August 1964.

Fant, G. Acoustic theory of speech production. 's-Gravenhage: Mouton, 1960.

Fant, G. Descriptive analysis of the acoustic aspects of speech. Logos, 1962, 5, 3-17.

Fant, G. Comments by G. Fant to Paper D3, A Motor Theory of Speech Perception, by A. M. Liberman, F. S. Cooper, K. S. Harris and P. F. MacNeilage. In Proceedings of the speech communications seminar. Vol. 3. Stockholm: Royal Institute of Technology, 1963.

Halle, M., Hughes, G. W., and Radley, J.-P. Acoustic properties of stop consonants. J. acoust. Soc. Am., 1957, 29, 107-116.

Jakobson, R., Fant, C. G. M., and Halle, M. Preliminaries to speech analysis. M.I.T. Acoust. Lab. tech. Rep., 1952, No. 13. (Cambridge: M.I.T. Press, 1965.)

Liberman, A. M. Some results of research on speech perception. J. acoust. Soc. Am., 1957, 29, 117-123.

Liberman, A. M., Cooper, F. S., and Gerstman, L. J. An experimental study of the acoustic determinants of vowel quality. Word, 1952, 8, 195-210.

Liberman, A. M., Cooper, F. S., Harris, K. S., and MacNeilage, P. F. A motor theory of speech perception. Proceedings of the speech communication seminar. Vol. 2. Stockholm: Royal Institute of Technology, 1962.

Lindblom, B. Spectrographic study of vowel reduction. J. acoust. Soc. Am., 1963, 35, 1773-1781.

Öhman, S. E. G. On the perception of Swedish consonants in intervocalic position. Thesis for fil. lic. degree. Royal Inst. Tech., Speech Trans. Lab., Stockholm, 1962, No. 25.

Öhman, S. E. G. Numerical model for coarticulation, using a computer-simulated vocal tract. J. acoust. Soc. Am., 1964, 36, 1038. (Abstract)

Öhman, S. E. G. Perception of segments of VCCV utterances. J. acoust. Soc. Am., 1966, 40, 979-988.

Penfield, W., and Roberts, L. Speech and brain-mechanisms. Princeton: Princeton Univer. Press, 1959.

Pipping, H. Inledning till studiet av de nordiska sprakens ljudlära. Helsinki: Söderström, 1922.

Stevens, K. N. Toward a model for speech recognition, J. acoust. Soc. Am., 1960, 32, 47-55.

INVITED PAPERS IV

Visual Shape Perception II

Chairman: John Mott-Smith
Data Sciences Laboratory
Air Force Cambridge Research Laboratories
Bedford, Massachusetts

MECHANICS OF VISUAL FORM RECOGNITION IN ANIMALS

W. R. A. Muntz
Psychological Laboratory
University of Sussex
Brighton, Sussex, England

This paper will describe some of the physiological and behavioral findings that have been obtained on visual form recognition in different animals, and it will discuss how far these findings help in understanding the mechanisms underlying form discrimination. Two problems will be emphasized: first, how animals, possessing only a limited number of neurones, are able to respond accurately to a very large number of visual forms (economy), and second, how they can respond appropriately to visual forms presented anywhere in the visual field, although quite different neurones will be excited on different occasions (receptor generalization).

Releasing Stimuli and the Concept of a Stimulus Filter

A lot of evidence is now available showing that animals usually respond to very specific, though often very complex, stimuli. Other aspects of the stimulus situation are ignored, although they may appear to us to be more important. Thus male sticklebacks will court a crude model of a female stickleback which bears little resemblance to a fish, provided that it has a swollen red abdomen, while much more realistic models (to humans) lacking the red abdomen will be ignored. The shape shown in Figure 1 provides another well-known example; when it is moved to the right (and presumably resembles a short-

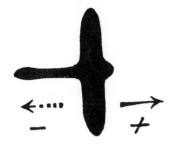

Fig. 1. Model of a bird of prey, releasing no escape reactions when sailed to the left, but releasing escape when sailed to the right. (Reproduced from Tinbergen [1951] by courtesy of the Clarendon Press, Oxford.)

necked hawk) it causes flight reactions in ducklings, but when it is moved to the left (and resembles a long-necked duck) it is ignored. A large number of similar examples have been described by ethologists (see Tinbergen, 1951, for a summary), and the restricted stimuli to which the animals respond have been called "releasing stimuli." A releasing stimulus is usually associated with a single response. Thus the swollen red abdomen of the female stickleback releases the response of courting only; the responses of nest building, or fighting, have different releasing stimuli. Restricting responses to releasing stimuli in this way is clearly economical, since most of the stimuli reaching the receptors will be ignored. In certain circumstances, however, it can also be disadvantageous, since it leads to inflexible behavior. For example, frogs are said to die of starvation when surrounded by dead flies, because the flies do not move and therefore do not fill the requirements of the releasing stimulus.

The concept of a stimulus filter has often been used in this connection: only some stimuli, the releasing stimuli, can pass the filter and activate the mechanism. This concept of a stimulus filter has not only been applied to instinctive behavior (Marler, 1961), but has also been applied profitably to other types of behavior (Broadbent, 1961).

In many animals physiological data suggest that the filtering of stimuli takes place near the receptor surface. Thus, in the vertebrate eye, microelectrode recordings from the ganglion cells of the retina have shown that already at this stage, two synapses from the receptors, the neurones are responding to specific aspects of the visual field, and that unimportant aspects of the stimulus situation are being filtered out. For example, on-off fibres only fire at the onset or cessation of illumination; only changes of illumination are signaled to the brain by such fibres, and the absolute level of illumination is ignored. Different

optic nerve fibres extract different types of information, and the
"releasing stimulus" to which they respond may be very complex, such
as a small dark convex object moving in a certain direction (Lettvin,
Maturana, McCulloch, and Pitts, 1959). Information is now available
for the retinal ganglion cells of fish (Jacobsen and Gaze, 1964), frogs
(Lettvin et al., 1959), pigeons (Maturana, 1962), rabbits (Barlow, Hill
and Levick, 1964), cats (Kuffler, 1953), and monkeys (Hubel and Wiesel,
1960), and in every case they have been shown to act as filters. The
situation is similar in invertebrates. Thus Ratliff, Miller, and Hartline (1958) have shown how the Limulus eye enhances contours, a
physiological mechanism for simultaneous contrast. In the octopus,
Young (1964) has shown that the dendrites in the superficial layers
of the optic lobes lie mainly in the vertical and horizontal planes,
and has suggested that this may correlate with Sutherland's (1958)
finding that octopuses can distinguish easily between vertical and
horizontal rectangles, but cannot distinguish obliques.

It is clearly not true that all filtering is done so close to the receptor
surface: the work of Hubel and Wiesel (1962), for example, shows
how much can be done at later stages. Nevertheless it is equally true
that a great deal of filtering is done very soon after the receptor
mosaic: this is true for every animal for which data are available.
It is also clear that the early filtering of significant information by
the retina makes for efficient utilization of the limited number of
optic nerve fibres available.

The evidence summarized also shows that the filters, or stimulus
analyzers, are reduplicated over the receptor surface. There is not
one analyzer which in some way scans the whole field, but a large
number of analyzers each responsible for a small part of the visual
field.

In spite of having a limited number of stimulus filters most animals
can be trained to recognize a very large number of different shapes.
All the information discarded by the filters has been irrevocably lost,
so that such shapes must be recognized by the outputs of the filters
being recombined in various ways. A good example of how this can be
done occurs in color vision. Recent evidence (Brown and Wald, 1964;
Marks, Dobelle, and MacNichol, 1964) confirms the classical view
that there are only three filters, a red, a green, and a blue, but the
outputs of these can be combined to yield a large number of color
sensations. Nevertheless it remains true that information has been

lost, and many physically distinct stimuli are perceptually indistinguishable.

Central Projections of the Different Filters

In many animals the different filters project to different parts of the
CNS, so that their outputs are spacially separated. This is very
marked, for example, in the frog, where Lettvin et al. (1959) have
shown that the outputs of the four classes of retinal ganglion cell they
describe project to four superimposed maps on the optic tectum. An
even greater separation exists between these four classes of fibre and
a fifth class of fibre, the blue-sensitive on-fibres, which project to a
different part of the brain altogether, the dorsal thalamus (Muntz,
1962b).

Similar situations occur in other animals. In the fish the separation
of the tectum into layers is not so marked. The tectum contains only
three layers, and the top and bottom layers receive on fibres, off
fibres, and on-off fibres, while the bottom layer receives sustained
on and sustained off fibres (Jacobsen and Gaze, 1964). The fish also
differs from the frog in that color coded fibres pass to the tectum
(Jacobsen, 1965), whereas in the frog they project to the thalamus.
In pigeons it is not known whether the tectum is divided into functionally
different layers or not, but Maturana (1962) has shown that no color
coded fibres pass to the tectum in these animals: these, as in the
frog, pass to the thalamus.

In the mammals no detailed data are available for the optic tectum,
but the lateral geniculate nucleus is divided into layers, and the
different layers have different functions. Walls (1953) likened the
geniculate to a pile of maps, and said ". . . laminae No. 1, No. 4, and
No. 6 are related to each other as are three maps of the same country,
one of which is geodetic, a second climatological, and the third
argicultural." The recent physiological work of DeValois, Smith,
Karoly, and Kitai (1958), Daniel, Kerr, Seneviratne, and Whitteridge
(1961), and Bishop, Kozak, Levick, and Vakkur (1962) confirm this
view. Neurones having different properties are also separated in the
mammalian cortex, though here the separation is into columns, not
layers (Hubel and Wiesel, 1962; Powell and Mountcastle, 1959).

The Problem of Receptor Generalization

Animals not only have to recognize stimuli, they also have to be able

to recognize stimuli irrespective of where they fall on the receptor
surface. A frog must, for example, react appropriately to a fly whether
the image of this fly falls on the upper half of the retina or the lower
half, on the right retina, or the left. The same considerations apply to
learned behavior: if an animal learns to respond to an object seen
with the left eye, it must continue to respond correctly if the object is
now seen through the right eye.

This phenomenon may be called receptor generalization, to distinguish
it from stimulus generalization (Muntz, 1962c). Stimulus generalization is presumably determined by the properties of the stimulus
analyzers; receptor generalization, on the other hand, must be
determined by the interconnections between the different analyzers. It
is possible that the physical separation of the outputs of the different
stimulus filters underlies this function: if filters of one class project
to a distinct part of the CNS, then a few "collecting neurons," which
fire in response to activity in any of the neurons in this area, indicate
the occurrence of a specific stimulus, irrespective of its locus. Hubel
and Wiesel have described "complex neurones" in the cat's striate
cortex which respond to a given specific stimulus falling anywhere over
large areas of the visual field, and suggest that they "collect" from
"simple neurones" in the cortex in exactly this manner (see Figure 2).

The retinal projections to the brain of the frog provide a clear
example of different releasing stimuli activating filters which project
to spacially separate areas of the brain, and result in different
responses. Thus, under suitable conditions (Boycott, Mrosovsky, and
Muntz, 1964), the orientating response of frogs to light is released
most strongly by blue light (the releasing stimulus), and there is
strong evidence that the stimulus analyzers involved project to the
dorsal thalamus (Muntz, 1962b). Other visual responses, such as the
optomotor response, must involve optic nerve fibres projecting to the
tectum, and here blue light is relatively ineffective, the most effective colors
being green and yellow (Birukow, 1949). Thus, considering these two specific responses, orientation to a light source is mediated by filters with
specific spectral characteristics and projecting to the thalamus, while the
optomotor response is mediated by filters projecting to the optic tectum,
and having quite different spectral characteristics. "Collecting" neurones
in the thalamus and tectum can then lead directly into the appropriate
response mechanisms, so that the orientating response will occur to the
blue light anywhere in the visual field, and the optomotor response
similarly to moving stripes anywhere in the field.

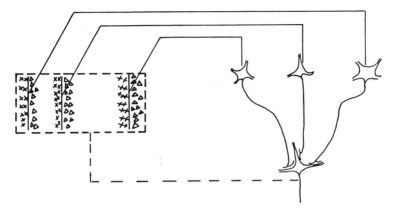

Fig. 2. Possible scheme for explaining the organization of complex receptive fields. (A number of cells with simple fields, of which three are shown schematically, are imagined to project to a single cortical cell of higher order. Each projecting neurone has a receptive field arranged as shown to the left: an excitatory region to the left and an inhibitory region to the right of a vertical straight-line boundary. The boundaries of the fields are staggered within an area outlined by the interrupted lines. Any vertical-edge stimulus falling across this rectangle, regardless of its position, will excite some simple-field cells, leading to excitation of the higher-order cell. [Reproduced from Hubel and Wiesel (1962) by courtesy of the Cambridge University Press, Cambridge.])

The work of Lettvin et al. (1959) shows that several filters project to the tectum, whereas only one projects to the dorsal thalamus (Muntz, 1962a). However, as already described, the outputs of the different filters are also segregated within the tectum. A scheme which could apply to this part of the brain is shown in Figure 3. In this scheme two types of information are collected separately. First, "collecting neurones" from the four maps yield four outputs which give information about what has occurred irrespective of locus, and these underlie receptor generalization. Second, vertical neurones are assumed to pass through the four maps and be fired by activity in any one of these; these vertical neurones result in a fifth map giving information as to the locus of a stimulus, but no information as to what it is. Such a scheme has the advantage of economy, since four maps have been reduced to one with little loss of information. The position of the dorsal thalamus in this model is uncertain: there is some evidence of a separate map in this area, and the whole thalamic system may be entirely separate throughout.

The scheme as it stands must be a great oversimplification. One immediate difficulty concerns what would happen when more than one

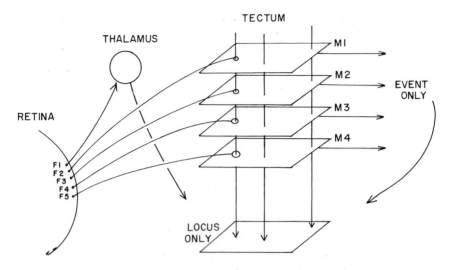

Fig. 3. Diagram of the retinal projections of the frog's brain. (Four classes of retinal analyzer project to four superimposed maps (M1-M4) in the optic tectum; a fifth class projects to the thalamus.)

event occurs in the visual field, since in such cases there is no way of knowing which horizontal output should be attached to which vertical output. The simplest way of overcoming this problem is to postulate some mechanism of mutual inhibition between the horizontal and vertical outputs of the system, such that only one of each of the outputs can be active at any given time. This would mean that the animal could "pay attention" to only one stimulus at a time. This concept of a limited amount of attention is common in psychology, and Mast (1911) has shown an effect of this type in the phototactic behavior of the toad. He found that if a toad, moving towards a source of light, entered a lateral beam of light, it ignored it and continued towards the first beam, even if the lateral beam was considerably brighter. The toad, through "paying attention" to the first beam, fails to respond to the second, although if they had both been presented simultaneously, it would have chosen the brighter of the two.

Such physiological and anatomical evidence as is available for the frog can be interpreted on the foregoing scheme. The histological pictures of Pedro Ramon (see Figure 4) show terminal arborizations of the optic nerve fibres ending at different levels in the surface layers of the tectum: these may represent the superimposed maps discovered through the physiological experiments of Lettvin et al. The tectal

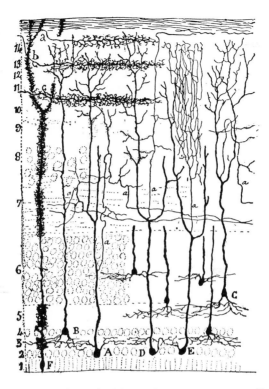

Fig. 4. Structure of the frog's optic tectum, according to
Pedro Ramon. (Reproduced from Santiago Ramon y Cajal,
Histologie du Système Nerveux [Madrid: Instituto Cajal,
Consejo Superior de Investigaciones Cientificas, 1955],
by courtesy of the Instituto Cajal.)

neurones run perpendicular to the surface and penetrate these maps,
and these must represent the vertical outputs postulated above.
Lettvin et al. have recorded from some of these tectal neurones,
without, however, performing any detailed analysis. They divided
them into two groups: "newness" neurones, and "sameness" neurones.
Members of the former class have very much the properties suggested
here for the vertical outputs. Thus they have distinct visual fields,
and no longer respond to a specific stimulus: almost any stimulus
will release a response in them. They also have a property of rapid
habituation: they rapidly cease responding to any given stimulus, but
remain responsive to others. The "sameness" neurones cannot
easily be fitted into the above scheme; their behavior is complex and
some form of mutual inhibition appears to be occurring. A vertical
organization can also be shown in the mammalian lateral geniculate

nucleus, running perpendicular to the layers (Bishop et al., 1962).

A final case of receptor generalization that will be considered, and which has been studied in detail by many people, is interocular transfer. Here again the mechanism underlying the phenomenon may be the projection of different filters from the two eyes onto the same areas of the brain, by way of the optic chiasma and the corpus callosum. Hubel and Wiesel (1962) have shown that many of the cells in the cat's striate cortex, which respond to specific complex stimuli, may be fired by stimulating either eye with the appropriate stimulus, although the cell will respond more strongly to stimuli falling on one or the other eye. Behavioral data have been obtained on the rat which agree in detail with these physiological findings. After monocular training the animals recognize stimuli equally well through either eye, but show much more responsiveness through one eye than the other (Muntz, 1963).

Summary and Conclusions

1. In many animals stimuli are analyzed by perceptual filters, which lie near the receptor mosaic. These filters respond to specific attributes of the visual field, and only stimuli which can pass these filters (releasing stimuli) can influence behavior.
2. Perceptual filters, or stimulus analyzers, are distributed over the receptor surface; there is not one analyzer which in some way scans the whole field, but rather a large number of analyzers each responsible for a small part of the visual field.
3. The outputs of the different filters project to physically separate parts of the brain, and often influence different pieces of behavior.
4. The separation of the filters' outputs may underlie receptor generalization, for if analyzers of one class project to a given part of the CNS a few "collecting neurones" from this area will indicate the occurrence of a given stimulus, irrespective of its position.

Acknowledgment

This work forms part of a project on stimulus analyzing mechanisms financed by the American Office of Naval Research (Contract Number N62558-2453) and the Nuffield Foundation.

References

Barlow, H. B., Hill, R. M., and Levick, W. R. Retinal ganglion cells responding selectively to direction and speed of image motion in the rabbit. J. Physiol., 1964, 173, 377-407.

Birukow, G. Die Entwicklung des Tages- und des Dämmerungssehens im Auge des Grasfrosches (Rana temporaria L.). Z. vergl. Physiol., 1949, 31, 322-347.

Bishop, P. W., Kozak, W., Levick, W. R., and Vakkur, G. J. The determination of the projection of the visual field on to the lateral geniculate nucleus of the cat. J. Physiol., 1962, 163, 503-539.

Boycott, B. B., Mrosovsky, N., and Muntz, W. R. A. Black and white preferences in the frog (Rana temporaria) and other Anura. J. exp. Biol., 1964, 41, 865-877.

Broadbent, D. E. Human perception and animal learning. In W. H. Thorpe and O. L. Zangwill (Ed.), Current problems in animal behavior. London: Cambridge Univer. Press, 1961. Pp. 248-272.

Brown, P. K., and Wald, G. Visual pigments in single rods and cones of the human retina. Science, 1964, 144, 45-51.

Daniel, P. M., Kerr, D. I. B., Seneviratne, K. N., and Whitteridge, D. The topographical representation of the visual field on the lateral geniculate nucleus in the cat and monkey. J. Physiol., 1961, 159, 87P-88P.

DeValois, R. L., Smith, C. J., Karoly, A. J., and Kitai, S. T. Electrical responses of primate visual system. I. Different layers of macaque lateral geniculate nucleus. J. comp. physiol. Psychol., 1958, 51, 662-668.

Hubel, D. H., and Wiesel, T. N. Receptive fields in optic nerve fibres in the spider monkey. J. Physiol., 1960, 154, 572-580.

Hubel, D. H., and Wiesel, T. N. Receptive fields, binocular interaction and functional architecture in the cat's visual cortex. J. Physiol., 1962, 160, 106-154.

Jacobsen, M. Spectral sensitivity of single units in the optic tectum of the goldfish. Quart. J. exp. Physiol., 1965, 49, 384-393.

Jacobsen, M., and Gaze, R. M. Types of visual response from single units in the optic tectum and optic nerve of the goldfish. Quart. J. exp. Physiol., 1964, 49, 199-209.

Kuffler, S. W. Discharge patterns and functional organization of mammalian retina. J. Neurophysiol., 1953, 16, 37-68.

Lettvin, J. Y., Maturana, H. R., McCulloch, W. S., and Pitts, W. H. What the frog's eye tells the frog's brain. Proc. IRE, 1959, 47, 1940-1951.

Marks, W. B., Dobelle, W. H., and MacNichol, E. F. Visual pigments of single primate cones. Science, 1964, 143, 1181-1183.

Marler, P. The filtering of external stimuli during instinctive behavior. In W. H. Thorpe, and O. L. Zangwill (Ed.), Current problems in animal behavior. London: Cambridge Univer. Press, 1961. Pp. 150-166.

Mast, S. O. Light and the behavior of organisms. New York: Wiley, 1911.

Maturana, H. R. Functional organization of the pigeon retina. In Proceedings of the twenty-second international Congress, International Union of physiological Science, Leiden, 1962, Vol. 3. R. W. Gerard and J. W. Duyff (Ed.), Information processing in the nervous system. Amsterdam: Excerpta Medica Foundation, 1964. Pp. 170-180.

Muntz, W. R. A. Effectiveness of different colours of light in releasing the positive phototactic behavior of frogs, and a possible
function of the retinal projection to the diencephalon. J.
Neurophysiol., 1962, 25, 712-720. (a)

Muntz, W. R. A. Microelectrode recordings from the diencephalon
of the frog (Rana pipiens) and a blue sensitive system. J.
Neurophysiol., 1962, 25, 699-711. (b)

Muntz, W. R. A. Stimulus generalization following monocular
training in Octopus. J. comp. physiol. Psychol., 1962, 55,
535-540. (c)

Muntz, W. R. A. Stimulus generalization following monocular
training in the rat. J. comp. physiol. Psychol., 1963, 56,
1003-1006.

Powell, T. P. S., and Mountcastle, V. B. Some aspects of the
functional organization of the postcentral gyrus of the monkey: A
correlation of findings obtained in a single unit analysis with
cytoarchitecture. Johns Hopk. Hosp. Bull., 1959, 105, 133-162.

Ratliff, F., Miller, W. H., and Hartline, H. K. Neural interaction
in the eye and the integration of receptor activity. Ann. N.Y.
Acad. Sci., 1958, 74, 210-222.

Sutherland, N. S. Visual discrimination of the orientation of
rectangles by Octopus. J. comp. physiol. Psychol., 1958, 51,
452-458.

Tinbergen, N. The study of instinct. Oxford: Clarendon Press, 1951.

Walls, G. L. The lateral geniculate nucleus and visual histo-
physiology. Univ. Calif. Publ. Physiol., 1953, 9, No. 1.

Young, J. Z. A model of the brain. Oxford: Clarendon Press, 1964.

SOME RECENT STUDIES IN VISION RELEVANT TO FORM PERCEPTION

Bela Julesz
Bell Telephone Laboratories, Incorporated
Murray Hill, New Jersey

It would be a relatively easy task to take the stand of the devil's
advocate and emphasize the premature nature of studying form perception with all its frustrations and unfounded speculations. This
attitude would seem quite natural for the author whose work could be
best characterized by his constant avoidance of the formidable problem
of form and his reliance on artificially created random stimuli devoid
of all familiarity cues. Instead of taking such a destructive approach I
shall give a short account of some recent experiments which may be

somewhat relevant to form perception. The emphasis in these experiments is on the methodology used, since it is now fairly certain that only new techniques in experimentation and bold, unorthodox models in generalization will bring us closer to an understanding of perception.

A New Phenomenon in Figure-Ground Reversal

Many students of perception believe that the prerequisite for a form to emerge is the phenomenon of figure and ground. The name itself is somewhat deceiving. In figure and ground perception the use of "figure" is really figurative and does not mean the form of any recognizable object. It refers rather to a definite perceptual change which occurs when two domains which have a common boundary are viewed. Whichever is seen as sharp, definite, having a "thing" character, is called the figure, while the rest is perceived as some "substance" and is the ground. From Rubin's studies we know that this phenomenon occurs regardless of whether the two domains are amorphic or not, and a quick reversal might occur depending which of the domains are attended to (Rubin, 1915).

This monocular figure and ground phenomenon has a binocular counterpart. Perhaps you recall how random-dot stereo images are generated (see Figure 1). Here a two-dimensional array of randomly selected black-and-white dots is identically displayed in left and right

1	0	1	0	1	0	0	1	0
1	0	X	A	A	B	B	0	0
0	0	Y	B	A	B	A	1	1
0	1	0	0	1	1	1	0	1
1	1	A	B	A	B	A	0	0
0	0	B	A	B	A	B	1	0
1	1	0	1	0	1	1	0	0
1	0	A	A	B	A	X	0	1
1	1	B	B	A	B	X	1	0
0	1	0	0	0	1	1	1	1

1	0	1	0	1	0	0	1	0
1	0	A	A	B	B	Y	0	0
0	0	B	A	B	A	X	1	1
0	1	0	0	1	1	1	0	1
1	1	B	A	B	A	B	0	0
0	0	A	B	A	B	A	1	0
1	1	0	1	0	1	1	0	0
1	0	Y	A	A	B	A	0	1
1	1	Y	B	B	A	B	1	0
0	1	0	0	0	1	1	1	1

Fig. 1. Illustration, using a small matrix of letters and numbers, of the method by which random-dot stereo images are generated. (When the matrix size is increased and the characters are changed to black and white brightness values the images are monocularly random, without shapes. When stereoscopically viewed the correlated rectangles can be seen in vivid depth above or behind the surround. In Figure 3 only the center rectangle of Figure 1, having both a nasal and a temporal disparity, was used. This produces some periodic stripes which can be seen monocularly too.)

fields, except for some areas which are also identical, but horizontally shifted relative to each other (Julesz, 1960; Julesz, 1964).

If we imagine a "model" in which the left and right fields are combined with increasing horizontal shifts prior to the combination (e.g., subtraction) and staggered above each other we obtain a set of depth planes. In each depth plane the correlated points form clusters which when viewed as figures give the cross sections of objects (see Figure 2). The correlated domains consist of clusters of points having minimum value, whereas the uncorrelated domains are randomly textured in the various depth planes (Julesz, 1960; Julesz, 1964). Therefore, stereopsis might be though of as attending to the correlated clusters as if they were the "figures" and ignoring the rest as being the "ground" in the various depth planes.

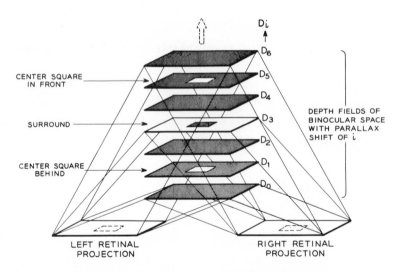

Fig. 2. Illustration of a heuristic model in which the various "depth planes" (D_i) are derived by subtracting the left and right fields after various amounts of horizontal shift (i) relative to each other.

There is a second connection of figure and ground with depth perception. It is a well-known characteristic of figure and ground that when a part is viewed as a figure it is perceived in depth as being somewhat in front of the ground. This can be demonstrated by viewing first monocularly and afterwards stereoscopically ambiguous random-dot stereo pairs (see Figure 3). Since the ambiguous stereo pairs consist of a periodic pattern in the center which can be seen monocularly

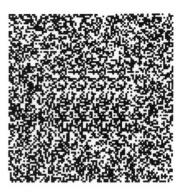

Fig. 3. Random-dot stereo pair in which the center square
has a disparity in both directions and when viewed stereoscopically can be perceived either in front or behind the
surround.

as being imbedded in randomness, the periodic pattern when viewed
stereoscopically can be seen either in front or behind its surround,
but only in one way at a time. In this experiment we view monocularly
one of the stereo pairs first and decide to see the center periodic
pattern either as figure or ground and while doing so we open the
second eye. The stereoscopically viewed ambiguous pattern is either
in front or behind depending whether it was previously perceived as
figure or as ground.

After this discussion of figure and ground phenomena I should like
to turn to another topic which seems quite remote from the previous
notions; but please be patient with me for a short time.

What are the perceptual processes which occur when viewing a
simple outlined polygon? According to the neurophysiological findings
of Hubel and Wiesel (1959, 1962) the striate cortex of the cat extracts
slits and edges of given orientation from the input stimuli. Both the
position and the orientation of these retinal receptor fields (slit-
detectors) are meticulously preserved in the cytoarchitecture of the
visual cortex. Jack Schwartz (of New York University) and I have
begun to investigate the problem of how simple figures, such as
outlined polygons, might be recognized in such an orientation-position
mapping. One recognition mechanism might be based on scanning
sequentially each side of the polygon and noting the temporal order of
vertices where the jump from one set of orientation detectors to
another occurs. A conceptually simpler but actually more complex
model might be based on parallel organization. Here each possible

slit detector combination forms a complex unit which might simultaneously process each side of the polygon in question. In order to
decide whether in perception the sequential process in time is
preferred or not, I tried to utilize the notion of the temporal "moment."

The temporal "moment" was intensively studied by von Uexküll
(1928) as the smallest resolvable time unit in perception. He defined
the moment (in agreement with earlier attempts by Exner and Wundt)
as the "time period in which one perceives all stimuli, regardless of
their objective order, as simultaneous." This is the temporal counterpart of visual acuity, which is the smallest separation between two
points, so that the two points can be still resolved. Illig (1953) and
Brecher (1937) studied the optical moment intensively and found
that it is relatively constant for all people, at about 100 msec. The
moment in vision is relatively insensitive to changes in light adaptation,
intensity of light, duty ratio of flashes, spatial extent of presentation,
etc., in contrast to critical flicker frequency.

In the experiments to be reported (and demonstrated) next, the
optical moment was measured for various polygons (pentagons,
hexagons, etc.) under two conditions. First, the sides of the polygon
were presented for ten subjects cyclically in nonsequential order at
various speeds (see Figure 4). Second, the same sides were presented
cyclically in sequential order at various speeds. The sides were thin

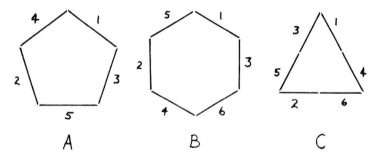

Fig. 4. Nonsequential presentation of sides of various
polygons: (A) Pentagon, (B) Hexagon, and (C) Triangle
(half-sides).

bright slits in a black background. It was found that the extent of the
presentation (both the visual angle of the diameter of the polygon and
the width of the slits) and the contrast had negligible effects on the
moment. In the experiments, the criterion for the optical moment was

the maximum time of presentation when the polygon in question was
perceived as a single Gestalt. Since this limit is lower in frequency
than the critical flicker threshold, the perceived polygon appears to
be flickering, but it is impossible to tell the order in which the sides
appear. The results of these experiments are summarized in Table 1.
It can be seen that the required speed is about 50% higher, and thus
the moment time is 50% lower for the sequential case. This finding
disproves the parallel hypothesis in which each side of the polygon is
processed by a slit detector and connected simultaneously to a complex
polygon detector. Since in the experiments for both the sequential and
nonsequential presentation the same perceptual criterion of seeing
a Gestalt was used, we might expect that the polygon detector would
be insensitive to the temporal order of the occurrence of edges. This
expectation is in disagreement with the findings.

Table 1. Optical Moments

Mean Moment Frequencies in Hz		
Case	Nonsequential	Sequential
A	15.8	10.2
B	25.7	18.5
C	26.2	19.8
D	17.6	11.4
E	25.3	17.8

In addition to these orientation-sensitive simple and complex units,
Hubel and Wiesel found hypercomplex units, such as corner detectors.
In some of our experiments instead of the sides of the polygon its
vertices were presented both in sequential and nonsequential order
(see Figure 5). The results are also included in Table 1, and though
the vertices require a somewhat shorter moment the ratio between
sequential and nonsequential presentation is about the same. The
fact that, regardless of the complexity of the features, their sequential
presentation is easier to perceive than any departure of the sequential
order is interesting in itself. This finding, together with the typical
times for the moment, might suggest that this sequential read-out
mechanism might be related to the occipital alpha-rhythm, as found
in EEG. There are several theories by Brecher (1937) and Illig et al.

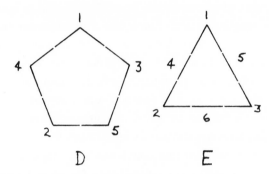

Fig. 5. Nonsequential presentation of vertices (and sides)
of various polygons: (D) Pentagon, (E) Triangle.

(1954) which regard the alpha-rhythm as a triggering mechanism.
Some temporally subsequent input stimuli reach the same "street-car"
and the schedule for the next "read-out" (street car) is governed by
the alpha-rhythm. Both the "street car" theory and the role of the
alpha-rhythm are very speculative and require very thorough further
elucidation.

After this detour it is time to go back to the problem of figure-
ground. The previous discussion on the optical moment was, of
course, relevant to the problem of form perception but also served
another purpose. It kept the observers' attention focused on the sides
of the polygon (during the demonstration), which assured that they
were perceived as the figure and that the black inside of the polygon
with its surround was perceived as the ground. In the experiments
reported next, the subjects were instructed to perceive the polygon
as being cut out of a solid black sheet placed over a blurred white
opening. After the perceptual reversal takes place, an unexpected
thing happens. Regardless of any speed of presentation, the black
hexagon can be perceived as moving very slowly in an eccentric path.
Subsequently, the sides become hidden one at a time behind the black
surround, but after emerging the side appears at the place where
the subjects were expecting it. This "figural constancy" occurs at
very low speeds, several times longer than the measured moment.
Thus, with figure-ground reversal the required memory storage ex-
pands too. This phenomenon is in agreement with findings which
conclude that often only figures are remembered and not the ground.
Nevertheless, the experiments we have performed might have some
interest, since they show under controlled conditions that figure and

ground reversal is not a simple spatial phenomenon depending on which side of a contour is attended to, but is already a complex spatial-temporal phenomenon.

Multidimensional Scaling of Figure-Lattices Hidden in Randomness

Visual texture discrimination is a further generalization of figure and ground. It might be regarded as ground and ground discrimination in a sense. In previous experiments, I used two computer-generated random fields side by side having different statistical properties (Julesz, 1962). The subjects were asked to report how different the two displays looked from each other. The basis of discrimination was not that of scrutinizing the stimulus, but a spontaneous, effortless sensation of two separate fields (Julesz, 1962). The main result of these experiments was: that the common statistical parameters by themselves are not very good descriptors of texture discrimination. The visual field undergoes a preprocessing first, that of extracting clusters formed by proximate points having similar brightness values. It is a few relatively simple properties of clusters which are the basis of discrimination.

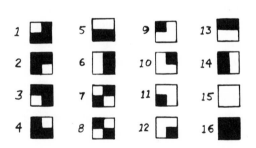

Fig. 6. The set of all 2 × 2 arrays of black and white dots with their number codes.

In the forthcoming experiments attempts were made to include some simple form cues. The patterns to be discriminated were chosen from a modest set of all 2 × 2 arrays of black-and-white dots. There are 16 such patterns (see Figure 6). These 16 different patterns could be regarded as characters of a foreign alphabet. There are 16(15)/2 = 120 different ways of pairing any two of these characters and we could rank order them according to their similarities (or confusion errors committed). Such a study already has been undertaken by Roger Shepard.[1]

----

[1] Personal communication.

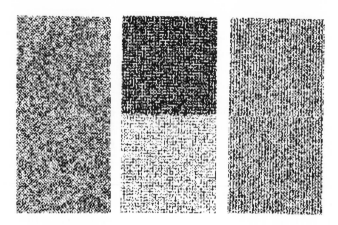

Fig. 7. Lattice pattern pairs side by side. (A few examples
from the 120 stimuli used: [7 and 8], [15 and 16], and
[6 and 14].)

My experiment is a greatly modified version of this. The 2×2
matrix of a given pattern is many times repeated in both dimensions
keeping one row and one column in between which is filled with black-
and-white random dots. Though the same pattern is periodically
repeated several hundred times the slight noise in between makes
the pattern unrecognizable. After 16 such lattice patterns (hidden in
randomness) were generated, each possible pair was presented side
by side to a group of 36 observers. They were asked to "sort" the
pairs into five grades according to their dissimilarities. Some of
the stimuli are shown in Figures 7 and 8.

Before any detailed evaluation of the data is made, a three-
dimensional abstract space can be conjectured, based on intuition and
subjective judgment, in which the 16 different lattice forms are
regarded as 16 points in a Euclidian space and their distances from
each other are kept similar to the psychological dissimilarities (see
Figure 9). It is a priori plausible that there are two strong dimensions,
and a third less obvious one. The strongest dimension is brightness
(i.e., the number of white dots in the 2×2 matrix). Since this can
be 0, 1, 2, 3, and 4 the 16 points have to be grouped along these 5
brightness values. The next dimension is the orientation of the line
clusters formed. Since apparently a vertical stripe is still vertical
after a 180 degrees rotation, it is assumed that a 360 degrees range
of the stimulus space is mapped to only 180 degrees in the abstract
psychological space. The third dimension is the distance from the

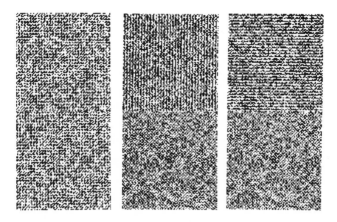

Fig. 8. Similar to Figure 7. (Stimuli: [9 and 12], [7 and 14],
and [5 and 7].)

brightness axis which could be interpreted as the strength of connectivity. In a Cartesian system the diagonal connectivity is weaker
than the horizontal or vertical ones, since the center of the picture
elements is $\sqrt{2}$ times more distant.

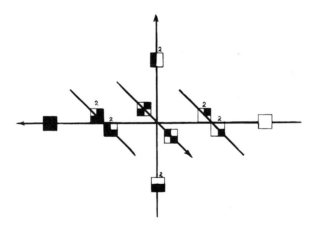

Fig. 9. Idealized qualitative stimulus space in three-dimensions. (Interpoint distances between stimuli [Euclidian metric]
are qualitatively related to the psychological dissimilarities.)

After this idealized abstraction the actual results are now discussed.
First of all, these results were obtained from 36 subjects instead of
1 observer. Second, the subjects were naïve and were unaware of
certain subtle changes in the stimuli. The last but perhaps most

important departure from the previous model is that some quantitative results were sought instead of the more or less qualitative considerations discussed previously.

In order to evaluate the dissimilarity (or confusion) matrix, the nonmetric multidimensional scaling procedure (or "analysis of proximities"), originally developed by Shepard (1962), and refined by Kruskal (1964), was used. The problem of multidimensional scaling is to find n points whose interpoint distances match in some sense the experimental dissimilarities of n objects. In the Shepard-Kruskal procedure the fundamental hypothesis is that dissimilarities and distances are monotonically related. It is a surprising fact that the rank order of the dissimilarities is itself enough to obtain a very tightly constrained solution. The departure from monotonicity is defined by a mathematical quantity called, by Kruskal, the "stress" and the best-fitting configuration is sought which has minimal stress in a given dimension. The number of dimensions of the configuration space is of course crucial. Indeed n points can always be placed in an (n-2) dimensional space with zero stress, (i.e., such that their interpoint distances have the same monotonically ordered hierarchy). But, if we want to place the n points in an (n-3) or lower dimensional space, then we will notice that the possible solutions become very limited if at all feasible. If the number of objects is large and the dimension of configuration space is small, then the solution is very tight and precise although we ignored the actual numerical values of the data and kept only their rank order.

The Shepard-Kruskal procedure has been written as an iterative program for the IBM 7090 computer, and it is a very convenient package. The figures presented next are the actual output from the computer by a General Dynamics microfilm printer. First of all, the actual stresses for our data are 4% in three-dimensions, 9% in two-dimensions, and 16% in one-dimension. The problem whether the configuration is three- or two-dimensional depends on two things. First, is the increase in stress sudden enough as we lower the dimensions to suggest that we have surpassed the real dimension number of the configuration space and started to collapse a useful axis? Second, can we give a proper psychological interpretation of all dimensions? In our case both the 4% and 9% stresses seem small enough to be accepted as possible dimensions. In Figure 10 you can see a two-dimensional projection of a three-dimensional solution

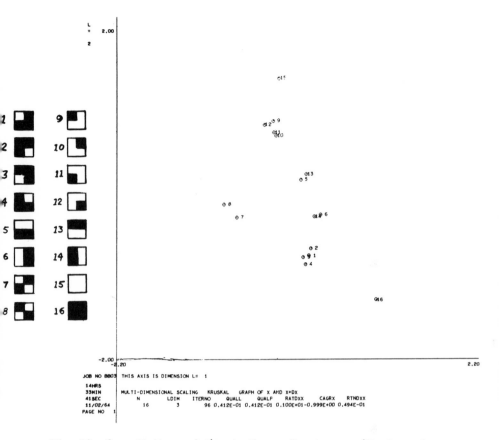

Fig. 10. Quantitative solution in three-dimension. (Portrayed is the two-dimensional projection of the solution. Table 2 shows the co-ordinates of the three-dimensional solution.)

(Table 2 gives the co-ordinates in three-dimension) and in Figure 11 the monotone best-fitting curve in the scatter diagram (where the abscissa represents the distances, and the ordinate the dissimilarities, between the 120 point pairs). The less the departure (scatter) from this "best-fitting" monotonically ascending curve, the better the configuration space is recovered (Kruskal, 1964). Figures 12 and 13 show the same two diagrams for the two-dimensional solution. Finally, the one-dimensional solution is shown where the large stress indicates that one meaningful dimension has probably been ignored, although the remaining dimension, as you can see, is the most important axis; viz., brightness (see Figure 14). In two-dimensions, the brightness axis goes through Points 15 and 16 (which are the zero

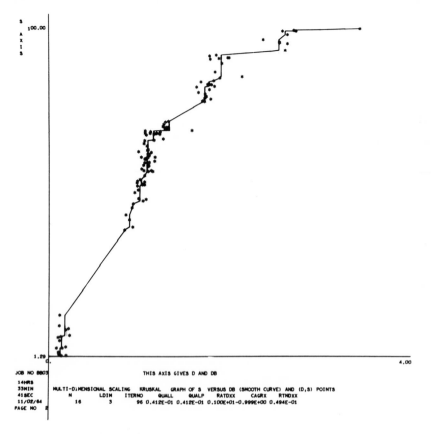

Fig. 11. Scatter diagram for the three-dimensional solution.
(Abscissa = interpoint distances, ordinate = psychological
dissimilarities. Line = best fitting curve with minimal stress.)

and four white dot patterns). The cluster made up of the Points 9, 10,
11, and 12 corresponds to one brightness level change from point 15,
the (5, 13), (6, 14), and (8, 7) points are two brightness levels remote
from 15, whereas 1, 2, 3, and 4 are 3 brightness levels distant from
15 (and one level away from 16). In all these slides a Euclidian metric
was used. (A Minkowskian 1-metric, also called city-block metric,
was tried, but then the axes cannot be freely rotated and the slight
possible improvement in the results does not justify the difficulties
encountered.) Several of the iterations gave similar results in two-
dimensions except for the (5, 13), (6, 14), and (7, 8) point pairs which
often became pairwise interchanged (see Figure 15). These 3-point
pairs correspond to the 0-, 45-, and 90-degree orientations and are

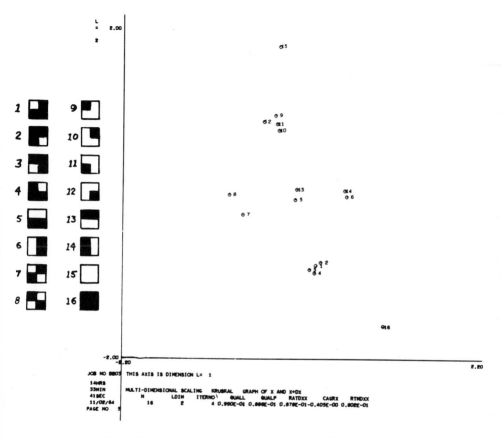

Fig. 12. Quantitative solution in two-dimensions.

about equidistant from each other. Thus, they have to be placed on the vertices of an equilateral triangle in a plane perpendicular to the brightness axis.

Of course, you might argue that the three-dimensional solution would automatically lead to this result, which is very similar to the suggested model we derived by intuition. Unfortunately, the three-dimensional solution is not so neat (as Table 2 shows). Naturally, the principal brightness dimension can be found easily in the three-dimensional configuration. However, the addition of a third dimension is not only meaningless for the rest of the points but introduces so many additional degrees of freedom that the "tightness" or metric determinacy of the earlier solution is lost. Therefore, the multi-dimensional scaling process has to be modified somewhat. It is not

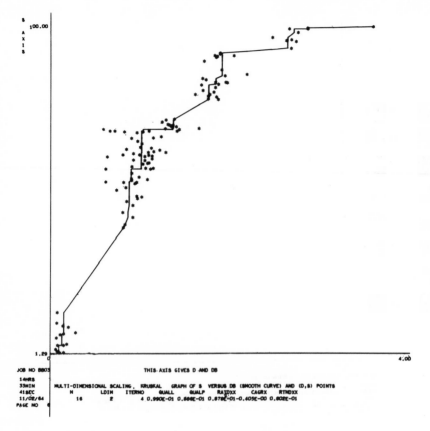

Fig. 13. Scatter diagram for the two-dimensional solution.

possible to find the optimal minimum dimensions for all n points at
once, so we have to take a subset of k points for which one (or more)
additional dimensions might be recovered and successfully interpreted,
letting the remaining (n-k) points stay in the lower dimensional space.
The search for such subsets could be made automatically in the
iteration programs.

As has been shown, all the 2 × 2 lattice patterns can be placed in a
three-dimensional space, where one axis can be interpreted as a
brightness and in which orthogonally drawn axes of different orientations correspond to the orientations of the line-clusters in the displays. There are a few deviations from the suspected solution.
Horizontal and vertical clusters are not quite equal when compared
with other patterns. This is due to the fact that the separation between
the two half-fields took place along a vertical boundary. Therefore,

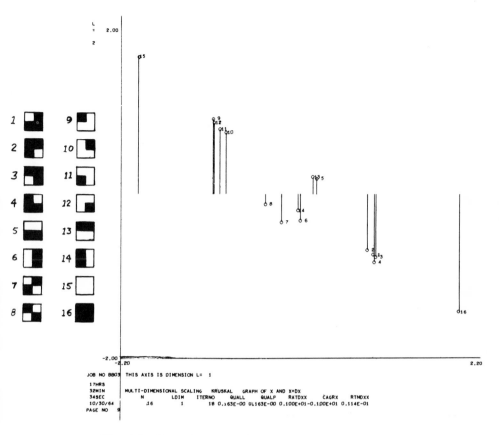

Fig. 14. Quantitative solution in one-dimension

vertical patterns are sooner discriminated than horizontals. But
this is only a side effect of presentation. There is a small discrimination effect within the same orientation according to whether
the white-black stripes are left-right or right-left, similarly up and
down or down and up, etc. This is a slight effect, but interestingly
the naïve subjects were able to notice it, whereas differences in
diagonal staircases of white dots in a black surround versus black
dots in a white surround passed unnoticed (see Figure 7, first display).

It should be emphasized again that in these stimuli the form cue
is hidden from consciousness and manifests itself only through the
properties of the connected clusters. Therefore, the results obtained
might be very different from experiments where the 16 2 × 2 matrices
are regarded as an alphabet. For instance, whereas in that case
patterns that differ by changing all black squares to white and vice

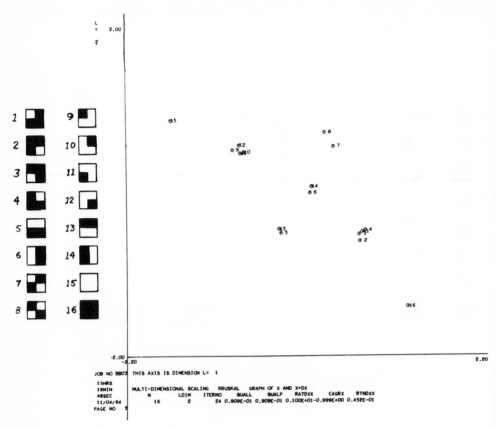

Fig. 15. Quantitative solution in two-dimensions (using different iteration from Figure 12).

Table 2. Three-Dimensional Solution

Stimuli*	Co-ordinates of the 16 points in abstract space		
	I	J	K
1	.215	-.745	-.404
2	.236	-.654	-.467
3	.144	-.760	-.460
4	.171	-.844	-.368
5	.110	.195	-.528
6	.357	-.235	.449
7	-.696	-.272	.049
8	-.858	-.113	.128
9	-.239	.912	.359
10	-.205	.733	.282
11	-.232	.772	.392
12	-.348	.862	.257
13	.181	.259	-.477
14	.281	-.263	.548
15	-.170	1.433	1.060
16	1.052	-1.280	-.821

* Number code given in Figure 6.

versa are often confused;[2] in the experiments reported here, such patterns (differing along the dimension of brightness) are the most distinct.

It would be desirable to increase the size of the matrix to 3×3 or 4×4, and see whether the increased complexity would result in additional psychological dimensions. But, unfortunately, already a 3×3 size means $2^9 = 512$ patterns which require several ten thousands of measurements even if the symmetrical pairs are discarded. Of course, there is no need to span the entire space of possibilities, and some interesting 6×6 or larger arrays could be selected and compared to see what other dimensions could be perceived besides brightness and orientation. Perhaps the width and curvature of the formed lines might serve as a cue. There are many things which one could try with this technique, and my purpose was only to demonstrate that nonmetric multidimensional scaling could become a useful technique in form discrimination.

In this paper the relatively simple problem of figure and ground was attacked from different angles, and already complex processes of memory reorganization, attention shift, etc., were noticed. The phenomena studied were just borderline cases preceding real form perception. It frightens me even to think of the problems which might occur when real form recognition is investigated. On the other hand, we might be more optimistic. After all, what do the neurophysiologists find in the visual cortex? They find just mappings of mappings. Perhaps the enigma of form lies in the enormous number of parallel processings where many extracted features are weighted simultaneously. Any such feature which can be identified by neurophysiological or psychological methods might be a step in the right direction.

References

Brecher, G. Die Momentgrenze in optischer Gebiet. Z. Biol., 1937, 98, 232.

Hubel, D. H., and Wiesel, T. N. Receptive fields of single neurons in the cat's striate cortex. J. Physiol., 1959, 148, 574.

Hubel, D. H., and Wiesel, T. N. Receptive fields, binocular interaction and functional architecture in the cat's visual cortex. J. Physiol., 1962, 160, 106.

Illig, H. Der optische Moment. Dissert. München: 1953.

---

[2] R. N. Shepard, personal communication.

Illig, H., Pflanz, M. and von Uexküll, J. Experimentelle Untersuchungen über die kleinste Zeiteinheit (Moment) der optischer Wahrnehmung. Pflüg. Arch. ges. Physiol., 1954, 257, 124.

Julesz, B. Binocular depth perception of computer-generated patterns. Bell System Tech. J., 1960, 39, 1125.

Julesz, B. Visual texture discrimination. IRE PGIT, 1962, IT-8, 84.

Julesz, B. Binocular depth perception without familiarity cues. Science, 1964, 145, 356.

Kruskal, J. B. Multidimensional scaling by optimizing goodness of fit to a nonmetric hypothesis. Psychometrika, 1964, 29, 1 and 115.

Rubin, E. Synsoplevede figurer. Copenhagen: Gyldensdalske, 1915. [Cond. trans. of pp. 35-101 of Ger. ed.: E. Rubin, Figure and ground. In D. C. Beardslee and M. Wertheimer (Ed.), Readings in perception. New York: Van Nostrand, 1958. P. 194.]

Shepard, R. N. The analysis of proximities: Multi-dimensional scaling with an unknown distance function. I and II. Psychometrika, 1962, 27, 125 and 219.

von Uexküll, J. Theoretische biologie. Berlin: Springer, 1928.

Contributed Papers

CONTRIBUTED PAPERS I

Visual Recognition

Chairman: Paul A. Kolers
Research Laboratory of Electronics
Massachusetts Institute of Technology
Cambridge, Massachusetts

TEMPORAL EFFECTS IN THE PERCEPTION OF LIGHT AND FORM

Daniel Kahneman
Department of Psychology
Hebrew University
Jerusalem, Israel

In recent years, there has been a marked upsurge of interest in the temporal characteristics of visual perception. The quantization of psychological time into moments (Stroud, 1956; White, 1963), the temporal sequence of operations on the visual input and the speed of extraction of information from visual displays (Averbach and Sperling, 1961) are now important topics of investigation. The series of studies to be described here was motivated by the same interest. It represents an attempt to study the role of time as an independent variable of stimulation so as to provide a background for inferences in which time appears as a dependent variable in the description of the perceptual process.

Duration-Intensity Reciprocity for Acuity and for Brightness.

The main empirical law describing the effects of exposure duration as an independent variable is the Bunsen-Roscoe law of reciprocity between intensity and duration of stimulation. The finding of reciprocity of this type for a particular feature of the visual response demonstrates that the visual system is capable of perfectly integrating (up to some critical duration t_c) certain relevant aspects of the input.

We have been concerned in three separate studies with the reciprocity law as it applies to the acuity performance of a dark-adapted observer. A Maxwellian view and central fixation were used in all these studies, the target appearing in the center of an 8-degree circular field. (Apparatus and procedures have been described elsewhere: Kahneman, 1964; Kahneman, 1966a; Kahneman and Norman, 1964.)

In the first study (Kahneman and Norman, 1964), intensity thresholds were obtained at different durations for the identification of triads of binary digits appearing as black figures on a briefly illuminated background. Duration-intensity reciprocity was found to hold for both the identification task and the apparent brightness of the illuminated background on which the target appeared. Apparent brightness was determined by matching the brightness of flashes of different durations to that of standard flash of 10 msec. The main finding of this study was that different critical durations were obtained for the two tasks.

Results for one 0 are presented in Figure 1. It can be seen that reciprocity for the identification task holds up to a critical duration

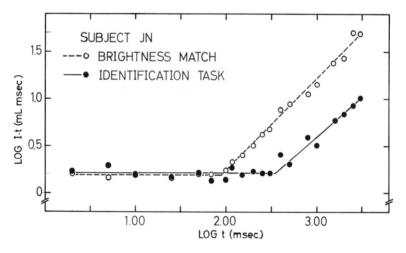

Fig. 1. Log energy required for two tasks (identification of triads of binary symbols and matching the brightness of a flash to a standard flash of 10 msec) as a function of log stimulus duration.

of about 350 msec, whereas t_c for brightness is only 100 msec. In the range between t_c for brightness and t_c for identification, the apparent brightness of a stimulus at threshold decreases steadily with increasing duration, whereas the energy required for identification remains constant.

The values of t_c for the identification task (200 to 350 msec for different observers) are high, but not exceptional: values of t_c ranging from 200 to 300 msec, have been reported for the span of apprehension (Hunter and Sigler, 1940) and for the identification of words (Scharf, Holohan, and Morningstar, 1963); under some conditions, t_c reaches 1,000 msec in the detection of movement (Brown, 1957). As a whole, such data indicate that different mechanisms of temporal integration operate in responses to different features of the stimulus. They also suggest that the interpretation of the critical duration as some sort of sensory latency (Graham and Ratoosh, 1962; Hartline, 1934) cannot apply to all cases of reciprocity.

A second study (Kahneman, 1964) was designed to investigate the variation of t_c as a function of stimulating energy for the resolution of the Landolt C. Previous studies, beginning with McDougall's work (1904) on the action-time of lights of different luminances, have agreed that the upper limit of temporal integration is inversely related to the level of stimulating energy (e.g., Barlow, 1958). We found that this generalization does not apply to the resolution of the Landolt C: for three Os, t_c for this task was a U-shaped function of stimulating energy, with values of 350 to 1,000 msec at the highest level of energy studied (45 mL × msec). Control experiments were carried out to investigate the possibility that the unexpected upturn of t_c at high levels of energy is due to the size or retinal location of the target. These variables, which were confounded with energy in the main experiment, apparently do not play an important role in the determination of t_c. A particular value of t_c appears to correspond to every value of stimulating energy.

This conclusion was confirmed and elaborated in a third study (Kahneman, 1966a). Our hypothesis at the time was that differences in figure-ground contrast could account for the different characteristics of temporal summation in tests of acuity and of brightness discrimination. In the latter task, t_c has often been found to decrease monotonically from about 100 msec at absolute threshold to low values of 10 to 20 msec for strong background illuminations (and correspondingly high energies of test increment). In brightness discrimination tasks, the contrast between figure and ground is minimal, whereas contrast is usually maximal in investigations of acuity performance. An acuity experiment was therefore undertaken, in which the independent variables were energy level, amount of contrast, and mode of presentation (black or gray target on illuminated ground, bright target on dimmer ground, and bright target on black background).

The results of this experiment are presented in Figure 2. The

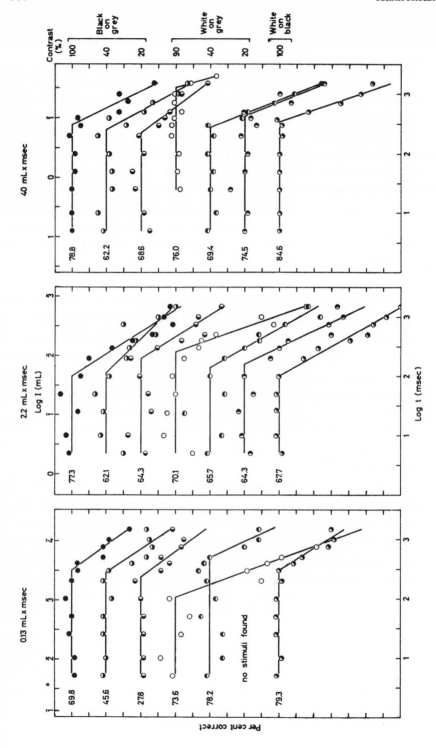

dependent variable in the figure is the probability of correct identification of the gap in a Landolt C. Duration and luminance for any experimental point may be read off the bottom and top scales, respectively. In a plot of this type, the reciprocity relation is displayed by a horizontal line, and the lines of negative slope indicate the failure of reciprocity beyond the critical duration. The luminance corresponding to t_c may be read off the top scale. Measurements of figure-ground contrast follow the definitions proposed by Luckiesh (1944, p. 108).

This complex set of data may be summarized as follows:

1. The reciprocity relation appears to hold in all cases, although considerable variability is observed in some conditions.

2. For any one level of energy, closely similar values of t_c are found for all conditions, with the exception of the 90% contrast, white-on-gray presentation.

3. In most conditions of presentation, t_c varies as a U-shaped function of energy, with a clear exception in the case of the 90% contrast, white-on-gray presentation.

The most surprising feature of these results is that the white-on-black presentation behaves very much like most other conditions, while the 90% white-on-gray presentation does not. An interpretation which accounts for both results is that figure-ground contrast as such has little or no effect on temporal summation in this acuity task[1]; t_c

Fig. 2. Landolt C's were exposed in three modes of presentation and various levels of figure-ground contrast as indicated in the right-hand margin. (Each curve represents the average probability of detection of the gap [corrected for chance] for two 0s at a given luminance-duration product [E]. The top scale indicates background luminance in the black-on-gray and white-on-gray conditions, or the luminance of the figure in the white-on-black condition [unilluminated background]. Each vertical division equals 10% success. The horizontal lines represent the mean achievement for brief durations [indicated at left of each curve]; their vertical location is arbitrary. Lines of negative slope were drawn by inspection. Missing data for the 90%, white-on-gray case at the highest energy could not be obtained because of limitations of light source.)

_____

[1] An interpretation of the discrepant values of t_c in acuity and in brightness discrimination is presented later. See footnote 3.

appears to be determined by the luminance-duration product <u>for the</u> <u>brighter part of the field</u>.

Figure 3 summarizes the data of Figure 2 in accordance with this interpretation. The critical duration t_c is plotted against the luminance at t_c of the brighter part of the field (i.e., the background in the black-on-gray presentations or the target in the white-on-gray and white-on black presentations). The data for these highly heterogeneous conditions are fairly well fitted by a single function, in which t_c reaches a very high value (1 sec) for the highest luminance studied.

The data of these experiments lead to the following conclusions:

1. There are at least two distinct processes of temporal summation, of which one applies to brightness [and apparently to the b-wave of the ERG (Johnson, 1958)], while the other applies to the perception of form and quite possibly also to the perception of movement (Brown, 1957). The dichotomy suggested here could well be related to the hierarchy of operations on visual inputs recently described by Hubel and Wiesel (1962).

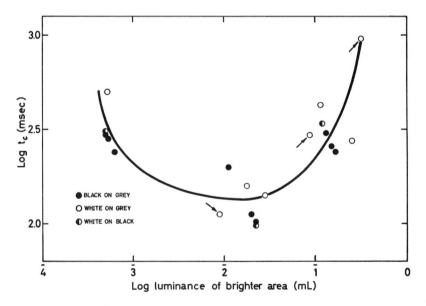

Fig. 3. Log t_c as a function of log luminance of brighter area of stimulus in three modes of presentation. (Data derived from Figure 2. The arrows indicate results for the 90%, white-on-gray presentation [see text]. Curve drawn by inspection.)

2. The critical duration for the form process is a complex function of stimulus luminance (see Figure 3).

3. Interpretations of t_c as a sensory latency (Graham and Ratoosh, 1962) or as the duration of an elementary sensory response (Blackwell, 1963; Johnson, 1958) do not appear applicable to the very high values of t_c obtained in the present experiments.

Visual Masking and Temporal Summation

The idea that visual masking may be closely related to temporal summation was independently advanced by Eriksen and Hoffman (1963) for masking by light, and by Kinsbourne and Warrington (1962) for masking by visual noise.

According to this theory, a target and a masking stimulus which follow one another in quick succession are effectively simultaneous within a single "frame" of time, in analogy with a double exposure of a photographic plate. In the case of masking by light, such super-position results in reduced figure-ground contrast; in the case of masking by visual noise, contour interactions prevent the resolution of the masked target. It follows from this view that similar masking effects should be obtained regardless of the order of presentation of target and mask.

The interpretation of some cases of masking as due to temporal summation has at least one important advantage: it provides a frame-work for the understanding of monoptic and dichoptic masking effects. The rules which describe what happens when two different stimuli are simultaneously presented to the two eyes also apply to cases of successive presentation. The dichoptic masking of a figure by visual noise (Schiller, 1965) corresponds to binocular rivalry and binocular contour interaction (Flom, Heath, and Takahashi, 1963); the failure of dichoptic masking by light is an instance of the dominance of contours presented to one eye over homogeneous illumination of the other eye. Significantly, dichoptic masking of one flash by another depends on the relative proximity of their contours (Battersby and Wagman, 1962). Dichoptic metacontrast effects are weak or absent (Alpern, 1953), except under conditions favoring apparent movement (Kolers and Rosner, 1960), a phenomenon which may be obtained binocularly. There appears to be little doubt that the cases of simultaneous and successive presentation have much in common, nor is there any doubt that summation between successive stimuli occurs.

Whether the notion of summation is sufficient to explain all masking effects is, of course, an entirely different question.

A direct test of the summation model was attempted in an experiment (Kahneman, 1965) in which we investigated the effects of pre- and post-exposure light fields on the apparent contrast of a black figure. A matching procedure was used: the standard stimulus was a gray square of given figure-ground contrast, presented for 2 sec on a light background; the comparison stimulus was a black square (100% contrast) preceded and followed by 1 sec of homogeneous illumination of the entire field with no change of background luminance during the presentation of the figure. In effect, the conditions of exposure of the comparison stimulus simulate the most common arrangement of tachistoscopic experimentation. The 0's task was to adjust the duration of exposure of the black comparison square to a match with the grayness of the standard stimulus. The main results of this experiment are presented in Figure 4.

According to a summation model, the apparent contrast of a black figure presented under standard tachistoscopic conditions should be a linear function of exposure duration, passing through the origin: The amount of light flux which reaches the eye from the "black" area of the figure during the period of summation is inversely related to exposure duration, while the light flux absorbed from the background remains constant. It is apparent in Figure 4 that lines through the origin can be drawn only through the points representing the higher values of contrast and longer durations. Marked deviations from the summation model are present at short durations of exposure, and an additional effect of interference with apparent contrast is required to account for these data.

The phenomenology of the situation suggested a hypothesis concerning the nature of this interference. At very short durations of exposure, the percept is a vague moving blur, totally lacking in bounding contours. No value of contrast can be assigned to this form-less stage, in which the figure is phenomenally absent. The hypothesis was therefore advanced that the pre- and postexposure fields reduce apparent contrast in two ways: directly, by brightness summation, indirectly, by interference with the formation of bounding contours which are presumably essential to figure-ground contrast.

In an attempt to test this hypothesis, an outline of the square was

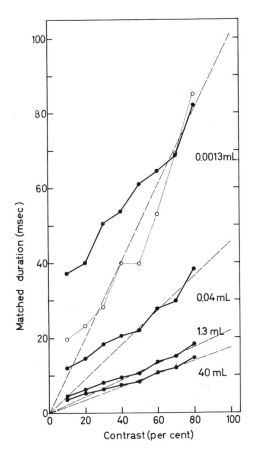

Fig. 4. Filled circles: a black square subtending 4 degrees 24
minutes is presented in a circular field of 8 degrees, preceded
and followed by illumination of the entire field; luminance of
background remains unchanged during exposure. (The duration
is determined for which the apparent contrast of the square
matches each of the contrast values indicated on the abscissa.
Background luminance is the parameter.) (Unfilled circles:
as above, but exposure of the black figure is preceded and
followed by presentations of a thin outline of the square
[width of line, 5'].)

presented in the pre- and postexposure fields, presumably supplying
a contour which would permit the formation of a perceived form and
the judgment of its contrast. This manipulation was intended to overcome the interference effect, and it appears to have succeeded:

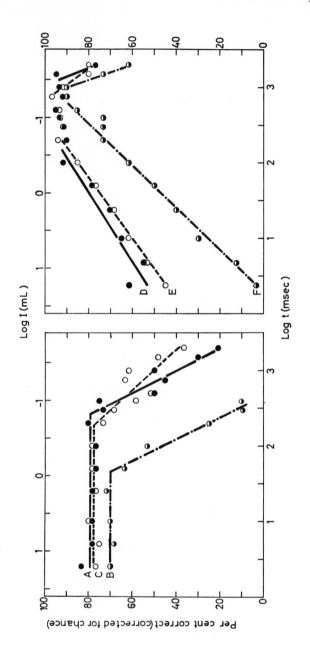

results for this condition (unfilled circles in Figure 4) tend to fall
fairly close to a line through the origin, in accordance with the brightness summation model.[2]

The effects of brightness summation and interference on acuity
performance were studied in a further experiment (Kahneman, 1966b).
Reciprocity functions were obtained for the resolution of a Landolt C
presented at 40 mL × msec. In different conditions, exposure of the
target preceded, followed, or was superimposed on a 2-sec flash of
light illuminating the entire field.

It can be seen in Figure 5 that reciprocity holds up to a value of
about 300 msec when no flash is presented (Curve A), or when flash
and target are separated by 1.5 sec (Curve C). Reciprocity also holds
when the target is superimposed on the flash (Curve B), but only up
to a t_c of about 50 msec, characteristic of the brightness process.[3]

Fig. 5. Performance in detection of gap of a Landolt C
presented at 40 mL × msec for different combinations of
duration (bottom scale) and luminance (top scale). (Average
for 2 subjects. The target is exposed in different temporal
relations to a 2-sec flash of homogeneous light at 1 mL:
A - Control, no flash; B - Superposition on illuminated
background; C - Interposition between flashes [ISI = 1,500
msec]; D - Target followed by flash [ISI = 0.1 msec];
E - Target preceded by flash [ISI = 0.1 msec]; F - Target interposed between two 1-sec exposures of light
[ISI = 0.1 msec].)

---

[2] A possible methodological contribution of this study should be noted.
According to the summation model, extrapolation of the lines through
the origin to 100% contrast yields an estimate of summation time for
brightness. These estimates are in good agreement with determinations of t_c for brightness discrimination, at similar levels of adapting
luminance (Biersdorf, 1955). With the contrast-matching method, a
critical duration for brightness may be estimated with fair reliability
in 15 to 20 minutes of testing.

[3] Under these conditions, which are closely related to those of standard
brightness discrimination tasks, the luminance of the Landolt C is
maintained at the adapting level of 1 mL, while the luminance of its
background is raised briefly. As exposure duration is increased beyond t_c for brightness, the background becomes dimmer, and apparent
contrast between the C and its background decreases; this reduction of
contrast results in impaired acuity performance. By this mechanism,
t_c for brightness determines t_c for acuity under these special conditions.

Kahneman

Under conditions of backward and forward masking, however, reciprocity breaks down: in these situations (Curves D, E, F) acuity
performance rises with increasing exposure duration.

The failure of reciprocity under conditions of masking can be
predicted from a summation model: the longer of two equal-energy
stimuli has a better chance of escaping some of the effects of brightness summation. However, this model also predicts, erroneously, that
the greatest reduction of the contrast of the target should occur when
it is superimposed on the flash: the maximal reduction of contrast
should be obtained when target and flash are actually simultaneous
(Curve B); performance with successive presentation (Curves C, D,
E, F) can only be better than in this limiting case. In fact, performance
for short target-exposures is definitely worse in Curves D, E, and F
than in Curve B. To account for these results, it is again necessary
to assume some interference of the light with the formation of the
figure, occurring in both forward and backward masking.

The work described here was an attempt to link some phenomena of
masking to a view of temporal summation, in the hope of eventually
relating both processes to a concept of temporal frame (Boynton, 1961),
moment (Stroud, 1956; White, 1963), or perceptual rhythm (Kolers,
1959). In view of such aspirations, our experimental results are
rather discouraging. While the assumption that different moments
correspond to different perceptual functions is not unlikely, the close
dependence of t_c on stimulus luminance is not parsimoniously explained in terms of a scanning mechanism. In addition, the fact that
summation, mutual interference or apparent movement may all occur
when different visual stimuli are exposed in quick succession presents
formidable problems of logic and method to the investigator interested
in the structure of psychological time. The only safe general conclusion to be drawn from recent research in this area appears to be
that even relatively simple questions, such as the nature and locus of
temporal summation must now be considered unsolved (Boynton, 1961).

Acknowledgment

It is a pleasure to thank J. Norman and M. Kubovy for their many
suggestions and enthusiastic participation in the work reported here.
A. Koriat, D. Max, and D. Pasternak worked long and diligently in
gathering the data.

References

Alpern, M. Metacontrast. J. opt. Soc. Amer., 1953, 43, 648-657.

Averbach, E., and Sperling, G. Short term storage of information in vision. In C. Cherry (Ed.) Proceedings of the Fourth London symposium on information theory. London: Butterworth, 1961. Pp. 196-211.

Barlow, H. B. Temporal and spatial summation in human vision at different background intensities. J. Physiol., 1958, 141, 337-350.

Battersby, W. S., and Wagman, I. Neural limitations of visual excitability: IV. Spatial determinants of retrochiasmal interaction. Amer. J. Physiol., 1962, 203, 359-365.

Biersdorf, W. R. Critical duration in visual brightness discrimination for retinal areas of various sizes. J. opt. Soc. Amer., 1955, 45, 920-925.

Blackwell, H. R. Neural theories of simple visual discriminations. J. opt. Soc. Amer., 1963, 53, 129-160.

Boynton, R. M. Some temporal factors in vision. In W. A. Rosenblith (Ed.), Sensory communication. New York: Wiley, 1961. Pp. 739-756.

Brown, R. The effect of extent on the intensity-time relation for the visual discrimination of movement. J. comp. physiol. Psychol., 1957, 50, 109-114.

Eriksen, C. W., and Hoffman, M. Form recognition at brief durations as a function of adapting field and interval between stimulations. J. exp. Psychol., 1963, 66, 485-499.

Flom, M. C., Heath, G. G., and Takahashi, E. Contour interaction and visual resolution: Contralateral effects. Science, 1963, 142, 979-980.

Graham, C. H., and Ratoosh, P. Notes on some interrelations of sensory psychology, perception, and behavior. In S. Koch (Ed.), Psychology: A study of a science. Vol. IV. New York: McGraw-Hill, Pp. 483-514.

Hartline, H. K. Intensity and duration in the excitation of single photoreceptor units. J. cell. comp. Physiol., 1934, 5, 229-247.

Hubel, D. H., and Wiesel, T. N. Receptive fields, binocular interaction and functional architecture in the cat's visual cortex. J. Physiol., 1962, 160, 106-154.

Hunter, W. S., and Sigler, M. The span of visual discrimination as a function of time and intensity of stimulation. J. exp. Psychol., 1940, 26, 160-179.

Johnson, E. P. The character of the B-wave in the human ERG. AMA Arch. Ophtahl., 1958, 60, 565-591.

Kahneman, D. Temporal summation in an acuity task at different energy levels — A study of the determinants of summation. Vision Res., 1964, 4, 557-566.

Kahneman, D. Exposure duration and effective figure-ground contrast. Quart. J. exp. Psychol., 1965, 17, 308-314.

Kahneman, D. Time-intensity reciprocity in acuity as a function
of energy and figure ground contrast. Vision Res., 1966, 6,
207-216. (a)

Kahneman, D. Time-intensity reciprocity under various conditions
of adaptation and backward masking. J. exp. Psychol., 1966, 71,
543-549. (b)

Kahneman, D., and Norman J. The time-intensity relation in visual
perception as a function of observer's task. J. exp. Psychol.,
1964, 68, 215-220.

Kinsbourne, M., and Warrington, E. K. Further studies on the
masking of brief visual stimuli by a random pattern. Quart. J.
exp. Psychol., 1962, 14, 235-245.

Kolers, P. A. Serial processes in visual perception. Proceedings of
the fifteenth international congress of psychology, 1957.
Amsterdam: North-Holland, 1959.

Kolers, P. A., and Rosner, B. S. On visual masking (metacontrast):
Dichoptic observation. Amer. J. Psychol., 1960, 73, 2-21.

Luckiesh, M. Light, vision and seeing. New York: Van Nostrand,
1944.

McDougall, W. The variation of the intensity of visual sensation
with the duration of the stimulus. Brit. J. Psychol., 1904, 1,
151-189.

Scharf, B., Holohan, C. M., and Morningstar, M. E. The visual
duration threshold as a function of intensity. Amer. Psychologist,
1963, 18, 456.

Schiller, P. H. Monoptic and dichoptic visual masking by patterns
and flashes. J. exp. Psychol., 1965, 69, 193-199.

Stroud, J. M. The fine structure of psychological time. In H.
Quastler (Ed.), Information theory in psychology, Glencoe, Ill.:
The Free Press, 1956. Pp. 174-207.

White, C. T. Temporal numerosity and the psychological unit of
duration. Psychol. Monogr., 1963, 77 (12, Whole No. 575).

THE ROLE OF SHORT-TERM VISUAL MEMORY IN VISUAL INFORMATION PROCESSING

Ronald J. Massa [1]
Data Sciences Laboratory
Air Force Cambridge Research Laboratories
Bedford, Massachusetts

Introduction and Summary

Recent experiments (Averbach and Sperling, 1961; Massa, 1961; Massa, 1964; Sperling, 1960; Sperling, 1963) indicate the existence of a short-duration memory function in many aspects of human visual operation. This short-term visual memory (STVM) has several properties suitable for "smoothing" information flow to the higher centers of the brain from pairs of retinal images which change in response to saccadic movements of the visual fixation point. The experiments reported have not, however, indicated where the short-term memory function is performed in the anatomy of the visual system, nor have they completely defined the attributes of this memory.

Perhaps more significantly, short-term visual memory may provide the functional mechanisms suitable for the separation of the signal detection and information perception aspects of vision. The memory appears eidetic, or pictorial, on its input side. Its read-in mechanism is essentially instantaneous, and characterized by the integration of the physical stimulus to provide the signal detection aspects of vision. Apparently anything which can be "seen" can be read into memory. When the visual fixation point changes, or new information — even peripheral information — enters the visual system, the old information is written over very quickly. This feature must be present to provide for rapid response to new information which signals danger or otherwise compels the immediate attention of the human.

Once the information is read into the STVM it is stored for significant fractions of a second — sufficiently long for holding a visual image between successive fixation points. The information stored is read-out slowly — not in pictorial units such as patterns of light and dark — but in perceptually meaningful units for the task at hand. The letters in the experiments of Averbach and Sperling (1961), and the

---

[1] Now at the Space Systems Division, Avco Corporation, Lowell, Massachusetts.

geometric forms in the experiments reported by the author (Massa, 1961), are examples of perceptually meaningful units for the subject's tasks in these experiments. The read-out scan is slow, taking perhaps tens of milliseconds per English letter. It is directed by higher centers of the brain in its search and information retrieval task, and apparently subject to a very limited span of attention in terms of perceptually meaningful units. The concept of "seven plus or minus two" discussed by Miller (1956) as a limitation on span of attention appears to be relevant to the STVM read-out scan.

The purpose of this paper is to propose a conceptual model for the role of short-duration memory in vision. This model and some of its attributes are presented in Figure 1. A major feature of this model lies in its separation of the signal detection and information perception aspects of vision through the operation of short-term visual memory.

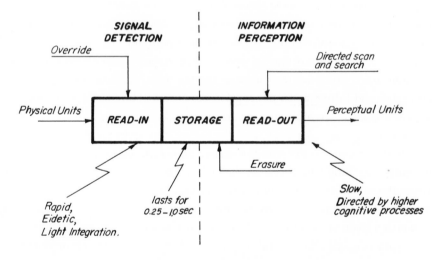

Fig. 1. A conceptual model, illustrating the role of short-duration memory in visual information processing.

Note that this conceptual model does not indicate anatomical locations for the specific read-in, read-out, or storage functions. Very little work has been done at present on the localization of these functions.

The approach to understanding visual information processing essentially regards the STVM as the "scratch-pad" on which a highly detailed pictorial rendition of the environment is retained while more time-consuming, but still basic, visual calculations are made under the direction of higher centers of the visual process. It provides a convenient and simple notion around which more definitive research can continue to increase our knowledge of visual operation.

A Brief Review of the Evidence

The existence of an intermediate short-term memory in vision is clearly demonstrated by the results published by Sperling (1960) and Averbach and Sperling (1961). The fact that the effective exposure duration of tachistoscopically displayed material is not determined entirely by the duration of the physical stimulus is the logical starting point for such a conclusion. Further, the results of Averbach and Sperling (1961) and Averbach and Coriell (1961) obtained with bar and circle response keys indicate that spacial relations are retained in the stimulus rendition in this memory. While these results — by themselves — do not prove that STVM is eidetic or pictorial, they are certainly consistent with this property.

Further, self-erasure (due to geometric proximity of unrelated items) and imposed erasure (caused by the presentation of masks or stimulus keys which offer geometric confusion with the stimulus array) properties of this memory demonstrated in the foregoing papers[2] also support the conclusion that the STVM is eidetic. In addition, these results raise questions as to whether such keys or masks (a) erase an already stored rendition of the stimulus, (b) interfere with the read-in to short-term memory, or (c) interfere with read-out from the memory. Certainly, performance which is degraded by a key or mask whose physical onset follows the cessation of the stimulus indicates that the mask does not interfere with read-in but does effect read-out. Such a result is discussed in Averbach and Sperling (1961) and later in this paper.

The high storage capacity demonstrated by Averbach and Sperling (1961) further indicates that STVM stores data in terms of physical stimulus units, i.e., pictorially, since the generally accepted concept of the span of immediate memory (Miller, 1956) does not apply to the stored data. Storage durations of 0.25 to 1 sec are also demonstrated by the results of Averbach and Sperling and the experiments discussed in the following paragraphs.

---

[2] Self-erasure is also treated extensively in Massa (1961) and post-exposure erasure with masking signals is considered in Silvestri, Massa, and Goldstein (1963).

The basic proposals made in this paper (as outlined in Figure 1) have
not been proven by a single experiment or a specific group of experiments reported in the literature. One reason why such a proof is not
available is that few, if any, experiments have been performed
specifically to evaluate or validate the concept of short-term visual
memory embodied in Figure 1. The evidence in support of this concept is fragmentary. However, the recent experiments described in
this paper, when viewed with the results of the work of Averbach,
Sperling, Coriell and the author cited earlier, relate many of these
fragments into the specific hypothesis presented here.

The basic experimental technique employed in this study involved
the use of 16 mm motion pictures to present two three-letter stimulus
arrays separated by a masking field. (See Figure 2 for a typical
experimental trial.) White pre- and postexposure fields were used in

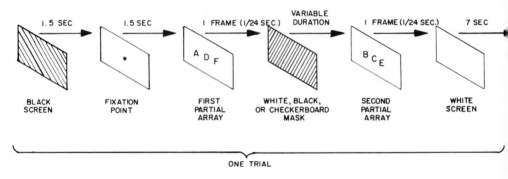

Fig. 2. Typical trial sequence for one-frame partial arrays
(shown for black mask).

all cases reported here. Two types of English letter arrays were
used — arrays forming six-letter words[3] and arrays consisting of
six nonsense letters. The basic time unit was a single frame of a 16
mm motion picture, projected at a controlled rate of 24 frames per
second. The total exposure duration of the frame was 41.6 msec with
a light-to-dark duty cycle of 50% due to the action of the projector
shutter. When projected, the six-letter images subtended horizontal
visual angles of approximately 14 degrees to the subject (the complete
projected image frame subtended approximately 25 degrees). A

---

[3] In all cases superposition of the two arrays results in a lineal
arrangement of the six letters as follows - A B C D E F.

fixed light level, well above threshold, was used throughout the reported experiments.

The effects of exposure duration on letter recall for typical six-
letter arrays are shown in Figure 3. Nearly all of the errors associated
with word recall are due to random factors such as eyeblink and
momentary inattention. The slight improvement in nonsense letter
recall with increasing exposure duration is probably due to the large
visual angle subtended by the letter arrays.

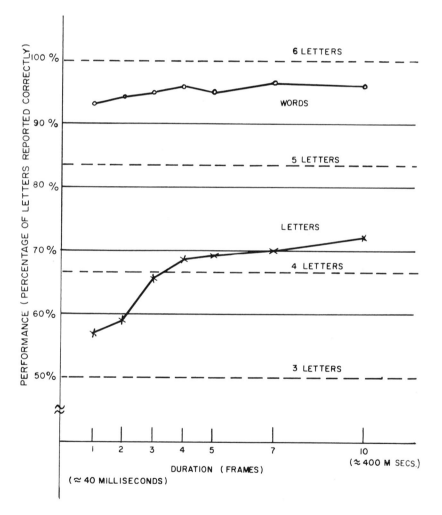

Fig. 3. Percentage of letters correctly reported versus stimulus
duration (15-subject averages). (Mask duration = 0.)

Total exposure durations of two (≈ 80 msec) and four (≈ 160 msec) frames (one and two frames for each three-letter array) were selected for the memory manipulation experiments. White, black, and checkerboard (noise) masks were used to separate the three-letter or partial arrays. The duration and nature of the intervening mask were the major experimental parameters.

Figure 4 depicts some of the results of this work[4]. Note that the zero delay point represents performance levels without the intervening mask (the data points are taken from Figure 3). For both white and black masks between the two arrays, word performance is only slightly affected (and this only for short duration masks). Letter performance, on the other hand, steadily increases for mask durations up to about 12 frames (1/2 sec). Both letter and word performance are essentially independent of exposure duration for black and white masks.

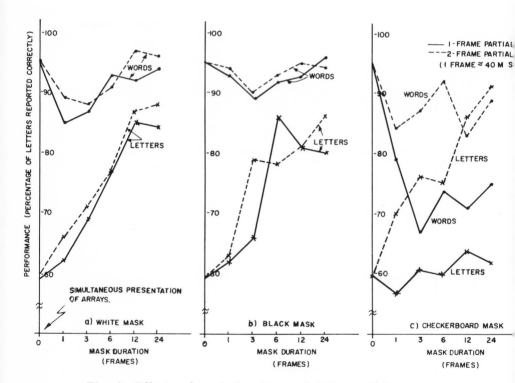

Fig. 4. Effects of mask duration on letter recall for one- and two-frame partials (100-subject average).

---

[4] These experiments are further discussed in Silvestri, Massa, and Goldstein (1963).

In all cases, performance with the <u>first</u> partial array is considerably
poorer than with the second partial array.

The checkerboard mask (the only mask which offers geometric confusion with the letter arrays) produces a very different subject
response. For one-frame partial arrays, word performance de-
teriorates rapidly with increasing mask duration and letter performance
does not improve as before. However, with two-frame partial arrays
and an intervening checkerboard mask, word and letter performance
both tend to be quite similar to the performance measured with white
and black masks.

The foregoing experiments are similar in many respects to those
originally performed by Baxt (1871) and more recently elaborated on
by Sperling (1963). The major difference in the current experiments
is the sequential presentation of related and unrelated letter stimuli
providing a second information bearing input to the memory following
a masking stimulus.

Conclusions

The experiments reported here support the following conclusions
regarding the nature of short-term visual memory.

1. The separation of a stimulus, whose element content (letters,
   in this case) exceeds the span of immediate memory, into
   discrete "chunks" which do not exceed the span of immediate
   memory improves information transfer by eliminating self-
   masking in the stimulus array, provided that the second "chunk"
   appears either after the memory has decayed or after its contents have been read-out. The fact that letter performance
   continues to rise for delays up to 1/2 sec between letter arrays
   indicates that memory decay rather than read-out time may be
   the key factor in eliminating self-erasure.

2. Short-term memory read-in is very rapid. A visual image can be
   read into memory as long as it can be distinguished from its
   surround (detected). This feature supports the notion that short-
   term memory is an "eidetic" or pictorial storage which operates
   similar to a television camera whose shutter opens to integrate
   light for relatively short durations, and whose photosensitive
   surface stores the image for from about 0.25 to 1.0 sec for later
   read-out.

3. The read-out or scan mechanism associated with short-term

memory is much slower and subject to confusion if the visual
image during scanning interferes spatially with the prior stimulus.
The stimulus duration of two frames (approximately 80 msec) is
apparently sufficient to read-in and scan three letters, since the
checkerboard mask (which effectively erases the first partial
array) is ineffective for two-frame exposures. This fact is
consistent with Sperling's (1963) conclusion that output scan rates
for letter stimuli are of the order of 10 msec per letter.

4. The differing rates of random-letter recall improvement for
black, white, and checkerboard masks indicate that both storage
duration and read-out success depend on the nature and intensity
of the visual field during read-out. Furthermore, the read-out
or scan process apparently continues for significant fractions of
a second after the cessation of the physical stimulus. Averbach
and Sperling (1960) concluded that the minimum duration of
short-term memory persistence was approximately 1/4 sec.

5. The ability to recall the second array under all mask conditions
indicates that the presence of new information during the scan
process overrides the old information and the memory output
scan. Thus, the operation of short-term memory — which is
particularly vulnerable during read-out — does not preclude
immediate response to new stimuli; nor does improvement in
memory read-out efficiency due to the presence of an intervening
mask affect the ability of the subject to relate the sets of letters
which form words in spite of the fact that the letters were
presented in successive exposures.

Note that 80% recall for random letters at 12-frame mask durations
(14 frames total trial duration) is almost one letter more (on the
average) than could be obtained with a 14-frame exposure to the
stimulus alone. It is reasonable to assume that even more startling
improvement could be obtained if more letters were included in the
stimulus. Such a result strongly suggests that short-term visual
memory can be manipulated to enhance information retrieval from
visual displays.

The ability of the subjects to relate the letters in successive exposures to form "words" and essentially take advantage of the learned
redundancies in these letter combinations, even with the highly
disturbing intervening checkerboard mask, is of particular interest
in this discussion of short-term memory. Apparently, once informa-

tion has been read-out of short-term memory, further manipulation of the stimulus is ineffective in destroying the information. Furthermore, it indicates that operations such as word and concept formation are not performed in this memory.

Acknowledgment

The work reported originated with the author's doctoral dissertation at M.I.T. and has since been supported in part by Melpar, Inc., and Laboratory for Electronics, Inc.

References

Averbach, E., and Coriell, A. S. Short-term memory in vision. Bell Syst. tech. J., 1961, 40, 309-328.

Averbach, E., and Sperling, G. Short term storage of information in vision. In C. Cherry (Ed.), Proceedings of the fourth London symposium on information theory. London: Butterworth, 1961. Pp. 196-211.

Baxt, N. Über die Zeit welche nötig ist, damit ein Gesichtseindruck zum Bewusstsein kommt und über die Grösse der bewussten Wahrnehmung bei einem Gesichtseindruk von gegebener Dauer. Pflüg. Arch. ges. Physiol., 1871, 4, 325-336.

Massa, R. J. Some aspects of human visual information transmission. Unpublished doctoral dissertation, Massachusetts Institute of Technology, 1961.

Massa, R. J. Information transfer in short-term visual memory. Paper read at International Conference of Microwaves, Circuit Theory and Info. Theory, Tokyo, September 1964. Summary in ICMCI 1964 Summaries of Papers, Part 3, Information Theory, Pp. 187-188.

Miller, G. A. The magical number seven plus or minus two: Some limits on our capacity for processing information. Psychol. Rev., 1956, 63, 81-97.

Silvestri, A. M., Massa, R. J., and Goldstein, S. Short-term visual memory. Sensory Communications Lab., Lab. for Electronics, tech. Rep., 1963, No. 63-3.

Sperling, G. A. The information available in brief visual presentations. Psychol. Monogr., 1960, 74 (11, Whole No. 497).

Sperling, G. A. A model for visual memory tasks. Human Factors, 1963, 5, 19-31.

SOME NEW STEREOSCOPIC PHENOMENA AND THEIR
IMPLICATIONS FOR MODELS OF STEREOPSIS

Lloyd Kaufman
Sperry Rand Research Center
Sudbury, Massachusetts

Stereopsis is based upon binocular disparity. Fixated points have common visual directions for the two eyes while more or less distant points have different visual directions. This difference in visual direction is disparity. The naïve observer is usually unaware that disparity exists. It is only under special circumstances that he can be made aware of his double images. But even then, small disparities, i.e., those that fall within Panum's area, go unnoticed. Hence, we say that fusion has occurred for these double images. The fusion accounts for the singleness of binocular vision but it is not necessary to stereopsis. Diplopic images can be seen in stereoscopic depth.

In spite of this latter fact, it is widely held that fusion is the basis for stereopsis. But the usage of fusion in this context implies something different from phenomenal fusion. It implies, instead, a neural fusion of representations of similar disparate stimuli. The neural fusion may or may not be accompanied by phenomenal fusion. According to some theorists, it is always accompanied by at least a partial phenomenal fusion of disparate inputs. This is realized as a shift in the apparent visual directions of diplopic binocular stimuli when both eyes view them at the same time. This shift has been termed allelotropia.

A model intended to account for the way in which disparate stimulus representations fuse was proposed by Boring (1933). This same model, which we call the projection field model, was independently formulated by Charnwood (1951), by Linksz (1952) and, most recently, by Dodwell and Engel (1963). This model represents a kind of theoretical concensus concerning stereopsis.

The projection field model postulates converging pathways from the two eyes which intersect to form a network. Stimuli imaged in the two eyes will produce signals which travel along these pathways to fuse at the intersections. The depth at which the signals fuse in the network depends upon the disparity of the stimuli. Hence, the depth of the representations in the network is isomorphic with respect to the perceived depth of the objects.

The geometry of the projection field model is the same as the geometry involved in drawing stereograms. It is in accord with Panum's rule of converging rays which is used to predict the amount of depth. In a sense, therefore, it is structurally the same as Johannes Kepler's projection theory which was intended to explain the singleness of binocular vision (Boring, 1942). The only difference is that the model has been internalized.

The model, as it stands, does not allow for the nature of the disparate stimuli which yield depth perception. Consider Julesz's (1960) regular stereogram. In disparate portions of the display dissimiliar dot clusters fall on corresponding places in the two eyes. The similar clusters fall on disparate places. Yet the clusters in one eye choose to interact with their similar contralateral counterparts rather than with the dissimilar clusters with which they are in register. This refutes von Tschermak-Sysenegg's postulate that the place in one eye that corresponds to a place excited by a contour in the other eye must be unstimulated, or stimulated by diffuse light, so that the action of this point would be inhibited by a contour imaged at a disparate ipsilateral place (von Tschermak-Sysenegg, 1952). According to this view, ipsilateral inhibition is the process which allows fusion of disparate contours. The refutation of this concept seems to be one of the important contributions of Julesz's patterns.

Since it is not possible to handle the fusion of similar stimulus representations in the face of competing dissimilar inputs peripherally, the model must be revised. One way out of this dilemma may be afforded by Julesz's difference field model.

Julesz suggested that the visual system may be responding to a binocular field made up of representations of the differences in brightness of micropatterns or point clusters in the monocular fields. The resulting difference field will contain a distinctive region corresponding to the binocular form which is seen in depth. Two such representations of the form must be present: one when the monocular field backgrounds are in register, and another when the regions representing the inner square are in register. This is accomplished by means of a convolving operation.

It is obvious that a difference field which contains a form corresponds to a fused image. The second difference field corresponds to another fused image and the amount of shift necessary to get it is related to the disparity. Hence, the difference field model is logically the same as the projection field model. The brightness subtraction operation can, however, get around the problem of form similarity in Julesz's regular stereogram.

There are, however, a number of stereoscopic phenomena which are inconsistent with both the projection field model and the difference field model. Consider a stereogram constructed from letters of the alphabet. We can place the letters asdqwadwadwadpoiuy in one eye and the letters asdpsnpsnpsnqpoiuy in the other eye. With the edge letters in register the inner region will contain similar triadic structures or patterns comprised of dissimilar letters. This produces a depth effect. The disparity between the triads mediates the depth response even though it is dissimilar physical forms which are both in register and disparate. This is not consistent with the projection field model.

Another interesting stereogram is one in which all the physical forms are identical but the brightnesses of the letters are of two different values. The brightnesses may be disparate. For example, abcde̲e̲e̲e̲e̲e̲e̲abcd in one eye and abcde̲e̲e̲e̲e̲e̲e̲abcd in the other. The underlined letters are different in brightness from the letters which are not underlined. Here identical forms are in register and there is no form disparity. The forms carry a brightness disparity. This is sufficient to produce stereopsis. If it is form that fuses then clearly stereopsis should not occur here. Does this mean that the depth producing disparity is necessarily a brightness disparity? This is clearly incorrect since ordinary stereograms do not present brightness disparities.

It is also possible to use entirely dissimilar forms as carriers of a brightness disparity. For example, an array of randomly selected letters carrying a brightness pattern may be placed in one eye and an array of a single letter replicated over the field in the other. If the latter pattern carries the same, but disparate, brightness pattern then depth will result.

It seems likely that any perceptible patterning can yield depth perception provided that the patterning is disparately represented in the two eyes. It does not depend upon physical contour or any other specific stimulus dimension but these dimensions can carry the patterning. In these terms stereopsis is the detection of a difference in the phases of correlated patterns.

This way of looking at the problem of stereopsis leads to certain predictions. One of these involves the following stereogram: If abcdefg is presented to one eye and bcdefgx is presented to the other, then the correlated sequence bcdefg is out of phase relative to the edges of the over-all patterns. In point of fact, viewing these patterns so that the correlated portions are in register produces a substantial depth effect. In an experiment to measure the amount of depth the correlated inner region was seen as 11.0 cm behind or in front of the edge letters, depending upon the direction of the phase difference relative to the dominant eye, at a viewing distance of 165 cm. The letters were about 0.4 cm apart, center to center.

It might be argued that this effect is nothing but Panum's limiting case in which a uniocular line is presented together with two other lines. The uniocular line fuses with one line and is disparate with respect to the other line. In this case the uniocular letters are disparate relative to one member of the identical binocular pair of letters. The depth effect results because fusion is independent of the particular forms involved. To test this notion the following stereogram was devised: The letters asdfgHJKLOsdfg were presented to one eye, and xcvbHJKLOxcvbp to the other. With the capital letters in register the four flanking letters in one eye are in register with dissimilar letters in the other eye. This leaves a right eye uniocular letter and a left eye uniocular letter on the ends of the combined image. With these letters in a matrix of similarly arranged letters a depth effect results. But only the capital letters go into depth. The depth effect measured about 9 cm in one experiment. The uncorrelated letters do not go into depth but the correlated letters do. Once again it is the phases of the letters relative to the edges of the pattern that seem to mediate the depth effect. There is no disparity in this or the foregoing pattern.

These demonstrations indicate that the difference field model is also incomplete. It is evident that convolving these patterns does not produce two difference fields. Two of them are necessary to see the inner region in depth. The effect does depend upon form but it is suspected that correlation between several different dimensions can produce the same results.

Another interesting facet of the foregoing stereoscopic demonstrations is that binocular rivalry is a frequent concomitant of the patterns. This was particularly true when the patterns contained different forms imbedded in similar structures. It also occurred when stereograms were viewed through narrow band red and green filters, one on each eye. In spite of considerable rivalry, and therefore suppression, depth was still experienced. Also, in brightness disparity patterns containing dissimilar forms, it was generally the forms imaged in the dominant eye that were visible and in depth. It must therefore be concluded that fusion, considered to be a combining of the half-images, was not necessary to depth perception. It is monocularly arising images which are modified by contralateral images which are seen in depth. These may be suppressed and depth can result.

This has implications for the applicability of Hubel and Wiesel's data to models of stereopsis (Hubel and Wiesel, 1959). It is clear that their slope detectors do not necessarily play a central role since brightness can mediate the depth as well as form. Also, rivalrous stimuli can be seen in depth. Dissimilar, and therefore rivalrous, forms would have antagonistic effects on their collector cells. We cannot conclude that the fusion or synergy at these cells is central to the problem of stereopsis. It is likely that centers at higher levels than the visual cortex are involved.

References

Boring, E. G. The physical dimensions of consciousness. New York: Appleton-Century, 1933. Pp. 118-119.

Boring, E. G. Sensation and perception in the history of experimental psychology. New York: Appleton-Century-Crofts, 1942.

Charnwood, J. R. B. Essay on binocular vision. London: Hatton Press, 1951.

Dodwell, P., and Engel, R. A theory of binocular fusion. Nature, 1963, 198, 39-74.

Hubel, D., and Wiesel, T. N. Receptive fields of single neurons in the cat's striate cortex. J. Physiol., 1959, 148, 574-591.

Julesz, B. Binocular depth perception of computer-generated patterns. Bell Syst. tech. J., 1960, 39, 1125-1162.

Linksz, A. The physiology of the eye. Vol. 2. New York: Grune & Stratton, 1952.

von Tschermak-Seysenegg, A. Introduction to physiological optics. Springfield, Ill.: Charles C. Thomas, 1952.

VISUAL ALEXIA

George Ettlinger
Department of Experimental Neurology
Institute of Psychiatry
London, England

Subhuman animals make many kinds of visual discrimination (e.g., of intensity, color, extent, position, orientation, and form); and they learn to attach significance to the objects and events which they see. Man, in addition, learns to recognize the significance of the forms (or shapes) which we call letters. He can read, and this is the visual perception of form at its most complex level. For reading also involves the use of language. It is the visual discrimination of forms which we have learned to recognize as representing the constituents of auditory/oral language. The dissolution of this perceptual process can only be studied in the neurological clinic.

In contrast to those disorders of reading which are frequently found to be associated with other disturbances of language (i.e., dysphasia) one kind of reading disorder, termed "visual alexia," is claimed to be relatively "pure" in that it is not associated with other kinds of visual perceptual disturbance or language defect to a significant degree. Visual alexia occurs only rarely. One constant feature is a homonymous field defect usually in the right half of the visual field. The role of other associated disturbances has been discussed elsewhere (Ettlinger and Hurvitz, 1962).

Certain features of visual alexia are of particular relevance in the present context. First, the reading of certain classes of written material may be severely disordered whereas other classes of material are read without error. For example, the alexic patient may be unable to read letters but he may read correctly arabic numerals, musical notation, or other special symbols or codes. Second, the patient may be unable to name (i.e., read) individual letters indicated to him by the examiner or to find individual letters (from an array, say, of 50 solid letters) named by the examiner; but yet, he can sort these same letters without error into groups where each group represents one particular letter. Third, the alexic patient is commonly unable to name colors indicated to him by the examiner or to find particular colors named by the examiner; and yet he can sort these same colors into hues and shades without error.

These features were, in general, shown by a case of visual alexia previously described (Casey and Ettlinger, 1960). In particular, although at first (and atypically) the reading of arabic numerals was severely defective, about 3 weeks after the onset of the alexia only 85% of single letters (capital or small) were correctly identified whereas by then 100% of arabic numerals could be correctly read. Moreover the reading of musical notation was virtually preserved even from the outset. Again, about 2 weeks after the onset of the alexia, only 80% of the attempts to read single letters or to find single named letters to command were correct, whereas at this time the patient was able to sort 96% of scattered letters without error. Finally, at an even earlier stage (about 1 week after the onset) only 70% of the attempts to name colors and 80% of the attempts to find named colors to command were correct, whereas at this same time the patient made no error in sorting the colors he was unable to name or find.

In interpreting these findings no attempt is made to present a formal model of the processes involved in reading and color naming. However, in partial explanation of the selective nature of the defect in visual alexia (i.e., letters cannot be read but numerals can), it is suggested that the child learns first to distinguish between the class of letters and that of numerals and only subsequently to identify the individual items within each class. Therefore individual neural systems concerned with letters and numerals may be formed. In partial explanation of the disorder of reading it is suggested that there may be a defect in matching across sense-modalities (i.e., in matching a visually perceived letter form against the range of possible letter sounds) irrespective of whether the patient is required to read the letter or to find it by command. Similarly, the defect with colors may be in the process of matching a perceived color against its possible names (that is, correctly differentiated colors cannot be matched with their language equivalents).

References

Casey, T., and Ettlinger, G. The occasional "independence" of dyslexia and dysgraphia from dysphasia. J. neurol. neuros. Psychiat., 1960, 23, 228.

Ettlinger, G., and Hurvitz, L. Dyslexia and its associated disturbances. Neurology 1962, 12, 477.

TWO OPERATIONS IN CHARACTER RECOGNITION: SOME EVIDENCE FROM REACTION-TIME MEASUREMENTS [1]

Saul Sternberg
Bell Telephone Laboratories, Incorporated
Murray Hill, New Jersey

Consider this simple task of recognition: A subject is presented with a stimulus and asked to judge whether or not it is a particular character. At some point in the process that leads to a response, a representation of the stimulus encounters a memory representation of the monitored character. What is the nature of this stimulus representation? In the formation of the representation, how much analysis of the stimulus is carried out?

At least two lines of approach to the problem of character recognition lead one to expect that the stimulus is processed to a considerable extent in the forming of its representation. First, in some artificial character recognizers the stimulus, before being tested, may be normalized or subjected to filtering operations such as "thinning," "smoothing," or "cleanup" (Doyle, 1960; Minsky, 1963; Selfridge and Neisser, 1963; Stevens, 1961; Unger, 1959). Other recognizers incorporate a stage in which features are extracted from the stimulus; these features are then tested in the subsequent decision process (Fischler, Mattson, Firschein, and Healy, 1962; Stevens, 1961). Indeed, it has been argued (Uhr, 1963) that if characters can be noisy or distorted, then this high degree of stimulus preprocessing is necessary in a workable recognition scheme. Second, in another domain, recent findings in neurophysiology show that the information available at the higher visual centers is not simply a point-to-point mapping of the retinal image (Hubel, 1963).

But whereas there seems to be a theoretical need for a highly processed stimulus representation, and whereas knowledge about some of the neural machinery is becoming available, the behavioral evidence is sparse. This is not very surprising. In a certain sense, the stimulus is lost until the response occurs. More specifically, the effects of most experimental manipulations can be attributed as easily to the operation of comparing stimulus and memory representations

---

[1] An expanded version of this paper will appear in Sternberg (1967).

as to the operation by which the stimulus representation is formed. What is needed are tools that allow the dissection of behavioral effects into those attributable to the first of these operations, and those attributable to the second. Such analysis would provide information about the nature of the operations, and therefore about the stimulus representation.

A tool of the required kind is perhaps provided by a recently discovered phenomenon in what may be described as a character-classification task. This is a generalization of the simple recognition task mentioned first. On each of a sequence of trials a character is presented as a test stimulus. The subject makes a positive response if the character is a member of a small "target" set of s characters, called the positive set, and a negative response otherwise. For example, the subject may be told to operate the right-hand lever if the test stimulus is one of the digits "3" or "7" and to operate the left-hand lever otherwise. In this condition the positive set is of size two. The ensemble of possible test stimuli may consist of all of the ten digits. The subject is encouraged to respond as rapidly as he can, while maintaining a low error-rate.

Results of a number of experiments on character classification suggest that the time between stimulus and response is occupied, in part, by an exhaustive serial-comparison process: A representation of the test stimulus is compared successively to a sequence of memory representations, one for each member of the positive set. Each comparison results in either a match or a mismatch. After the search is completed, a positive response is initiated if there has been a match, and a negative response otherwise.

A few of the findings (Sternberg, 1964, 1966) that support this theory are as follows: First, mean latencies of both positive and negative responses increase linearly with the number of characters in the positive set. This has been found for positive sets of up to six characters, with digit- as well as letter-ensembles[2]. Second, the mean

---

[2] For sets that consist of more than half of the ensemble this finding probably depends on preventing the subject from making use of the complement of the positive set. Such large sets have therefore been studied only in experiments in which a new series of digits is presented on each trial to define the positive set, and (a) the time interval between series and test stimulus is too short to allow the subject to find the complement and/or (b) the subject is required to recall the series after his binary response.

increase in latency per character has the same magnitude for positive responses as for negative responses. This equality shows that the search is exhaustive, rather than being terminated when a match occurs. Reaction time increases by about 38 msec for each member of the positive set, so that the average rate of search is between 25 and 30 characters per sec. Third, although the size of the positive set affects the reaction time, the size of the full ensemble does not, for ensembles that are at least twice as large as the positive set.

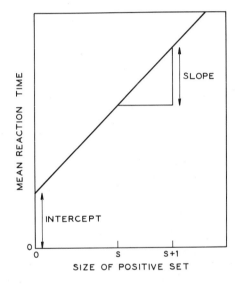

Fig. 1. Idealized data from a character-classification experiment. The slope is a measure of the mean time taken by the comparison of the stimulus representation to the memory representation of one character (Operation 2). (The zero-intercept is a measure of the mean time taken by the events before and/or after the series of comparisons, which include the formation of the stimulus representation [Operation 1].)

Figure 1 is an idealization of the data obtained in a character-classification experiment. Mean reaction time is plotted as a function of the size of the positive set. If one assumes that the serial-comparison theory is correct, one is led to the following interpretation of such data. The slope of the reaction-time function is a measure of the mean time taken by the comparison of the stimulus representation to the memory representation of one character. This comparison will be called Operation 2. The zero-intercept is a measure of the mean time taken by events before and/or after the series of comparisons. These include the formation of the stimulus representation, which will be called Operation 1. Whereas Operation 1 refers to processes that are carried out only once, Operation 2 may occur several times, once for each character in the positive set.

Table 1. Some Alternative Theories of Character Recognition

Theory	Operation 1	Stimulus Representation	Memory Representation	Operation 2
A	-	raw image	template	template-matching
B	-	raw image	feature list	feature-testing
C	image-refining	refined image	template	template matching
D	image-refining	refined image	feature list	feature-testing
E	feature-extracting	feature list	feature list	feature-list matching
F	labeling	label	label	label-matching

Several alternative theories of character recognition are described in Table 1. They differ in their stimulus and memory representations and, correspondingly, in the nature of Operations 1 and 2. In Theories A and B, Operation 1 is inconsequential, and Operation 2 is carried out directly on a raw image of the stimulus. In Theories C to F the stimulus representation is a processed version of the stimulus. In C and D it is a refined image; Operation 1 involves such processes as "thinning" and "cleanup." In E the representation is a list of relevant features of the stimulus; Operation 1 involves the extraction of features. In Theories A to E, Operation 1 produces a representation based on physical aspects of the stimulus. By contrast, according to Theory F, Operation 1 identifies the stimulus, producing a representation based on its name or meaning.

It will now be evident how a character-classification experiment might provide us with a dissection tool. In the present study the experimental manipulation is the degradation of the test stimulus. When the positive set contains just one character we have the simple recognition task in which the subject must decide whether the test stimulus is or is not a particular character. His decision takes longer if the test stimulus is degraded. This fact alone does not allow us to determine whether the increase in reaction time is due to Operation 1, or Operation 2, or both. One can make this determination, however, by varying the size of the positive set and evaluating separately the effects of degradation on slope and intercept.

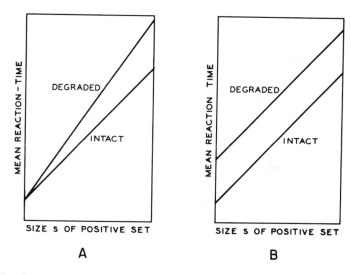

Fig. 2. Two possibilities for the effect of test-stimulus degradation on the reaction-time function. (Figure 2A corresponds to Theories A and B. Figure 2B corresponds to Theory F.)

Let us consider how the reaction-time function might change when the test stimuli are degraded. Two extreme possibilities are shown in Figure 2. Suppose first that Operation 1 was inconsequential, and the stimulus representation was a replica of the stimulus, as in Theories A and B. Then the increase in reaction time would have to arise from an increase in the duration of the comparison process. One would expect the slope of the function to increase, but not its zero-intercept (Figure 2A). At the other extreme, the stimulus representation might be a sufficiently processed version of the stimulus so that it incorporated none of the degradation. One example of such a representation is the name of the character, as in Theory F. In this case there would be no increase in the duration of the comparison process. The increase in reaction time would reflect an increase in the time to form the stimulus representation. One would expect an increase in the intercept of the reaction-time function, but not in its slope (Figure 2B).

Method

Apparatus. Test stimuli were digits produced by a Burroughs "Nixie" tube (Type 6844A). A beam splitter caused a checkerboard pattern that was transilluminated by an array of neon lamps (Type NE2H) to be superimposed on the digits. The degradation thus produced had previously been found to cause an increase in reaction time without substantially increasing the low error-rate. A warning signal and fixation aid was provided by an annulus that surrounded the digits and could be transilluminated by a second set of neon lamps. On either side of the Nixie display was a translucent panel that could be illuminated from the rear to provide feedback signals. The subject viewed the display binocularly from a distance of about 29 in. while seated in a dimly lit booth, his head supported by a chin rest. He rested his elbows on the table in front of him, positioning the fingers of each hand lightly on the table and immediately behind a lever which he could operate by flexing his fingers, thereby pulling it toward him. Near the beginning of its stroke the lever produced a contact-closure. The lever that was operated by the subject's dominant hand represented the positive response. The subject wore headphones through which a white noise was steadily delivered at a comfortable level, in order to mask apparatus and other sounds.

Trial Events. A trial consisted of the following events: (a) intertrial interval of 2.0 sec; (b) warning signal (illumination of annulus) for 1.25 sec; (c) display of test stimulus for 44 msec, either intact or degraded; (d) subject's response (operation of one of the two levers); (e) feedback light displayed for 0.75 sec from occurrence of response. (The panel on the side of the lever that had been operated was illuminated in green if the response was correct, in red if incorrect.) The time from onset of test stimulus to lever displacement was recorded with an accuracy of ±1 msec.

Test-stimulus Sequences. The purpose of the experiment was to determine the difference between reaction times to intact and degraded test stimuli for positive sets of size s = 1, 2, and 4. It was important to avoid confounding the variation in s with three other factors that might affect performance in this situation (Garner, 1962, pp. 19-52), namely: (a) response uncertainty, (b) stimulus uncertainty, and (c) systematic differences from digit to digit. This was accomplished by means of the arrangement shown in Figure 3.

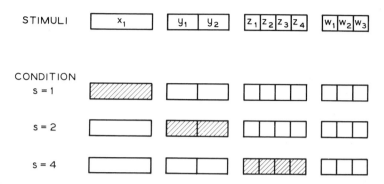

Fig. 3. Arrangement for varying size of positive set while
stimulus population and response frequencies remain fixed.
(Letters represent test stimuli and cell widths represent
their relative frequencies. Those cells in a row that are
hatched represent stimuli in the positive set in that condition.)

For a given subject, each of the ten subscripted letters represents a
particular digit, and the width of its cell represents the relative
frequency with which it occurred in the population of test stimuli. The
relative frequencies were 4/15, 2/15, 1/15, and 1/15 for x_1, each y,
each z, and each w, respectively. For a given subject the population
was the same in all three conditions; the important difference among
conditions was in the assignment of stimuli to responses. In the row
of cells associated with a condition, a hatched cell represents a digit
assigned to the positive set of that condition. In each condition the
test stimuli in the population were presented in a different random
order.

With this arrangement, the size of the positive set could be varied
without altering the relative frequency of the two responses. Furthermore, for a given subject the relative frequency with which a particular
digit occurred as a test stimulus and, a fortiori, the stimulus uncertainty, was the same from condition to condition. It should be
noted that in order to exploit the invariance of the test-stimulus
population so as to balance the effects of individual digits over conditions, data from the positive and negative responses in a condition had
to be pooled rather than examined separately; this was done in the
main analysis.

A fourth condition, with s = 3, was used for practice. For a given
subject, the positive set was composed of the digits represented by
w_1, w_2, and w_3. In order that the relative frequency of positive
responses be 4/15, as in the other conditions, the test-stimulus popula-

tion had to be altered slightly.

Design. Each of 12 subjects was run for two sessions lasting about 1 hour and separated by about a week. Each session had four parts, one for each value of s, and each part had two subparts, one with intact and one with degraded test stimuli. Part 1 was always the s = 3 condition. In the remaining parts a pair of subjects was assigned to each of the six possible orders of the s = 1, 2, and 4 conditions. One member of each pair had subparts in the order intact, degraded; the other member had the reverse order. For each subject the order of degraded and intact subparts and of conditions s = 1, 2, and 4 were reversed from Session 1 to Session 2. Trials were grouped in blocks of 18; there were 3 blocks per subpart except for condition s = 3, in which there were 2.

In each session, three different identifications of digits with the letters of Figure 3 were used, with two pairs of subjects assigned to each. The composition of the resulting positive sets is given in Table 2. For each subject the sets in the two sessions were "orthogonal": any two digits in the same set in Session 1 were in two different sets in Session 2.

Table 2. Composition of Positive Sets

Subjects	Session 1			Session 2		
	s = 1	s = 2	s = 4	s = 1	s = 2	s = 4
1-4	5	4,9	0,1,3,7	7	3,8	1,5,6,9
5-8	8	2,7	3,5,6,9	9	0,6	2,4,5,8
9-12	7	0,9	2,3,5,6	2	1,5	0,3,4,7

Subjects. Subjects, students at the University of Pennsylvania, were paid for their services. The 12 subjects were selected from a group of 20 on the basis of the accuracy of their performance in Session 1. Any subject who made more than 3 errors in the last 36 trials in any of the last 6 subparts in that session was eliminated.

Payoffs and Other Aspects of Procedure. For each block of 18 trials a subject received a score of one point per 0.01 sec in his mean reaction time and ten points per error. In each session the lowest-scoring half of the subjects were each paid at $1.00 bonus. In both sessions a subject was told his mean reaction time, number of errors, and score after each block in Part 1. After this he was told only his over-all errors, mean time, and score for each part at the end of that part. He was able to rest after each block.

At the beginning of Session 1 the ten digits were displayed serially several times, both intact and degraded. Before each part the subject was told the composition of the positive set. A right-handed subject, for example, would be told: "In the next part of the experiment, the digits for which the right-hand lever is correct are .... The other lever is correct for all other digits."

Results

Excluded from the analyses were the data from Part 1, the first block of each subpart, and the first three trials of each block. Also excluded were the occasional trials (2.2% in Session 1 and 2.5% in Session 2) on which the response was incorrect. There remained about 29 reaction times per subpart for each subject, which included times for both positive and negative responses.

Effects of Test-stimulus Degradation on the Reaction-time Function. To avoid possible effects on mean reaction times of individual differences among digits (see section on test-stimulus sequences), the times for positive and negative responses were pooled, and their arithmetic mean obtained. Means over subjects of the resulting values are displayed in Figure 4. Also shown are lines that were fitted by least squares, and their equations.

Results for intact stimuli in Session 1 ($\overline{RT}$ = 371.7 + 35.6 msec) are almost identical to those from a previous experiment[3] (triangular points, $\overline{RT}$ = 369.4 + 38.3 msec). In that experiment, test stimuli were intact, but instead of being flashed for 44 msec they were exposed until the response occurred.

The increases that degradation produced in the slope and zero-intercept of the reaction-time function are shown in Table 3 for the two sessions.

Table 3. Effects of Test-Stimulus Degradation on Estimated Parameters of the Reaction-Time Function (Estimated standard errors are based on 5 df)

Effect	Session 1	Session 2
Increase in mean zero-intercept produced by degradation (msec)	67.1 ± 5.7	63.7 ± 10.4
Increase in mean slope produced by degradation (msec per character)	7.6 ± 2.4	2.7 ± 3.8

---

[3] Experiment 2 in Sternberg, 1966.

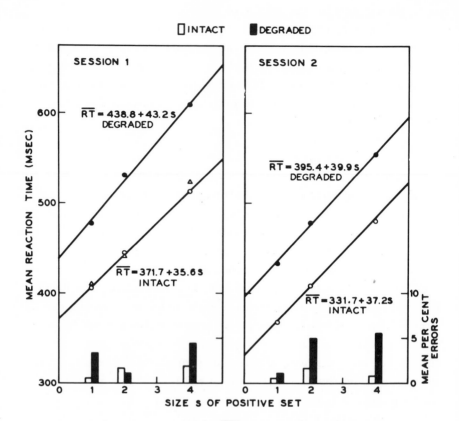

Fig. 4. Mean reaction time ($\overline{RT}$) and error percentage as functions of size of positive set for intact and degraded test-stimuli. (Left-hand and right-hand panels show data from Sessions 1 and 2, respectively. Each point [circles] represents about 29 observations from each of 12 subjects. Lines were fitted by least squares; their equations are displayed. Triangles represent data from a previous experiment.)

Degradation affected the intercept markedly in both sessions. (The difference between the effects in the two sessions is small, amounting to 3.4 ± 7.4 msec, where the standard error is based on 5df.)[4] The

---

[4] The experimental unit in these analyses was the pair of subjects having the same order of conditions s = 1, 2, and 4 but opposite orders of intact and degraded subparts. The data for each pair were averaged and then corrected for the mean part-of-session effect. Lines were fitted by least squares to the corrected values. For each of the six pairs of subjects, and for each session, the increases produced by degradation in slope and zero-intercept were determined. Estimates of standard errors were based on these values for each of the two sessions, or on the appropriate differences between them.

effect of degradation on the slope is substantially smaller than its effect on the zero-intercept and is significant in Session 1 only. (In Session 1 the value of the t statistic associated with the slope effect is 3.22 with 5 df, and the p value associated with the positive tail is 0.013. The corresponding p-value for Session 2 is 0.26.)[5] The difference between the slope effects in the two sessions is 4. 9 ± 3.3, where the standard error is based on 5 df. (Here the value of t is 1.49, and the p-value associated with one tail is 0.10.)

The reaction-time functions changed in two respects from session to session. First, as already indicated, the functions for intact and degraded test stimuli are more nearly parallel in Session 2 than in Session 1. Second, there was a general increase in speed, with the mean zero-intercept reduced by 41.7 ± 13.8 msec from first to second session (standard error based on 5 df). On the other hand, there appears to have been no general reduction in slope.

Comparison of Effects of Test-stimulus Degradation on Latencies of Positive and Negative Responses. The relation between the effects of degradation on latencies of positive and negative responses is relevant to theories of character recognition. The magnitudes of these effects were determined from the combined data for conditions in which s = 1, 2, and 4. Combining these data produced considerable overlap of the populations of test stimuli that contributed to positive and negative means, although these populations were not identical (see Figure 3). The results are displayed in Table 4. Evidently, the extent

Table 4. Comparison of Effects of Degradation on Latencies of Positive and Negative Responses (Data from conditions with s = 1, 2, and 4 have been combined. Estimated standard errors are based on the 11 df associated with subjects.)

Effect	Session 1	Session 2
Mean increase produced by degradation in positive-response latency (msec)	84.8	68.6
Mean increase produced by degradation in negative-response latency (msec)	84.2	70.6
Difference (msec)	+0.6 ± 8.1	-2.0 ± 8.5

[5] For the six experimental units (pairs of subjects) the differences between estimated slopes for degraded and intact test stimuli in Session 1 were 14.7, 12.0, 9.8, 6.5, 3.9, and -1.2 msec per character.

to which the response to a test stimulus is slowed by degradation does not depend on whether the stimulus is a member of the positive set.

Discussion

On the basis of these data, what can be said about the nature of Operation 1 and the stimulus representation it produces? The representation is apparently very far from a raw image of the stimulus, contrary to Theories A and B. It is sufficiently abstracted so that, in Session 2, the comparison operation can proceed unhindered by the degradation that was originally present. This conclusion follows from the virtual equality of the slopes of the two reaction-time functions in that session. The marked effect of degradation on reaction time was due, in both sessions, primarily to its effect on some part of the process other than the comparison operation. It seems plausible that the affected part of the process occurs before the comparison stage and is, in fact, Operation 1. (If so, then the magnitude of the effect of degradation on the zero-intercept, about 65 msec, provides a lower bound for the duration of Operation 1 with degraded test stimuli.)

The major effect of test-stimulus degradation, then, is on Operation 1. But it can affect the comparison operation as well. This is shown by the difference observed in Session 1 between the slopes of the reaction-time functions for intact and degraded stimuli. Visual degradation can influence Operation 2 only if there is residual degradation in the stimulus representation. It follows that, contrary to Theory F, what is represented is the physical stimulus, rather than the meaning or the name of the character.[6]

The effect of degradation on slope was less in the second session

---

[6] In his discussion of this paper, N. S. Sutherland attempted to salvage Theory F by proposing an alternative explanation of the difference between slopes. Stimulus representations could take the form of labels, and because of its ambiguity a degraded test stimulus might occasionally be represented by more than one. When this happened a serial-comparison process would be carried out for each label. The mean number of comparisons per character in the positive set, for degraded test stimuli, would therefore be greater than one, and this would produce the increase in slope. Multiple representations would also produce false positive responses. Sutherland's proposal must be rejected because, taken together with the magnitude of the observed slope effect, it leads to several predictions about these errors that are inconsistent with the data.

than the first, suggesting that some sort of learning occurred. This is not very surprising, since the degradation was produced by a fixed pattern, and the ensemble of test stimuli was the same from session to session. The improvement cannot be attributed to familiarity with particular positive sets, since their composition was changed from session to session (see section on design). Nor can it be attributed to a general increase in efficiency of the comparison operation, since the slope of the reaction-time function for intact stimuli does not decrease from session to session. On the basis of these data, however, one cannot decide whether the improvement results from Operation 1 becoming more effective at eliminating degradation from the representation, or from Operation 2 becoming less sensitive to the degradation that remains.[7]

The equality of the increases produced by degradation in the latencies of positive and negative responses is consistent with two aspects of the theory proposed here: first, that Operation 1 precedes and is therefore independent of the decision of whether or not the stimulus is a member of the positive set, and second, that the same number (s) of comparisons occur, whichever decision is required. On the other hand, the equality of effects seems inconsistent with theories according to which the amount of processing of the stimulus depends on whether or not it is a target. Such a theory, involving the self-terminating operation of a hierarchy of feature recognizers, has been put forward by Neisser (1963; 1964) for monitoring in visual search. He proposes that in his experiments on visual scanning a stimulus is tested first for gross features; it is processed further only if it passes the first test, and so on. More tests are carried out for targets than for nontargets. It seems plausible that the greater the number of tests, the greater the opportunity for stimulus degradation to have an effect. If this kind of theory were valid for the present experiment one might therefore expect stimulus degradation to have a greater effect on positive than on negative response latencies.

The effects on reaction time of experimental variations have occasionally been explained in terms of changes in the amount of time occupied by the sampling of information from the stimulus (e.g., Fitts, Peterson, and Wolpe, 1963; Stone, 1960). That this kind of

---

[7] This argument is one of several in the present paper that depend on the assumption that any effect of stimulus degradation on an operation will be revealed by a change in the duration of that operation.

explanation may be of limited usefulness for simple-reaction time has been shown, for example, by Raab and Fehrer (1962), who found that differences in the luminance of a 2-msec flash could produce differences of 120 msec in reaction time. The present experiment provides similar evidence for choice-reaction time. First, the effects on reaction time of both degradation (65 msec) and set size (as much as 130 msec) were greater than the duration of the test stimulus (44 msec). Second, the reaction-time function for intact stimuli appears to be unaffected by whether the test-stimulus exposure is brief or, as in a previous experiment, response-terminated.

It may be possible to apply the dissection tool described here to the general problem of explaining the invariance of object identification with respect to transformations of the stimulus (Attneave, 1966). The addition of a checkerboard is only one of many transformations to which a stimulus can be subjected without altering the classification response. But whereas the response is invariant with respect to the transformation, its latency may not be. If the latency is affected, then the investigation of the locus of the effect, as exemplified in the present study, may reveal something of the mechanism that underlies the response invariance.

Summary

Six alternative theories of character recognition are proposed. Analyses of reaction times in a classification task where test stimuli were either intact or degraded characters, and where there were relatively few errors, lead to the rejection of three of the theories. Under the conditions studied there appear to be at least two separate operations in the recognition of a character. The first produces an abstracted representation of the physical stimulus. The second is a comparison between stimulus and memory representations, and produces either a match or a mismatch. The method of reaction-time analysis that is introduced may have application to the general problem of object invariance.

Acknowledgement

The experiment on which this report is based was performed at the University of Pennsylvania with the support of Grant GB-1172 from the National Science Foundation.

References

Attneave, F. Some criteria for a tenable theory of form perception. In W. Wathen-Dunn (Ed.), Proceedings of the symposium on models for the perception of speech and visual form, 1964. Cambridge: M.I.T. Press, 1967. Pp. 56-67.

Doyle, W. Recognition of sloppy, hand-printed characters. Proc. west. jnt. Comput. Conf., 1960, 17, 133-142.

Fischler, M., Mattson, R. L., Firschein, O., and Healy, L. D. An approach to general pattern recognition. IRE Trans. Info. Theory, 1962, IT-8(5), S64-S73.

Fitts, P. M., Peterson, J. R., and Wolpe, G. Cognitive aspects of information processing: II. Adjustments to stimulus redundancy. J. exp. Psychol., 1963, 65, 507-514.

Garner, W. R. Uncertainty and structure as psychological concepts. New York: Wiley, 1962.

Hubel, D. H. Integrative processes in central visual pathways of the cat. J. opt. Soc. Amer., 1963, 53, 58-66.

Minsky, M. Steps toward artificial intelligence. In E. A. Feigenbaum, and J. Feldman (Eds.), Computers and thought. New York: McGraw Hill, 1963. Pp. 406-450.

Neisser, U. Decision-time without reaction-time: Experiments in visual scanning. Amer. J. Psychol., 1963, 76, 376-385.

Neisser, U. Visual search. Sci. Amer., 1964, 210 (6), 94-102.

Raab, D. and Fehrer, E. Supplementary report: The effect of stimulus duration and luminance on visual reaction time. J. exp. Psychol., 1962, 64, 326-327.

Selfridge, O. G. and Neisser, U. Pattern recognition by machine. In E. A. Feigenbaum, and J. Feldman, (Eds.), Computers and thought. New York: McGraw Hill, 1963. Pp. 237-250.

Sternberg, S. Estimating the distribution of additive reaction-time components. Paper read at Psychometric Society, Niagara Falls, Ontario, Obtober 1964.

Sternberg, S. High-speed scanning in human memory. Science, 1966, 153, 652-654.

Sternberg, S. Two operations in character recognition. Perception and Psychophysics, 1967, 2, in press.

Stevens, Mary E. Automatic character recognition: A state-of-the art report. U.S. Dep. Commer. NBS tech Note, 1961, No. 112.

Stone, M. Models for choice-reaction time. Psychometrika, 1960, 25, 251-260.

Uhr, L. "Pattern recognition" computers as models for form perception. Psychol. Bull., 1963, 60, 40-73.

Unger, S. H. Pattern detection and recognition. Proc. IRE, 1959, 47, 1737-1752.

REPETITION AS A DETERMINANT OF PERCEPTUAL RECOGNITION PROCESSES

Ralph Norman Haber
Department of Psychology
University of Rochester
Rochester, New York

Three recent experiments were undertaken to explore some theoretical and methodological issues regarding the measurement of word recognition processes. One of these issues concerns a serious confounding which results from the use of the method of limits, a method that permeates nearly all of the research in this area. This method yields a perfect correlation between the number of presentations of the stimulus word and the duration (or intensity) of each presentation. To the extent that repetition alone, without any changes in duration of the stimulus, leads to an increase in perceptibility, then an important independent variable is being masked, and confused with other variables.

In these three experiments, the method of limits was replaced by a modified method of constant stimuli, so that each word was presented for a predetermined number of trials, but with no changes in duration between trials. In all cases, the intertrial interval was never less than 8 sec, during which time the subject reported what he had seen on the preceding trial. To study the effect of repetition, some of the words were presented for only one flash, others for two, and so forth, up to 25 presentations for some of the words. Duration was also varied, but never during the presentation of a word. Thus, some words were presented at 10 msec (i.e., all of the trials for that word would be at 10 msec), some at 15, 20, and so forth. In this way, the effects of repetition were assessed by comparing the number of letters perceived for different numbers of trials, holding duration constant. Likewise, the effects of duration were assessed by comparing the number of letters perceived for different durations, holding the number of presentations constant. For any given word, the subject would not know how many presentations he was to receive, so that he had no control over the number of trials. Therefore, he had to assume that each presentation might be the last one. This latter procedure partially corrects another methodological defect in the method of limits, in which the subject normally determines how many presentations he will receive, which he can shorten or extend by varying the quality of his report.

In addition to the separation of repetition and duration, a second major innovation was introduced into these experiments. The response indicator employed in nearly all studies on word recognition has been that of guessing the entire stimulus. Persistence in the use of this has continued in spite of serious criticisms raised by a number of authors (e.g., Garner, Hake, and Eriksen, 1956; Goldiamond, 1958). It is nearly impossible to reconstruct what the subject might have seen from what he guessed, since the latter places such reliance on the subject's previous knowledge, his expectations and hunches, and the ease with which he can take advantage of the redundancy in the stimulus. In place of guessing, in these experiments, the subject was always required to report the letters that he saw after each presentation. In this way, the indicator provided an index of the subject's perceptions, rather than his guesses.

With the changes described, these experiments can begin to assess the independent effects of duration and repetition on the perceptibility or clarity of the letters of words.

In other respects, these experiments were similar to most previous studies on word recognition. The stimuli were always seven-letter, three-syllable pronounceable words. In most conditions, they were English, whose frequencies were determined from the Thorndike-Lorge word counts (1944). For each study, the words were printed on long paper tapes, which were automatically centered and exposed, one line at a time, in one channel of a three-channel mirror tachistoscope, built by Scientific Prototype Mfg. Corp. A second background channel with two faint fixation lines was always illuminated at 10 ft-L. Total illumination increased to 18 ft-L during the exposure of a word.

On a signal from the experimenter, the subject pressed a switch which triggered the flash of the word. Immediately after each presentation, the subject reported the letters that he was sure he perceived. The subject was always told when trials for a new word would begin. The subject was scored as having perceived a word only if on the last presentation of the word he reported seeing all seven letters. No control over eye fixation was utilized, although the subject was cautioned not to initiate a flash unless he was fixated in the spot where the middle of the word would appear.

The first experiment (Haber and Hershenson, 1965) used 504 frequent

English words, presented at five different durations, for from 1 to 25
trials each. Nine testing sessions of 1 hour each were required, with
the first two being used to determine the duration values. These were
specified for each of the 10 subjects separately, by finding the highest
duration at which each subject rarely saw all seven letters on the first
presentation. This base duration was approximated 15 msec for each
subject. The other durations were then set 5 msec less and 5, 10,
and 15 msec above this base value.

A marked effect of trials on the probability of seeing all seven
letters of each word was found for the base duration and the two above
it. The duration 5 msec below base (not shown) rarely permitted the
subject to perceive any letters, regardless of the number of trials,

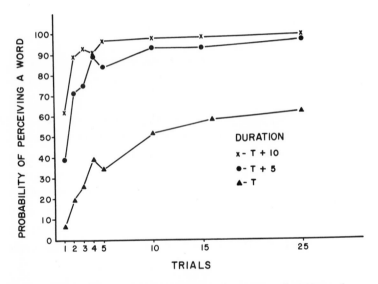

Fig. 1. Probability of perceiving a word as a function of
repetition trials (1 through 25) and duration (base, base plus
5 msec, and base plus 10 msec). (After Haber and Hershenson
[1965].)

whereas for the highest duration (not shown), the subject perceived
all of the letters on the first or second trial.

The phenomenal reports of each subject indicated that the first few
trials generally were blank (especially for the base duration), but with
further presentations, first the beginnings of letters would appear,
then whole letters, and often the entire word. The percept of the word
that developed with repetition was not fuzzy or unclear, nor was it

the result of a guess or hunch. It assumed a clear status, so that the subject was never uncertain about his reports, even though he had been unable to see anything a few presentations earlier. Many subjects reported afterwards that they thought the duration or intensity of the stimulus was being increased between trials, and they were quite surprised to find that there had been no changes made.

This first experiment demonstrated that repetition alone increased the probability of seeing words, independent of any changes in the duration of the presentations. Further this effect was found for a relatively large range of duration of exposures. Thus, the ascending method of limits did appear to confound duration with repetition, since either of these manipulations alone produced increases in perceptibility. Further, it showed that the phenomenal percept of the letters increased steadily with repetition, suggesting a developmental process for the appearance of the percept. This effect was independent of the duration of exposure.

The second experiment (Hershenson and Haber, 1965) was designed to extend the previous findings to meaningless words. Half of the 288 words were selected from the same lists as in the previous study, whereas the other half were seven-letter, three-syllable (if pronounced by an English speaker) Turkish words. For these, the subjects could not use many of the overlearned hypotheses or guesses that he knew would work for English words. Ten subjects were used, each tested in six sessions, three for English words and three for Turkish. All words were assigned to one of three durations (15, 20, or 25 msec) and one of eight numbers of presentations (1, 2, 3, 4, 5, 10, 15, or 25). As in the previous experiment, the subjects reported the letters that he perceived on each trial.

Figure 2 shows that repetition increased the clarity of letters, regardless of whether the subject knew the meaning of the words. Thus, the repetition effect was demonstrated for words about which the subject could use very few of his hypotheses regarding redundancy of the letters. Further, the rate of increase was similar for each language and duration. The relative perceptibility of letters of words from the two languages, as shown in Figure 2, was much greater for the letters of the English words. The subjects reported seeing more of the English letters on the first and each subsequent trial of English words as compared to corresponding trials for Turkish words, and these corresponding differences were massive. Meaning then seemed

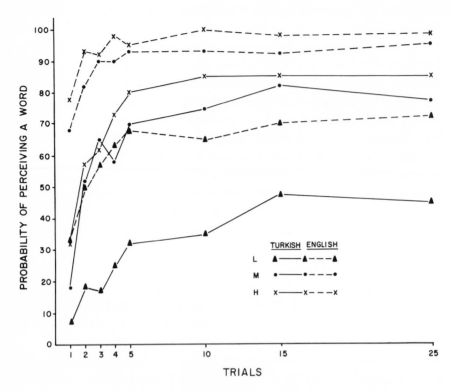

Fig. 2. Probability of perceiving a word as a function of
repetition trials, duration (low-15 msec; middle-20 msec;
high-25 msec), and language (English and Turkish). (After
Hershenson and Haber [1965].)

to play a role similar to duration in that both effected the initial perceptibility of the letters and the asymptotic performance, but not the
rate of increase in accuracy over trials.

The third experiment (Haber, 1965) examined one aspect of meaning
more directly. Only English words (totally 576) were shown, evenly
divided between rare and frequent. However, for half of the words,
immediately preceding the first trial for each, the word was exposed
for 5 sec whereupon the subject spelled it out loud. Then the regular
trials commenced. In other respects the procedure was similar to
the previous studies, though words were assigned to only one of two
durations. Sixteen subjects were tested individually in nine 1-hr
sessions each.

The major difference between this and previous studies was that for the words given prior exposure, while the subject knew exactly what each of the letters would be, he still was required to report which letters he could see. This condition high-lighted most strongly the difference between having the subject guess the word rather than asking him to report the letters he saw. For the words given prior exposure, requests for guesses would be meaningless.

Figure 3 presents the results of the effects of repetition for the base duration, as a function of word frequencies, and prior exposure. (The higher duration is omitted to save space, though the pattern of results was quite similar.) Giving prior exposure immediately before the trials of a word increased the probability of seeing its letters. A difference in perceptibility between rare and frequent words was also

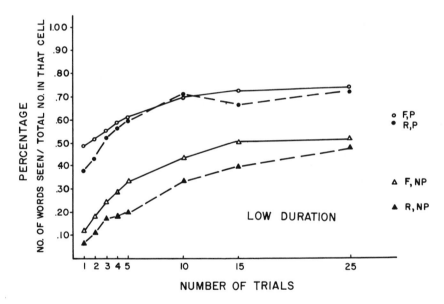

Fig. 3. Probability of perceiving a word as a function of repetition trials, frequency of word (R-rare)and (F-frequent), and prior knowledge (NP-no prior exposure; P-prior exposure). (After Haber [1965].)

found, but only when no prior exposure was given. Since these data were collected using a clarity rather than a guessing indicator, they suggest that as long as the differential frequency of the words was not eliminated by prior exposure, that differential effected the clarity of the letters directly, not just the ability to guess the highly redundant ones, as Pierce (1963) among others, has suggested.

The most important result of this experiment, however, was the similarity in rates of development of the percept as a function of any of the experimental variables. Specific prior exposure did not facilitate the rate of increase of seeing letters. It affected the amount of clarity — prior exposed words were seen more frequently — but not the rate of increase as a function of repetition.

Discussion

The pattern of results from these three experiments suggests both methodological and theoretical revisions in thinking about word recognition processes. Methodologically, they point to a rejection of the method of limits as a technique for presentation of stimulus materials. Because an effect of repetition can be established independently of changes in duration or intensity, continued use of the method of limits would represent a confounding of these two classes of variables.

Theoretically, these three experiments clearly indicate that repetition is an independent variable of recognition processes. The independence of repetition and duration needs to be qualified, however. If the duration is too brief, then repetition cannot bring the stimulus into a clear percept, regardless of the number of presentations. Likewise, repetition has no effect if the duration is so long that the entire percept is perfectly clear on the first presentation. However, near the lower end of the effective range, while a strong repetition effect is demonstrated, the asymptote for clarity does not approach 100%, regardless of the number of repetitions. When the duration is somewhat above the base value, while the initial presentation or two will result in only imperfect clarity, the function will eventually reach complete clarity.

These experiments were not designed to assess the relative importance of duration and repetition, but since these are the two variables confounded by the method of limits, a comparison of their effects was made. An attempt was made to determine whether perception was facilitated more by single presentations of long durations than by flashes of shorter durations but exposed for several trials. It was found that one long exposure was always superior to two or more shorter ones, summing to the same total, suggesting that duration accounted for more variance in clarity than did repetition. However, duration was varied in steps of 5 msec, a relatively coarse variation, which might have covered up sizable changes in repetitions. Therefore, this analysis should be repeated with durations varied in steps of a single msec. In this way, it might be that two flashes at 1 msec will be superior to one flash at 2 msec. In any event, a final conclusion awaits further research. Regardless of that outcome, however, the results from the three experiments already completed indicate clearly that repetition has a massive effect, increasing by over 50% the words in which all the letters are seen.

The intertrial interval in these experiments was never less than 8 sec, and sometimes a bit more if the subject was particularly slow in making a report. Haslerud (1964), in a replication of this design, reported that varying the intertrial interval systematically from 5 to 20 sec produced little significant change in the rate of development of the percept with repetition. This would suggest that further processing of the stimulus is not occurring during the intertrial interval, and that the size of the interval is not crucial as long as no interfering task is introduced.

Repetition is a variable of central importance in research on learning, and it is therefore somewhat surprising that it has not drawn much attention in perception. In part, this omission could stem from the assumed immediateness of perceptual experience. Even so, these results certainly indicate that repeated exposures of a stimulus help to bring its clarity up to strength. In this sense, perception of even highly familiar stimuli like words is not immediate at all, unless the initial presentation allows it to be.

In these experiments the effects of repetition are invariant over a number of quite different operations — duration, language, prior exposure, and frequency — operations that normally account for large portions of variance in most word recognition experiments. In these studies they account for variance in the level of clarity — each of them increases clarity — but they do not interact with repetition. They determine the clarity of the percept on the first presentation, and the ultimate clarity after many presentations, but seem to have little effect on the rate of increase in clarity with repetition.

This latter conclusion is supported by extensive curve fitting operations performed on the repetition functions from each condition in each of the three experiments. The fitting of a large number of different models was attempted and the only one that provided a fit to all of the data points was the negatively accelerated growth function:

$P_n = A - q_1/n$, where P_n is the probability of seeing all of the letters
of a word after the nth trial, A is the asymptote of the function after
many trials, q_1 is the probability of not seeing all of the letters on the
first trial, and n is the number of trials. The exponent of n was
empirically not significantly different from 1.00 for each function,
and hence does not appear in the equation. Since the starting probability
(q_1) and the asymptote (A) are highly related (r = + 0.85 over all
conditions of all experiments), the relation of repetition to the
probability of seeing the letters is specified by one parameter — the
probability of seeing all of the letters on the first trial. Thus, the
entire function in each condition can be generated by giving only one
trial per word. This suggests that some weight can be attached to
the conclusion that the effects of repetition cut across the other operations in these experiments, and is a highly stable effect.

Few models of perceptual behavior have incorporated repetition
effects. While Hebb (1949) has built his cell-assembly model on
repetition, he is concerned there primarily with the initial development
of an assembly from novel stimulation in infancy and childhood, and
has not discussed how repetition might affect already developed and
organized assemblies. By extension, however, it is possible to apply
the present results to his general theorizing. One possibility is that
the degree of arousal of a fully developed and organized assembly
mediates the perceptual experience of clarity — the more fully aroused
an assembly corresponding to a stimulus, the greater the experienced
clarity of the stimulus.

A number of variables would presumably determine the degree of
arousal of an established assembly. Among these are: (a) Stimulus
adequacy — the longer, or more intense, or more discriminable the
stimulus, the greater the likelihood that it will arouse an assembly.
This was shown in these experiments by the increase in clarity from
stimuli at higher durations. Presumably the same effect could have
been shown with changes in intensity, and that intensity and duration
are related by the Bunsen-Roscoe Law (See Kahneman, 1967). (b)
Initial organization — the more organized the assembly prior to
stimulation, the more likely it will be aroused by stimulation. Initial
organization would presumably be a function of a number of variables,
including the amount of prior experience with the specific stimuli
(e.g., frequency of appearance of words in print, and meaningfulness
of the stimuli), and prior knowledge or exposure of the stimuli. Finally,

(c), given an initial organization and level of stimulus adequacy, repetition of stimulation should boost the arousal of the assembly. This does not refer to repetition building or constructing the assembly, but merely in getting it all going. In this way, a poorly organized assembly, hit with an inadequate stimulus could still be brought to a high level of arousal by repetition of that stimulus. This is what happened, for example, in the second experiment with the low duration Turkish words, which achieved little clarity on the first trial, but which after repeated presentations over half of the Turkish words became perfectly clear. Also, as the present data indicate, there are lower limits to the inadequacy of the stimulus that can be overcome with repetition. Below some value of stimulus magnitude no increase in clarity can be achieved regardless of the number of repetitions. Finally, the present data suggest that the amount each repetition arouses an assembly is independent of the initial level of organization and stimulus adequacy, since neither of these parameters interacted with the rate of increase in clarity.

The extension of the Hebbian model is presented in this context, not because the data from these three experiments represent strict tests of the model, but because there is no comparable model to handle the effects of repetition. However, the model can provide considerable heuristic value to further research by suggesting the kinds of variables that should be investigated. The results of this further work can be used then to examine the adequacy of the model.

Acknowledgment

The three experiments reported in this paper were supported in part by a grant from the United States Public Health Service (MH-03244) to Yale University, where the research was completed. The author wishes to express his deep appreciation to Maurice Hershenson, with whom much of this work developed, and to Martha Breen, who assisted in the data collection in each of the experiments.

References

Garner, W. R., Hake, H. W., and Eriksen, C. W. Operationism and the concept of perception. Psychol. Rev., 1956, 63, 317-329.

Goldiamond, I. Indicators of perception; I. Subliminal perception, subception, unconscious perception: An analysis in terms of psychophysical indicator methodology. Psychol. Bull., 1958, 55, 373-411.

Haber, R. N. The effect of prior knowledge of the stimulus on word recognition processes. J. exp. Psychol., 1965, 69, 282-286.

Haber, R. N., and Hershenson, M. The effects of repeated brief exposures on the growth of a percept. J. exp. Psychol., 1965, 69, 40-46.

Haslerud, G. M. Perception of words as a function of delays between and summation of subliminal exposures. Percept. mot. Skills, 1964, 19, 130.

Hebb, D. O. The organization of behavior. New York: Wiley, 1949.

Hershenson, M., and Haber, R. N. The role of meaning in the perception of briefly exposed words. Canad. J. Psychol., 1965, 19, 42-46.

Kahneman, D. Temporal effects in the perception of light and form. In W. Wathen-Dunn (Ed.) Proceedings of the symposium on models for the perception of speech and visual form, Boston, 1964. Cambridge: M.I.T. Press, 1967. Pp. 157-170.

Pierce, J. Some sources of artifact in studies of the tachistoscopic perception of words. J. exp. Psychol., 1963, 66, 363-370.

Thorndike, E. L., and Lorge, I. A teacher's word book of 30,000 words. New York: Teachers College, Columbia University, 1944.

SOME EVIDENCE BEARING ON OPERATIONS OF "ANALYSIS" AND "INTEGRATION" IN VISUAL FORM PERCEPTION BY HUMANS

Joseph H. McFarland [1]
Department of Psychology
University of Denver
Denver, Colorado

Since the classic work by the Gestalt School, most experimental approaches to visual form perception have been based on synthetic models. Investigators have employed methods which are based on the methodological assumption that a perceived visual form is an indivisible unit of behavior, primarily dependent on topographic projection of retinal signals to the striate cortex. Experimental methods, based on more analytic assumptions concerning the functioning of the visual system are virtually nonexistent in the repertory of methods drawn upon by the experimental psychologist studying visual form

----

[1] Presently at the Psychology Department, Antioch College, Yellow Springs, Ohio.

perception. In summary, the employment of models which have
complementary synthetic and analytic features, characteristic of
scientific enquiry since Galileo, has not been a feature of most
investigations of form perception.

The neural model to be described here (cf. also McFarland, 1965a)
is based on both synthetic and analytic assumptions and has been
formulated in a manner that permits the development of both synthetic
and analytic experimental methods. In terms of this model, stimulation
of the retina and topographic projection to the cortex are necessary
conditions for form perception; but a neural network, which analyzes
the stimulus into parts and then integrates these part responses into a
whole response, is a primary determinant of the form, qua form,
perceived. Thus, with appropriate methods, study may be initiated
in terms of this model, as to an "analytic" response to parts of a
form and as to a "synthetic" response to the whole form.

A main feature of this model is the posited neural network within
the visual system that permits these hypothetical operations of
"analysis" and "integration." It is assumed that at birth, neuronal
convergences within the visual system are such that these operations
can occur (cf. Hubel and Wiesel, 1963). The "analysis" operation
entails production in first-order cortical units, by virtue of
converging projections from lateral geniculate units which have
appropriately adjacent receptive fields on the retina, of a sequence
of responses to line and to angle parts of a retinal stimulus. The
operation of "integration" entails the production of a response to these
part responses by virtue of converging projections from first- to
second-order cortical units, at some locus within the visual system
(cf. Hubel and Wiesel, 1959; 1965).

Two experiments are reported which employ methods designed to
provide information on the hypothesized operations of "analysis" and
"integration."

Experiment 1

The first of these experiments deals with analysis and employs a
method wherein the parts of an outline triangle (0.44 ft-L) are presented
simultaneously at increasing exposure times. The subjects report
on whether the form is complete or not; and, if there are incompletions, they report on the location of the incompletions. There are 16
subjects and each makes a total of 60 reports. It is assumed: (a) that

presenting a stimulus at some brief exposure time (2 msec) will "stop" stimulus processing after analysis but before integration is complete; (b) that presenting the same stimulus at increasing exposure times will increasingly permit integration to run its course; and (c) that perception under these conditions will reflect the hypothesized analysis and integration of parts.

The results show that with a 2-msec exposure, 28% of the reports are of only parts of the line triangle, viz., an incomplete triangle is reported; as exposure time increases, the percentage of part reports declines until at 128 msec only 0.1% of the reports are of an incomplete triangle (see Figure 1).

Consideration of the location of incompletions shows that, of the total incomplete reports, 38.7% have incompletions in an angle(s),

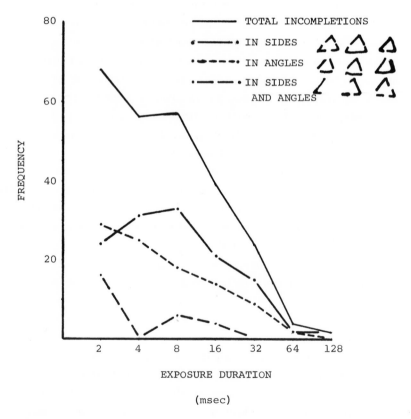

Fig. 1. Experiment 1, total reports of incomplete triangles as a function of exposure time and reports of incompletions by locus as a function of exposure time.

50.6% have incompletions in a side(s), and 10.6% have incompletions in both an angle(s) and a side(s). (Frequency of incompletions in angles alone and in sides alone are not significantly different from each other but are significantly different, p < 0.001, from incompletions in both an angle [s] and a side [s].)

Examination of the frequency of these three types of incompletions as a function of time shows a complex interaction (p < 0.001) (see Figure 1). When the degrees of freedom for this interaction are partitioned, however, only the interaction between incompletions in angles and incompletions in sides as a function of time is significant (p < 0.001).

Several features of these data provide support for the posited model. In that incompletions are frequent at brief exposure and diminish with increase in exposure, the data suggest that brief exposure stops stimulus processing during analysis, viz., before integration is complete, and longer exposure permits integration to run its course. The fact that frequency of incompletions in angles and incompletions in sides are comparable and both are significantly different from incompletions in angles and sides suggests that the hypothesized analysis entails resolving stimulation into responses to either line parts, viz., report of an incompletion in an angle(s), or angle parts, viz., report of an incompletion in a side(s). However, the fact that (a) the interaction between incompletions in angles and incompletions in sides as a function of time is significant, and that (b) both types of incompletions are comparable at the briefest exposure, but incompletions in angles show a linear decrease with time and incompletions in sides show a rise and then a decrease with time, suggests there are phases in the analysis of stimulation into line and angle parts, viz., analysis into lines and then analysis into angles.

Experiment 2

The second experiment deals with integration. Here, the same outline triangle employed in Experiment 1 is divided into three equal parts which are presented sequentially. Each part is presented for 10 msec and the two interpart intervals are maintained equal and varied from 0 to 100 msec. In one condition three line parts are presented and in a second condition three angle parts are presented; for both conditions the sequence is CCW. Subjects report whether all parts are simultaneous or not and whether all parts are joined to make a

complete triangle or not. There are 16 subjects and each makes a
total of 50 reports for each condition. By use of this method of
stimulus presentation, it is assumed (a) that neural response simulates
the hypothesized analysis of retinal stimulation into a sequence of part
responses, and (b) that perception reflects the hypothesized integration
of part responses.

The findings show that thresholds for perception of nonsimultaneity
and nonjoining of all parts are significantly higher ($p < 0.05$) when line
parts are presented in sequence (respective interpart intervals are 27
msec and 36 msec) than when angle parts are presented in sequence
(respective interpart intervals are 20 msec and 11 msec) (see Figure 2).

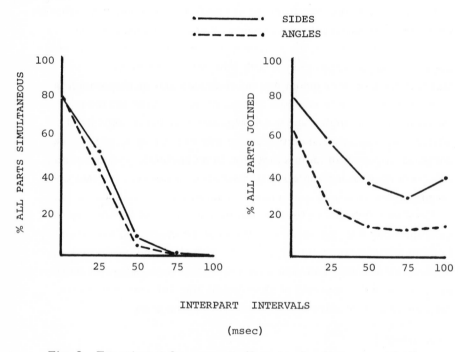

Fig. 2. Experiment 2, per cent all parts simultaneous and all
parts joined as a function of interpart intervals for sequential
side and sequential angle presentation.

These findings complement the previously reported findings in
suggesting a differential integration of responses to line versus angle
parts of a visual form. The present findings suggest that when a form
is analyzed into a sequence of responses to line parts, integration is
such that "normal" perception of the parts as joined and simultaneous

can occur at larger interresponse intervals than when a form is analyzed into a sequence of responses to angle parts. Thus, it can be inferred that the real time required for integration of sequential responses to angles is greater than that required for integration of sequential responses to lines.

Discussion

Several features of the results have provided support for the neural model of visual form perception posited here. First, the reports of incompletions either in angles or in sides (Experiment 1) at brief exposures is in accord with the posited analysis of a form into responses to line and angle parts. The fact that incompletions at angles diminish with increase in stimulus duration, and incompletions in sides increase and then diminish with increase in stimulus duration, has been viewed as indicating there are two phases in the processing of a stimulus. In the first phase a stimulus is analyzed into line parts; in the second phase the stimulus is analyzed into angle parts.

Second, the thresholds for both nonsimultaneity and nonjoining of all parts when lines versus angles are sequentially presented (Experiment 2) provide some support for the posited sequence of responses to line parts and to angle parts of a form. Although it may be argued that (a) "normal" perception of a form entails simultaneous responses to all line and angle parts of a form and (b) thresholds for nonsimultaneity and nonjoining under the conditions of sequential part presentation employed here can be related to mechanisms for temporal and spatial discrimination, the fact of differences between these thresholds for line versus angle part sequential presentation cannot simply be related to such mechanisms for temporal and spatial discrimination. Similarly, when the line parts of a stimulus are presented in different sequences, viz., clockwise versus counterclockwise, differences in thresholds of nonsimultaneity and nonjoining cannot simply be related to mechanisms for temporal and spatial discrimination.[2]

The interpretation offered for these differences is that during "normal" perception of a form there are sequential responses to lines and to angles of a form in first-order cortical units. Via converging projections from these first-order units to second-order units, these analytic responses are integrated and provide a basis for the

---

[2] A portion of this experiment is now reported in McFarland (1965b)

achievement of perceiving a form with parts simultaneous and joined.
The fact that thresholds of nonsimultaneity and nonjoining for
sequential responses to angles are lower than the thresholds for
sequential responses to lines (Figure 2) suggests that the real time
required for integration of sequential responses to angles is greater
than that required for integration of sequential responses to lines —
an interpretation in accord with that offered above, viz., a stimulus
is analyzed into angle parts in the second phase of stimulus processing.

In conclusion, it should be emphasized that the operations of
analysis and integration posited in the neural model advanced here
refer to neuronal relationships within the visual system and are based
primarily on a generalization to man of findings in the cat. These
findings, concerning the possible dependence of form discrimination
capabilities (Sutherland, 1964) on particular lateral geniculate-cortex
convergences present at birth (Hubel and Wiesel, 1963), make it
plausible to set aside both the Gestalt view of cortical field forces
(cf. also Lashley, Chow, and Semmes, 1951) and the Hebbian view (1949)
of random interconnections between neurons in Area 17, responding to
punctiform parts of the retinal stimulus, and neurons in visual
association areas. Based on this evidence, if it may be generalized to
humans (some steps in this direction have already been taken by Rudel
and Teuber, 1963), it has been assumed that discrete units in the
human visual system are capable at birth of responding to different
simple stimuli, viz., lines and angles, and that perception of a complex
form entails a higher order neuronal integration of the sequential
responses to such simple stimuli. This latter assumed integration
may well be the aspect of neuronal interrelations within the visual
system that is conditioned by organism-environment interaction.

Acknowledgment

This work was supported in part by National Institutes of Health,
Grant M-6403(A), United States Public Health Service

References

Hebb, D. O. The organization of behavior. New York: Wiley, 1949.

Hubel, D. H., and Wiesel, T. N. Receptive fields of single neurones
    in the cat's striate cortex. J. Physiol., 1959, 148, 574-591.

Hubel, D. H., and Wiesel, T. N. Receptive fields of cells in striate
    cortex of very young, visually inexperienced kittens. J. Neuro-
    physiol., 1963, 26, 994-1002.

Hubel, D. H., and Wiesel, T. N. Receptive fields and functional architecture in two non-striate visual areas (18 & 19) of the cat. J. Neurophysiol., 1965, 28, 229-289.

Lashley, K. S., Chow, K. L., and Semmes, J. An examination of the electrical field theory of cerebral integration. Psychol. Rev., 1951, 58, 123-136.

McFarland, J. H. Sequential part presentation: A method of studying visual form perception. Brit. J. Psychol., 1965, 56, 439-446. (a)

McFarland, J. H. The effect of different sequences of part presentation on perception of a form's parts as simultaneous. Proceedings of the seventy third annual convention of the American psychological association, 1965. Pp. 43-44. (b)

Rudel, R. G., and Teuber, H. L. Discrimination of direction of line in children. J. comp. physiol. Psychol., 1963, 56, 892-898.

Sutherland, N. S. Visual discrimination in animals. Brit. med. Bull., 1964, 20, 54-59.

ON MODELS FOR THE PERCEPTION OF VISUAL TEXTURE

Azriel Rosenfeld [1]
Budd Information Sciences Center
McLean, Virginia

Parameters and Stimuli

The appearance of "uniform texture" characteristic of probabilistically generated visual stimuli suggests that the brain may measure or estimate certain statistical parameters of such stimuli. These parameters would presumably describe the frequency distributions of various locally defined properties of the stimulus, such as values of the luminance and its gradient and spatial dependencies or periodicities in these values; they should probably also include explicit expressions of the tendencies for lines, edges, or patches of various sizes, shapes, and orientations to be present in the stimulus as a result of such spatial dependencies. As these examples suggest, the stimulus space over which the hypothetical parameter estimation process might operate is highly multidimensional, and many of the variables involved may be difficult to define quantitatively.

---

[1] Now with the Computer Science Center, University of Maryland, College Park, Maryland.

Past studies of visual texture perception have generally involved
only a few of the variables suggested by the foregoing. Emphasis has
been placed in most of these past studies on parameters related to the
"detail size" of the textured stimulus, such as "piece size" (Gibson,
1950), autocorrelation (Kaizer, 1955), conditional probability (Julesz,
1962; Pickett, 1964), spatial power spectrum (Rosenfeld, 1962a),[2]
luminance variance (Rosenfeld, 1962b), and "shaped piece content"
(Goldstein and Rosenfeld, 1964). (It is worth remarking that many of
these parameters have also been suggested as measures of photographic granularity, which may be regarded as relatively fine "detail.")

In order to perform quantitative studies of visual texture perception
which involve a manageable number of stimulus variables, it is
necessary to use stimuli in which the effects of other variables can
be controlled. This suggests the desirability of designing classes of
stimuli which can vary with respect to relatively few textural parameters. For example, one can use stimuli which are either "black"
or "white" at every point; this minimizes the influence of luminance
and luminance gradient variables. A more drastic restriction to
stimuli which are "one-dimensional" (luminance is constant across
the stimulus in one direction) can be used to minimize the significance
of form and pattern variables; methods of generating acceptable
stimuli of this type are described in Rosenfeld and Goldstein (1964).
Alternatively, a lesser degree of reduction in the effects of form and
pattern variables can be achieved by using stimuli the luminance of
which varies randomly in one direction. Computer programs for
generating stimuli of these types have been developed by various
investigators (Anderson, Rosenfeld, and Simenson, 1964; Julesz, 1962;
Pickett 1964). In order to impose constraints on this "random across"
type of stimulus without significantly disturbing its crosswise
randomness, one may impose them only on selected (e.g., alternating)
"rows" of the stimulus as suggested in Julesz (1962); however, this
"dilution" restricts the range of constraints which can be studied.

Experimental Tasks

A natural vehicle for the study of visual texture perception is the

---

[2] Techniques similar to those described in Rosenfeld (1962a; 1962b)
and Goldstein and Rosenfeld (1964) are discussed more fully in a
series of reports entitled "Semi-automatic target recognition device,"
issued by Litton Systems, Inc., Waltham, Mass., under Contract
AF 19(602)-2494 with the Rome Air Development Center.

choice experiment, generally involving stimulus materials which are uniformly textured and in which the task is one of discrimination, classification, ranking, or estimation of, or with respect to, textural parameters. For example, the studies described in Julesz (1962) involve tasks of discrimination between pairs of juxtaposed stimuli which are differently textured in a variety of ways; those in Pickett (1964), a classification task with respect to "coarseness" or detail size.

Another possible class of experimental tasks, perhaps more "realistic," might require subjects to indicate the direction of a texture gradient or to locate boundaries between differently textured regions in a nonuniform stimulus. Studies reported in Fried, Rosenfeld, and Gerstman (1965) have used constant-across "one-dimensional" stimuli in a task of boundary location with respect to mean luminance. Parameters more complex than mean luminance are difficult to study with such stimuli because of the limited amount of information per unit area which such a stimulus can contain. In other studies using random-across stimuli, currently in progress, mean luminance has been equalized by constraining all portions of the stimuli to be half "black" and half "white"; the variables under study are the frequency distributions of black and white "run lengths" (or one-dimensional "patch sizes").[3]

Models

A general class of models for the perception of statistical or "textural" properties of a stimulus is suggested by the following observations:

1. Suppose given a large collection of values of each of a number of locally defined stimulus properties. Significant peaks in the distribution of these values for a given variable should tend to correspond to "salient" perceived textural properties. Conversely, a distribution free of such peaks should tend to result in an appearance of uniformity with respect to the given variable.

---

[3] In both the boundary location studies of Fried et al. (1965) and the juxtaposed-stimulus discrimination studies of Julesz (1962) interpretation of the results must take into account the question (see Julesz, 1962) of whether or not the textures involved give rise to an "edge" when they are juxtaposed, as well as the question of their discriminability.

Texture perception may thus involve the application of "smoothing" and "peak enhancing" operations to distributions of stimulus parameter values so as to produce a "regularized" description of the stimulus.

2. Perceived texture can depend strongly on the "level of scrutiny" with which a stimulus is examined. This level may be related to the size of the "neighborhoods" over which the "local" stimulus properties are measured. Anatomically "natural" neighborhood sizes may exist, but level of scrutiny can apparently be influenced by set, intent, etc. as well, which suggests that it may be possible to select from among the range of sizes.

3. Performance at many texture-dependent tasks depends not only on the values of the "perceived" texture statistics, but also on the size of the sample for which these statistics are perceived – that is, on the stimulus size. This suggests that a model applicable to such tasks should involve both the stimulus statistics and the confidence levels which can be assigned to them.

4. For some local stimulus parameters, such as those which are measured by local processing "near" the eye, the supposed statistical analysis may take place in parallel; for other, "higher-order" parameters, the analysis may require sequential sampling of the stimulus, as suggested in the model proposed in Pickett (1964).[4] In analogy with Neisser (1963), significant differences in response latency (the experimental measurand in Pickett [1964]) might provide evidence on this question.

A complete model for visual texture perception and discrimination in two dimensions does not seem to be realizable at present. Since texture involves, among many other factors, the shapes of "patches" within the stimulus, a quantitative theory of visual form would seem to be a prerequisite to such a model. However, it may be[5] that visual form is more tractable from the model-making point of view when

---

[4] The results of studies with constant-across one-dimensional stimuli reported in Fried et al. (1965) indicate that the subjects could be influenced by the instructions to inspect the stimuli sequentially by scanning along them; however, this mode of inspection does not naturally generalize to two-dimensional stimuli.

[5] R. M. Pickett, private communication.

perceived in statistically constrained aggregates rather than in individual figures. This suggests that models for texture perception should continue to be studied side by side with models for the perception of visual form and pattern.

Acknowledgment

Much of the research described in this paper was performed under Contracts AF 49(638)-1143 and 1231 between The Budd Company and the Directorate of Information Sciences, United States Air Force Office of Scientific Research.

References

Anderson, N. S., Rosenfeld, A., and Simenson, N. F. A computer program for generating synthetic patterns. Comput. Sci. Ctr., Univ. Maryland, tech. Rep., 1964, No. 64-8.

Fried, C., Rosenfeld, A., and Gerstman, L. J. Sequential and parallel processing in boundary selections on one-dimensional pictorial stimuli. Percept. mot. Skills, 1965, 20, 789-801.

Gibson, J. J. Perception of the visual world. Boston: Houghton Mifflin, 1950.

Goldstein, A., and Rosenfeld, A. Optical correlation for terrain type discrimination. Photogram. Eng., 1964, 30, 639-646.

Julesz, B. Visual pattern discrimination. IRE Trans. Info. Theory, 1962, IT-8, 84-92.

Kaizer, H. A quantification of textures on aerial photographs. Opt. Res. Lab., Boston Univer, tech. Rep., 1955, No. 121.

Neisser, U. Decision time without reaction time: Experiments in visual scanning. Amer. J. Psychol., 1963, 76, 376-385.

Pickett, R. M. Perception of a visual texture. J. exp. Psychol., 1964, 68, 13-20.

Rosenfeld, A. Automatic recognition of basic terrain types from aerial photographs. Photogram. Eng., 1962, 28, 115-132. (a)

Rosenfeld, A. An approach to automatic photographic interpretation. Photogram. Eng, 1962, 28, 660-665. (b)

Rosenfeld, A., and Goldstein, A. Systems for generating one-dimensional patterns. Appl. Opt., 1964, 3, 547-548.

THE PERCEPTION OF RANDOM VISUAL TEXTURE

Ronald M. Pickett
School of Public Health
Harvard University
Boston, Massachusetts

Consider the remarkable ability we have of identifying types of bread or grades of sandpaper. With the slightest glance we can make reliable and valid distinctions among such images, even though such distinctions have to be based on what a statistician might describe as complicated, if not difficult, statistical analyses. The images undoubtedly are sampled in some sense since all the myriad of detail could not be apprehended in a brief glance. A sample of some one or more measures must be taken, and some one or more parameters of the over-all image estimated from these.

What measures are taken, what sampling plan is followed, and what parameters are estimated would be of interest from two standpoints. With this information the process of perceiving the particular class of imagery could be objectively described, and performance involving its perception under a range of task and viewing conditions could be predicted. In addition, one would begin to tap what may be a limited reservoir of sampling plans and statistical analyses which the visual system applies to such complex random imagery in general.

Studies of pattern perception employing various types of complex randomly generated images then may lead to the specification of some broad statistical decision models of visual perception. By working with imagery in which the microstatistics are well understood, e.g., distributions of element size, shape, orientation, and arrangement and so forth can be specified, statistical decision models can be developed. By interpreting measures of perceptual performance in terms of these models, answers to the type of questions mentioned here may be obtained.

With this kind of approach in mind, a program of research is currently under way investigating the perception of random visual textures. Several varieties of line- and dot-type textures, as well as mosaics, have been developed for the experimental program. Techniques for generating these displays have been developed for producing a large number of independent "large sample" patches of each variety of texture. The one type of texture which has been used in several recent experiments is the random-dot matrix.

Random-dot matrices described first by Green (1957) were
generated according to a Markov process (See Julesz [1962], and
Pickett [1963, 1964] for a detailed description). The dot matrices produced by such a process can be varied in appearance by changing the
transition probability (p). With p equal to 0.5 a matrix is produced
with a characteristic graininess or texture (Figure 1). The texture of

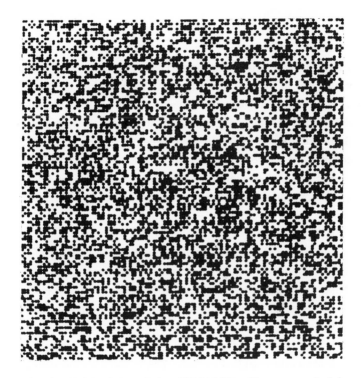

Fig. 1. A randon-dot matrix, 120 × 120 cells, generated from
a Markov process with transition probability equal to 0.5.

the matrix can be made "EVEN" by increasing p or "COARSE" by
decreasing p. The microstatistics of the resulting images can be
described as functions of p. In addition to the distribution of "transitions," the distribution of such measures of the image as interdot
distance, and length of run, can be specified for the vertical and
horizontal dimensions. The distribution of dot density can also be
specified for any shape and size of scanning window, and so forth. In
general, the sampling distributions of these measures can also be
specified or satisfactorily approximated.

Experimental subjects can be tested in regard to their sensitivity to the textural variation by having them sort a random sequence of matrices generated at various transition probabilities into the categories "COARSE" and "EVEN" relative to the texture of matrices generated at p = 0.5. Interpretations can be made of performance in terms of various statistical analyses which might have been made of the matrices, and inferences can be made about what measures of the image were taken, what sampling plan was employed, and what parameters were estimated.

A Typical Experiment

For a recent experiment matrices 120 × 120 cells in area similar to the one shown in Figure 1 were used. Twenty-four different matrices were made at each of 10 transition probability levels ranging from 0.38 to 0.62 in steps of 0.03 (0.38, 0.41, etc., with two sets at 0.50). Subjects viewed projections of these, one at a time, in a random sequence, making the forced choice of "EVEN" or "COARSE." They ran through the same sequence of 240 slides in three separate sessions. Session 1 is considered a training session, and the data reported are from Session 2 and 3 combined — 48 judgments at each of 10 transition probability levels.

The data are reported in terms of the per cent of "EVEN" responses and average response latency as functions of transition probability. With regard to the latency data, the subjects were told that they could take as much time as they wanted. They were self-paced through the task, and they ran individually. They were told that they should try to make their judgments within 10 sec.

Figure 2 shows how well they did. There were 20 subjects, and shown are the 20 individual accuracy functions. The fitted curves are normal ogives. Clearly the subjects did pretty well. If they were perfect discriminators each would show a step function with the vertical part of the step going through the solid symbol associated with each curve. The sigma of each ogive acts as a measure of the departure from such perfect performance. For the typical performance shown here the sigma is about 0.05, meaning that if the transition probability is either 0.45 or 0.55 the typical subject makes about 16% error in identifying the texture. Where the ogive does not go through the solid symbol, mean ±0.5, it indicates constant error.

Figure 3 shows the latency function for each subject. On the whole these functions show that the subjects take only 1 or 2 sec to make

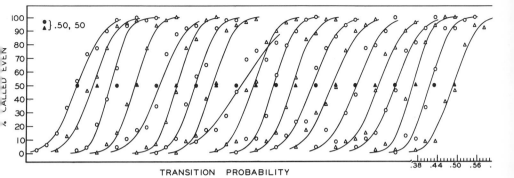

Fig. 2. Individual accuracy functions for the 20 subjects in the
experiment reported. (Subjects are numbered from left to
right.)

their judgments. The smooth curves are cubics fitted by least squares.
Notice that in each case the curve has a maximum, indicating that
every subject tended to take more time at or near p = 0.50. Where
the subject shows constant error in the accuracy function the maximum
of his latency function tends to shift accordingly.

While these data warrant a detailed discussion, it will have to
suffice here to point out some general properties. Variations in over-
all height and shape of the latency functions can be related, in part,
to variation in the parameters of the accuracy functions. A large
amount of the variation in latency though appears to be independent of
variation in accuracy. To the extent that it is, the latency data promise
to be an important additional source of information about the perceptual process. On the whole, however, there is obviously a very
large source of error in measuring the latency, and any detailed
inferences from the latency data will have to await a reduction in the
error. In future experiments it is hoped that this will be accomplished
by having subjects pay for their decision time.

Application of a Statistical Decision Model

Beyond these general observations, it will be helpful to consider the
data in terms of one possible statistical decision model. This will
provide a good example of the general approach to inferring a model,
and it will also suggest a point of departure for following out the
inferential chain over a program of experimental studies.

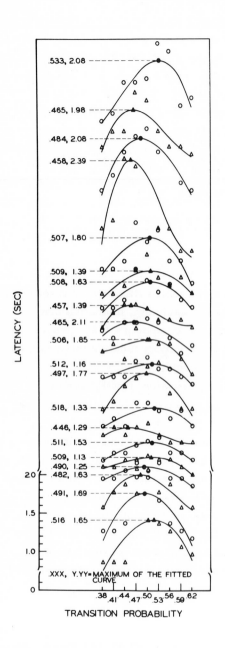

Fig. 3. Individual latency
functions for the 20 subjects
in the experiment reported.
(Subjects are numbered
from top to bottom.)

The model chosen is one in which the subject is assumed to estimate
the proportion of transitions in the matrix. He is assumed to collect
a sample of cells, note the proportion of transition cells in that sample
and to estimate the matrix (population) proportion from that sample.

His accuracy function may be considered the operating characteristic (OC) for the test. It represents the probability of "accepting the 'EVEN' (transition proportion greater than p = 0.5) hypothesis" at each level of p. Latency may be considered to be some direct function of the size of sample collected. For simplicity we will assume a linear relationship.

Perhaps the first thing to note is that the latency functions are very clearly of a general "inverted U shape." If latency is a direct function of sample size, this strongly suggests that the subjects are using a sequential sampling plan. The data may be interpreted then in terms of a sequential test of transition proportion, where the subject tests whether the proportion is greater than, or equal to, p = 0.5 (or whatever his criterion is, if he has some constant error).

The normal ogive fitted to the accuracy function is assumed to approximate closely the OC function for the test, and its parameters for a typical subject with mean = 0.5 and sigma = 0.05, are translated into the parameters of the sequential test, α = 0.16, β = 0.16, p_0 = 0.45, p_1 = 0.55 (see Wald [1959] p. 89 for details of this translation). Figure 4 shows the test diagrammatically. The parameters of the test determine the slope and width of the "keep looking" band. When the

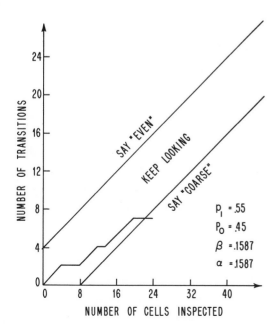

Fig. 4. A diagram of a sequential test of transition proportion equal in sensitivity to a typical subject.

cumulative number of transitions represented by the random walk goes outside the band the texture decision is made. In Figure 5 are approximations to the OC and average sample number (ASN) functions for the test diagramed in Figure 4.

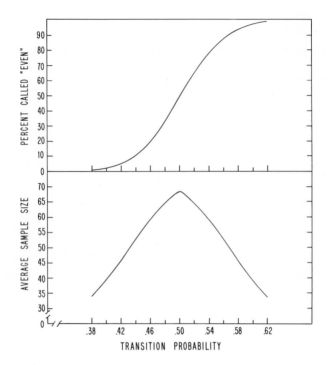

Fig. 5. Approximations to the operating characteristic and average sample number function for the sequential test.

At this point the model permits some interesting interpretation. The ASN function suggests that the typical subject uses at most an average of 70 cells of data from the 120 X 120 cell matrix. It also suggests that the amount of information extracted is halved when p is as extreme as 0.38 or 0.62. The rate of extraction, however, appears to be constant at about 30 cells per second for all levels of p.

Discussion

Clearly, there are several other aspects of the matrix related to "COARSENESS," besides transition proportion, which the subjects could measure, sample and estimate. They could be using any one or combination of such other measures as run length, interdot distance,

variability of dot density, etc. To the extent that models which involve
measuring and estimating such aspects can be specified, the performance could be interpreted in terms of them also. Then one could see
how each model could account for performance under variation in task,
or viewing conditions. There is evidence to show, for example, that
the test of transition proportion does not make complete sense because
of the way that the subject improves in performance as matrix size is
increased. The ASN function shows that the typical subject should not
need more than 200 cells of data to do as well as he does,[1] yet his
accuracy increases dramatically as we increase the amount of data at
his disposal from 200 to 400 to 1,600 and in this latest experiment to
14,000 cells of data. This is shown in Figure 6. If all he needs is 200
cells of data, he should not show this kind of improvement. This
suggests that the subjects are probably attending to some other aspect

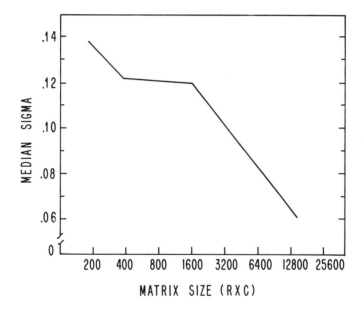

Fig. 6. Data from two separate experiments combined to show
the effect of matrix size on accuracy.

---

[1] The ASN function shows a maximum of about 70, but that value is the
mean of a skewed distribution of sample size. The 200 cell figure
represents a conservative upper limit for that distribution at which
truncation could occur without significantly affecting performance.

of the matrix than transition proportion. What that other aspect is, of course, would have to be inferred by applying other models to see which can reasonably account for the perceptual performance. Whichever one can account for changes in performance due to variation in matrix size would then be forced to account for any changes due to variation in matrix shape, and so on.

While there are clear limitations to this kind of trial and error approach, it does promise some very quantitative and specific information about an interesting area of visual perception. The success of this approach is dependent mainly on choosing the right kind of imagery. It must be a kind the microstatistics of which can be almost completely specified. The microstatistics, in turn, need to be of a relatively well-understood variety for which appropriate statistical decision models have been developed. To a workable extent this can be achieved by generating imagery from well-understood and relatively simple random processes.

Acknowledgment

The work reported here was supported by the United States Air Force under Contract AF 33(615)-1086.

References

Green, B. F. The use of high-speed digital computers in studies of form perception. In J. W. Wulfeck and J. H. Taylor (Ed.), Form discrimination as related to military problems. Washington: NAS-NRC, 1957. Pp. 65-75. (Pub. No. 561).

Julesz, B. Visual pattern discrimination. IRE Trans. Info. Theory, 1962, IT-8, 84-92.

Pickett, R. M. Computer generated pictures for pattern perception research. Paper read at Users of Automatic Information Display Equipment Meeting, Miami Beach, October 1963.

Pickett, R. M. The perception of a visual texture. J. exp. Psychol., 1964, 68, 13-20.

Wald, A. Sequential analysis. New York: Wiley, 1959.

COMMENTS ON THE SESSION

Paul A. Kolers
Research Laboratory of Electronics
Massachusetts Institute of Technology
Cambridge, Massachusetts

A profound change has occurred in the study of perception within the past 10 years or so. In older papers of the more psychophysical kind, the principal formulations are in terms of energy exchanges, regarding the subject as a passive detector, or simple transducer, and perception as a mirroring of the physical environment. The new approach regards the observer as an active operator rather than a passive detector; as an organism that is seeking or extracting information from the display that is presented to him; and perception as an instrumental act. Our concern here is to sketch out the nature of the black box that we use to represent the observer.

The current way of representing the operations in the black box is in terms of flow charts, which are a handy way of expressing processes or operations. As with any form of representation, however, they can be misleading. We have no clear-cut ways to begin that guarantee success. The only thing available to us now is a kind of phenomenology of process that Professor MacKay, for example, illustrates brilliantly, and which some of our colleagues in linguistics also act out. Here, one sits back and does a kind of Gedanken experiment saying, well, what must be the case, what sorts of operations must be going on, given this input to arrive at that output? But phenomenologies are terribly slippery and we want to formulate somewhat more explicitly than by mere descriptive adjectives what we hope to put into these little squares and triangles that we use in our flow charts. Sometimes there is a rigidity to flow charts that tends to obscure the fact that processes going on in an early stage in behavior (early in the subject's acquisition of skill) are not necessarily the same as those occurring later on. An example of this occurs in the study of reading as a perceptual skill, where we find that the processes the reader goes through change drastically as he moves from letter identification to the identification of words to the point where he can read text at rates perhaps of 600-1,000 words per minute. Clearly the kinds of operations that someone goes through reading at the rate of 1,000 words per minute are not the same as those he goes through when he is first learning to read. Flow chart models tend to be indifferent to the changes in a behavioral sequence that occur during its development, which I regard as a serious weakness in them, although the way they emphasize the active encoding processes that the observer goes through and illuminate the hierarchical structure of perceptual organization are their strong features.

In the series today we began at the level of primitive operation. Dr. Kahneman has described his experiments on brightness and contour; Dr. Massa then talked about the half-life of brief visual presentations; Sternberg has concerned himself with the attributes of the stimulus that the observer extracts in even a simple reaction-time experiment; Kaufman has worried about the co-ordination of partially conflicting information; Dr. Ettlinger has shown us that even simple textual material, numbers on the one hand and words on the other, may be encoded by different neurophysiological "routines"; and Dr. Haber has now described some autogenous processes that the observer goes through to clarify or make more perceptible to himself what it was that he was presented with. So much to begin. I would like to make some specific points about the papers seriatim and then Dr. Sutherland will do something of the same sort of thing.

Kahneman has shown us that even the primitive operations of brightness and contour detection have different rates of formation. Interesting in its own right, I think this has some bearing on the thorny question of the temporal quantum, the temporal unit of perception, and on the whole notion of the "unit" of perception itself. One wonders whether it is meaningful to talk about a temporal quantum and whether, assuming that we do believe that perception is chopped in some way over time, whether we should not better talk about temporal quanta, in the plural, assuming that different operations the perceiver performs occur at different rates. Some rates have been identified. Rates in the region of 30 cps, for example, have been identified for a detection of order, for the ability to tell which of two similar kinds of things came first. We are stuck perenially with the number 10 cps. Brightness enhancement — the Bartley-Brücke effect — occurs in the region of 6 to 8 cps. A large number of experiments have shown that 3 cps or something of the order of 300 msec is the formation time for a simple visual figure that the subject knows he has to detect. It is hard to believe, therefore, that the visual system is dominated by a single period. Different events that may be going on simultaneously occur at different rates.

There is an old search concerned with the identification of perceptual units, and many people have performed many kinds of factor
analyses trying to identify what in the stimulus is the unit of perception. One assumes they are seeking to invent a table of the perceptual
elements whose combinings, as in Mendeleev's table of the chemical
elements, describes a percept made up from so many thises and thats.
I would like to turn it around and say that perhaps this is a fruitless
search. Perhaps there is no unit in the stimulus, but that the unit is
an operation or encoding routine. The kinds of encoding routines that
the subject goes through may have their optimal rates quite independent
of what the stimulus is. What the subject sees then is not constructed
from the units of the stimulus, as a wall is made from bricks; rather,
what the subject sees represents the results of encoding routines or
cognitive operations that work on whatever materials are available.
To pursue the metaphor, the unit would be in the machine that makes
the walls more than in the materials it uses for the construction. We
are then obliged to account for the reasonably good fidelity of the
visual system in reporting the objects of the environment. Many
people who think about this very soon recognize the epistemological
problem that in some way the observer is required to identify what
he is looking at before he begins to process it, for often in fact one
does not know what he is seeing until he knows what he is looking at.
There is some kind of early recognition process that occurs, for we
are bombarded with information and select only parts of it to attend to.
How we select what it is we will see is at the heart of the problem of
recognition.

Dr. Massa has taken a point of view which emphasizes the kinds of
operations that occur in visual short-term memory. I am inclined
to think that it is not quite so simple as he may feel. There are at
least three points of view associated with what goes on in this kind of
short-term memory. One can talk about erasure, as the Bell Telephone people do; one can talk about an impairment in figure formation
as some other people do; or one can talk about an interference with
the extraction of the distinctive features of the stimulus. These are
all concerned with the fact that some visual target presented some
time after an earlier one is able to interfere with the perception of
the earlier one. What is in contention is what the nature of this
interference is. Does the interference occur because the subsequent
stimulus interferes with a naming function at some center to which the

fully processed earlier stimulus has been delivered, thereby erasing
its purely visual representation from consciousness? One might so
characterize the erasure notion. Another notion would say that it
takes the perceptual system a certain amount of time to form a percept; the second stimulus coming along within this critical time of the
first interferes with its formation, so that a fully processed version of
the first stimulus never even reaches the stage of reportability. Third,
there is some interference by the second stimulus with the subject's
operation, not on figure formation, but on feature extraction. We should
not assume that we have the answer yet.

I want to make a couple of small points about Dr. Sternberg's paper.
One is his identifying of this scanning rate as occurring at 30 cps.
This number has come up two or three times now in the past couple of
days. Professor Schouten the other day told us that the curious, sudden
appearance of a stable form occurred when he rotated his discs in the
region of 30 cps, Hirsch and Sherrick a couple of years ago reported
that the perception of the order of two similar stimuli has a lower
threshold in the region of 30 cps. And now Professor Sternberg tells
us about an interior scanning rate, a memory scan, in the region of 30
cps. Merely because of the similarity of the number I am led to ask
what the nature of the representation is that is being processed in
memory. If one has to extract some features from the stimulus array
in order to make a discrimination of order, this is already evidence
for one abstracting function. Is the sequential scan that Dr. Sternberg
believes occurs based on the same information as that used in the
detection of order, or does it involve still another kind of extraction?
Only in the former case could one talk meaningfully about exhaustive
serial search, while, given the complexity of the processing that occurs,
it is hard to believe in the likelihood of so simple a method. More
than one property of the array would have to be processed at a time
to meet the temporal processing rates Sternberg describes.

A second point that I would like to make is that in all of his data,
performance is better in Session 2 than it is in Session 1. Merely to
say that this is perceptual learning really does not do anything. Learning of what? Is it a learning in the sense of optimizing the motor
reaction time, or is it a learning of the categories of discrimination,
of what it is that one has to extract from the stimulus array? One
might say, for example, that what occurs during the learning is a
sharpening up of the categorial attributes of the stimulus. The initial

encoding of the stimulus involves, one might assume, a large amount of irrelevant or redundant information; with practice the subject learns how to identify certain features of the stimulus and is able to improve his performance because he can do a better job of saying yes or no on less information than he required earlier on. Is this compatible with simple serial search? I do not think so.

The principal point in contention, as I understand it, between what Sternberg gets in his reaction-time experiments and what Neisser gets in his scanning experiments is whether one has to go through an exhaustive serial search in order to make this kind of identification, which is what Sternberg asserts, or whether the perceiver can simultaneously process in terms of a large number of distinctive features of the stimulus.

Kaufman has done the extraordinary job of summarizing what comes out to be a theory of binocular perception in about 15 min and a tingle. His assertion is that stereopsis, that is, the depth perception that comes from noncongruent information presented to the two eyes simultaneously, that stereopsis depends on the detection of a difference in the phases of correlated patterns. The question is, what is a pattern? If one is willing to take the classical view and say that one gets stereopsis on the basis of disparity of brightness or disparity of form, one can assume that there are certain primitive detectors in the system that are tuned for brightness or that are tuned for "form," and so on. But it strains the imagination after a while to believe that there are also detectors in the system that are going to be sensitive to triadic patterns of the kind that he finds give one depth. And I am sure that with his ingenuity he can invent many other kinds of displays that will also give depth, and in each case one would be obliged to say that there is a detector for this disparity, until finally we would have as many detectors as William James has instincts, and without really solving the problem of depth. Now there is an implication to this kind of view which is that for such disparities to be detected a certain amount of processing has to occur in each of the two eyes separately, a certain amount of monoptic processing and recognizing of features whose existence is then signaled to some higher centers.

There is an alternative point of view, however, which would take the position that depth itself is a cognitive event, not a simple physiologically determined event of the same order as brightness, acuities, and so on. To this point of view one brings the following evidence, namely,

that the first time you look at the kinds of patterns that Julesz first
described or that Kaufman has described, it takes a surprisingly long
time to get a depth experience, 4 min or 5 min or so. After looking
at a number of different kinds of patterns for some protracted period
of time, the amount of time it takes to get a depth experience drops
dramatically. I understand that Dr. Julesz is able to get depth even
from flashes just a few microseconds long of moderate brightness.
Now, why should this be the case? How can one go about acquiring
skill in seeing depth, if seeing depth is primarily a matter of correlating the phases of patterns?

Finally, also in this line, this notion of detectors of various kinds
seems to have been emphasized in large part because of the brilliant
work of Lettvin, Maturana, McCulloch, and Pitts, on the one hand, and
Hubel and Wiesel, on the other, who have identified what they consider
to be various kinds of detectors for various kinds of orientations. I
would like to make a very simple observation — that a cat is not a man
and that, you know, people are not cats. Nobody has ever demonstrated,
for example, that the kind of depth human beings characteristically
report in a rotating Archimedes spiral can be obtained from a cat. I do
not know that anybody has shown that it cannot be, but nobody has ever
shown that it can be; and given Lashley's evidence about the effects of
proximity of contours in lower animals and the inability of cats to
discriminate anything but the simplest kinds of figure-ground
phenomena, one would doubt that this depth effect is possible with them.
There are not only differences in structure between the cat's eye and
the man's eye, there are differences in intelligence between cats and
men, and one would assume that part of the difference in intelligence
represents a difference in the ability to learn to code the environment
in new and different ways.

Dr. Ettlinger has told us that what one might think were similar kinds
of textual material, namely numbers on the one hand, words on the
other hand, probably involve different encoding routines, so that a
given damage to the brain leaves one differentially handicapped to deal
with these two sorts of things; furthermore that some visual functions
are retained, in the sense that the subject can continue to sort letters,
and yet not be able to identify them by name or operate on them to
command when their names are involved.

And, finally, Dr. Haber's paper talks to the interesting phenomena
that occur under periodic reinspection of a given stimulus. I know I

do, and I am sure you all do too, look at some data curve we have many times before being able to interpret it satisfactorily. This kind of phenomenon is characteristic of much creative perceiving. Picasso, for example, will leave an unfinished work in some prominent corner of his studio and walk by it for months at a time until he is seized by inspiration — that is "sees" what he wants — and paints the picture. That is all I want to say. Dr. Sutherland will make some comments.

COMMENTS ON THE SESSION

N. S. Sutherland
Laboratory of Experimental Psychology
The University of Sussex
Falmer Brighton
Sussex, England, and
Research Laboratory of Electronics
Massachusetts Institute of Technology
Cambridge, Massachusetts

I do not want to take up too much time, so I will concentrate on just three of the papers we have heard. These are the three that are closest to my own general area of interest. I shall finish by making one brief, general comment about the papers as a whole.

First of all, Sternberg's extremely elegant work on the recognition process. He investigated what happens when a subject has to identify test digits as either belonging or not belonging to a set of target digits. Sternberg refers to test digits which belong to the set of target digits as "positive"; those which do not belong he calls "negative." He comes to three main conclusions.

First, he thinks that the test digit is compared serially with the target digits. The comparison process does not take place in parallel. The evidence for this is that when he increases the size of the target set, the slope of reaction time against the number in the target set is linear.

Second, he finds that the search process is exhaustive. That is, when a subject gets a match between the test digit and a target digit he does not stop and give the response. All target digits are searched. Sternberg comes to this conclusion because the slope of reaction time against number of target digits is roughly the same whether the test digit is a positive instance or a negative instance.

Third, and this is what Sternberg is mainly concerned with in the experiment he reported today, he concludes that the processing of the test digit is largely completed before the comparison process starts. His evidence is that if you add noise to the test digit, the main effect is to shift the whole reaction-time function upwards, not to change the slope. Sternberg's model and his experiments are extremely elegant and neat. I would like to pose one or two questions which may complicate the picture a bit.

The first thing that I wondered about is just how specific these results are to Sternberg's situation. I find it very hard to believe, for example, that if he allowed subjects a lot of practice with the same target set, we would still get this linear slope of reaction time against the number of digits in the target set. In the extreme case if you think how long it takes to identify words as French or English, the reaction time for this is certainly not determined by processing individual words at the rate of 30 a second serially. So, this is the first thing, just what would happen if you allowed subjects very much more practice with a given target set instead of changing it all the time?

Second, Sternberg concludes that the search process is exhaustive and this is extremely puzzling. On the face of it, it seems a crazy system; having found a match, why does the subject not stop his search and give the positive response? I have tried to think of some way around this and there is one possibility which Sternberg may be able to rule out from other evidence, but perhaps it is worth mentioning. Consider a set of target digits 1, 4, 7, and 9. Now supposing the subject orders the digits, say simply in order of magnitude. If he has a test digit 3 which is a negative digit and he always goes through the target digits in order of magnitude, he could cut off the search for the negative one as soon as he reaches the number "4" in the target set. In general, when the test digit is negative he can cease his search as soon as he reaches a target digit bigger than the negative test digit. And this would mean that he would not have to process all digits when the test digit was negative. In the example I have given with a test digit of 3, he would know it was negative after he had processed two target digits. If the test digit were 4, he must again only process two target digits but now the test digit is positive. It seems to me a system of this sort would also result in getting about the same slopes

for negative and positive test digits. But now the process is not
exhaustive; the subject cuts off his search when he is satisfied that he
has matched a positive digit or when he is satisfied that he has gone
above the value of the negative digit.

Third, just a word about the main experiment Sternberg presented.
He comes to the conclusion that most of the processing of the test
digit is done before the comparison with the target digit takes place.
But there is a slight difference in slope when he adds noise, so he
thinks that possibly the processing in some way is not complete. It
may be worth considering the following possibility: the processing
may be complete before the comparison is made but in some cases
when noise is added the subject may be unable to make up his mind so
that he might be doubtful, say, whether the test digit was a 3 or an 8.
In a case like that, he might be tempted to look for both, and this in
itself would cause the slight difference in slope. In other words, I do
not think we can infer unequivocally that there is some processing
still left to do before the comparison process starts.

Next, I would like to say a word or two about Haber's paper. He
showed that if a word is presented for a very brief period, a period
shorter than the threshold of seeing, the probability of seeing the
word increases with the number of repetitions of the word, where the
repetitions are separated by an 8-sec gap. Now is seems to me that
there are rather a lot of different mechanisms that might be at work
here and I would like to see some of these discussed and perhaps
spelled out. One possibility, is that at each flash subjects can concentrate only on some part of the word and the more they concentrate
on one part, the less they concentrate on another. This would lead to
subjects building up the word by picking up a letter here on one
presentation, and a letter there on another. That is rather a dull
possibility, and perhaps it can be ruled out. A second possibility, perhaps a more interesting one, is that what is happening is that fragments
of each letter are being stored on each trial without any processing.
I do not know how you would get at that, but this would mean that the
subject could store unprocessed information for a time of at least 8
sec, which would be an interesting result. A third possibility is that
each flash enables the observer to rule out some hypothesis about what
the word or the letters could be. That is, while he may not see individual letters or the whole word on a given flash, he may be able to
delete a number of possible alternatives. Thus, his probability of

getting onto the right alternative would increase over flashes. Well, these are three possible things that may be going on, and perhaps they are all going on. I do not know what sort of evidence one could get to find out which one of these is actually taking place. There may be other possibilities as well.

Finally, Kaufman has presented some extremely beautiful demonstrations showing that stereoscopic depth perception may depend on correlating information from the two eyes in very much more complicated ways than anybody has hitherto suggested. He has shown two main things. First, stereoscopic depth perception does not depend on subjective fusion, it occurs in conditions where there is extreme rivalry between the two eyes, and second, although seeing depth does depend upon some sort of phase shift between parts of the pattern on the two eyes, the actual thing which has shifted may be extremely abstract. The clearest case of something very abstract is Kaufman's triads of letters; where "wad" occurs on one eye and "psn" on the other shifted with respect to surrounding letters that are common to both eyes, you get a depth effect. Now, as far as one can see, there is no form similarity between these two triads. What we have got is a sort of beat in each case and it is simply the position of the beat which is shifted, and this is enough to give a depth effect. This is in a way rather terrifying since it implies a very complicated mechanism. What I would like to see is some demonstrations of what sorts of shifts do not give a depth effect. I do not know whether Kaufman would expect a depth effect if instead of repeating three letters using different triads on the two eyes, he repeated say three letters on one eye and had a recurrence of a triad of three colors on the other eye carried always by the same letter again with a shift in phase between the two triads. We may ask two questions. First, is any shift that can be detected by successive monocular inspections enough to give a depth effect? Second, if the beats are produced by two completely different mechanisms such as size and color, can they still be put together on the two eyes to give a depth effect?

Finally, just one general point to which I do not attach too much weight. Dr. Kolers has already pointed out that the papers have one thing in common, and that is, that they all involve a search for models in a rather sophisticated way. All the speakers see perception as an active process and are looking for an active model of the recognition process. Now it seems to me they also have one negative feature in common. I am not using "negative" in a pejorative sense. Although all this work is about recognition, the speakers all take the actual process by which patterns are classified for granted. None of the models attempts to answer what I regard as the 64-dollar question; namely, how it is that a given pattern is classified under the class of patterns with which it is, in fact, classified. This process is completely taken for granted. Now, that is not intended as a criticism because I have investigated this question, which I conceive as the central question of pattern perception, in animals and other people have investigated the same problem in man. I have tried to answer directly the question of which features of patterns are used in classification and how the actual processing takes place to get to the stage when we get a common output for patterns of a given class. Direct work on this problem has not really met with very sensational success. It is rather interesting that this question can be bypassed. We have heard today of some very elegant and interesting work on other aspects of the recognition process such as the time constants of the process or the way in which labels are attached to stimuli after classification. It may be that we shall only be able to get back to the central question of just how patterned stimuli are classified, when some of these other issues have been resolved.

CONTRIBUTED PAPERS II

Experiments on Speech Perception

Chairman: James L. Flanagan
Speech and Auditory Research Department
Bell Telephone Laboratories, Incorporated
Murray Hill, New Jersey

VOICE AND HEARING IN THE BULLFROG[1]

Robert Capranica [2]
Research Laboratory of Electronics
Massachusetts Institute of Technology
Cambridge, Massachusetts

Lawrence Frishkopf
Bell Telephone Laboratories, Incorporated
Murray Hill, New Jersey

Moise H. Goldstein, Jr.
Department of Biomedical Engineering
The Johns Hopkins University
Baltimore, Maryland

The bullfrog's uses of vocalization as a means of communication are quite in keeping with his generally limited patterns of behavior. His repertoire of calls is small, probably including a "territorial growl," a release call (used by a male or infertile female to discourage a clasping male), and a distress cry. His best known call, however, from which his common name derives, is related to mating. It consists of a sequence of several croaks, each having an almost periodic wave form (repetition rate about 100/sec) and lasting somewhat less than 1 sec. This vocalization is produced only by the males, and appears to give females a means of locating males. Capranica (1965) has demonstrated that the males of a colony of bullfrogs in his laboratory

---

[1] A more thorough discussion of the substance of this paper may be found in Capranica (1965).

[2] Now with the Bell Telephone Laboratories, Murray Hill, New Jersey.

terrarium will produce the mating call in response to a restricted class of sounds. For example, the mating calls of 34 anuran species were presented to these frogs and they responded only to bullfrog calls. Capranica has also been able to evoke calling from these frogs by using synthesized croaks, allowing evaluation of those features of an acoustic stimulus necessary to evoke this highly selective response. The results are best summarized in terms of three spectral regions: A low region (L) centered at about 200 cps, a mid-region (M) centered at about 500 cps, and a high region (H) centered at about 1,400 cps. To evoke the mating call, it is necessary that the following stimulus conditions apply:

1. Energies in L and H must both be above minimum values.
2. The ratio of energy in region M to energy in region L must be sufficiently small. If, to a signal that evokes calling, a component of sufficient energy is added in region M, calling is suppressed. This suppression does not depend on the ratio of energies in M and H.

The stimuli were generated by exciting filters in the L and H regions with periodic pulses (rate usually 100/sec) or noise. Although both could evoke calling, the pulsatile stimuli were more effective. Suppression was obtained by adding a 500-cps sinusoid. The sounds were gated by an electronic switch to achieve a gross temporal pattern similar to the natural mating call.

These behavioral results are closely related to the electrophysiological findings of Frishkopf and Goldstein (1965) who recorded single-unit activity from the eighth nerve of bullfrogs. They identified two kinds of units. Both types exhibited sharply frequency-dependent sensitivity (tuning curves). "Simple" units were maximally sensitive to tone bursts of frequency between 1,000 cps and 1,500 cps, and could not be inhibited by acoustic stimuli. All "complex" units could be inhibited by acoustic signals, and although these units exhibited maximal sensitivities (for excitation) over a considerable frequency range (the majority being most sensitive to frequencies below 500 cps), a frequency of approximately 500 cps most effectively inhibited all of them.

This work indicates a close relation between coding in the afferent auditory pathway and the conditions that are necessary for producing a highly selective behavioral response to a vocal signal.

Acknowledgment

This work was supported in part by the United States Army, and Air Force under Contract DA 36-039-AMC-03200(E); in part by the National Science Foundation (Grant GP-2495), the National Institutes of Health (Grant MH-04737-04), and the National Aeronautics and Space Administration (Grant NsG-496).

References

Capranica, R. R. The evoked vocal response of the bullfrog: A study of communication by sound. Research Monogr. No. 33. Cambridge: M.I.T. Press, 1965.

Frishkopf, L., and Goldstein, M. Responses to acoustic stimuli from single units in the eighth nerve of the bullfrog. J. acoust. Soc. Amer., 1963, 35, 1219-1228.

INFORMATION AND COMPLEX SIGNAL PERCEPTION

J. C. Webster and R. B. Chaney, Jr.
United States Navy Electronics Laboratory
San Diego, California

The perception of speech has been explained in terms of physical correlates of the acoustic signal, and physiological correlates of the speech-producing mechanism. Psychologists have studied speech perception in terms of information theory, verbal learning, factor analysis, and selective attention. The broader field of perceiving complex auditory signals has likewise been studied by psychologists using concepts of information theory, selective attention, and short-term memory.

The tack to be taken in this paper is that psychological variables (meaningfulness, short-term memory, response complexity, past experience, and information content) are at least as important as physical aspects in determining the speed and accuracy of response in the perception of complex auditory signals.

Bartlett (1932) has demonstrated the effects of an individual's prior experience on perceiving and remembering, and Underwood (1961) has stated that "...the two most potent variables influencing verbal learning ... are ... meaningfulness and similarity...."

In the field of selective attention as exemplified by competing aural messages, it has been found by many investigators that one message could be more easily selected from another if the messages differed in level (Egan, Carterette, and Thwing, 1954), frequency bandwidth (Egan et al., 1954; Spieth and Webster, 1955), or location of sound source real (Spieth, Curtis, and Webster, 1954; Broadbent, 1954), or apparent (Broadbent, 1954; Treisman, 1961).

Webster (1961) carried out an experiment to find what dimensions in short, one-syllable speech sounds are used to select one of two competing messages from the other. It was found that sound source (message in left versus right ear), origination or basic frequency (woman's versus man's voice) identification (ah versus $\overline{ee}$), and inflection (up as a question versus down as a statement) in that order were easiest to use as orienting dimensions on which to select one message from a second competing message. Six binary choices were correctly made in one second on this type of material. The unanswered question was whether this order of "where," "who," "what," and "how" was more closely related to the physical characteristics of the speech signal or to the relative meaningfulness of the signal. Or, restated: Was the "who" dimension relatively easy because the basic voice frequencies were roughly an octave apart or because one sounded like a "man," the other, "a woman"?

The role of past experience and/or meaningfulness of the sounds could be evaluated if sounds similar in physical (acoustical) composition but completely different in meaning could be tested together. To this end a series of experiments was planned using speech sounds, music, laboratory sounds, and sonar sounds.

The plan can best be explained in terms of speech versus music. In speech the difference in formant structure differentiates the vowels, say, "ah," from "$\overline{ee}$." In music, differences in formant structure differentiate, say, a clarinet from an oboe. A difference in fundamental frequency of about one octave for speech (nonsinging) usually spells the judged difference between a male and female voice. A similar difference in music would separate an oboe from an English horn or a soprano clarinet from an alto or bass clarinet.

The assumption is that although trained musicians might separate bass and soprano (oboes or clarinets) as easily as they do male and female voices, the general nonmusical listener would not. In general terms, the experience of the listener and/or the meaningfulness of the sounds have as much to do with their perception as the physical differences in their wave form.

The first of the planned series of experiments using sounds whose physical dimensions are roughly equivalent but whose perceptual correlates are unequivalent deals with speech versus sonar sounds. The aim was to see if meaningfulness in terms of a subject's experience can be related reliably to the perception of different complex signals.

Two types of signals, speech and sonar, were selected which were similar in their physical dimensions, but which differed considerably in the kind and amount of experience the observers have had in hearing them. These particular sounds were chosen since it is fairly easy to select observers with similar experience in listening to speech (at least at the gross level required here) and for whom their experience with sonar was likely to be pretty much an all-or-nothing proposition. Table 1 shows the experimental dimensions. In the speech category, a sound was either (ah) or (ēē) spoken with an inflection appropriate for either a question or a statement and spoken either by a male or female voice. It was heard in either the right or left ear, and was either short or long in duration.

Table 1. Information Identification - Multidimensional Signals

Dimension	Stimulus	
	Speech	Sonar
A. Content	/a/ or /i/	Reverb. or whale
B. Inflection	Rising-falling	Rising-falling
C. Duration	0.5 Sec - 1.0 Sec	0.5 Sec - 1.0 Sec
D. Frequency	Male-female	1 Octave separation
E. Source	Right-left ear	Right-left ear

From a sonar repertory, typical signals were selected which corresponded physically to the speech signals. The critical thing about each of the binary distinctions listed in Table 1 is that each is 100% discriminable when heard in isolation. It is only when they are compounded into a single signal for identification in the face of a competing signal that they become difficult to identify.

Two groups of 12 observers were used, one experienced in listening to sonar signals, and the other naïve in this respect. Both groups, however, had similar backgrounds in speech and language. Each observer heard pairs of tape-recorded signals, one member of the pair in each ear. During each sequence (consisting of 24 pairs) he was

instructed to attend to one particular aspect of one dimension (the short
signals, or those in the right ear, for example) and record as many of
the remaining dimensions as he was able by throwing each of four
switches to one of two positions. This process was repeated until each
aspect of each dimension had served as the orienting dimension about
which the other decisions had been made.

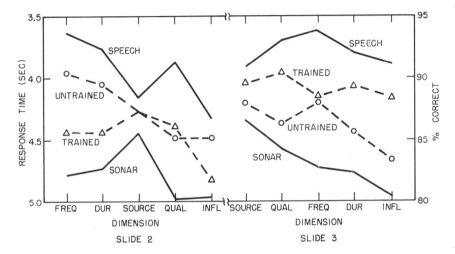

Fig. 1. Response times and accuracies for trained and untrained subjects listening to competing pairs of speech and
sonar signals in relation to the dimensions of the signals.

Figure 1 shows a summary of the results in terms of response
time and accuracy. Speech signals, for both trained and untrained
listeners combined, require the least time for greater accuracies
than sonar signals. Trained listeners, averaged over both speech and
sonar signals, are more accurate but take longer to respond. When
the scores on the five dimensions are rank-ordered from least to most
response time, the order is frequency, duration, source, quality, and
inflection (left side). When ranked on accuracy, the order is source,
quality, frequency, duration, and inflection.

However, the noteworthy point is that the rank-ordering changes with
signal, speech versus sonar; and with past experience, trained (in
sonar) versus untrained. And this is what was expected, namely, that
it is not the physical variables per se that determine the speed and/or
accuracy of perception, but factors relating to the meaningfulness of
the dimensions to the subjects. The meaningfulness varies with type
of signal and experience with it.

Two points of interest show up when details (not shown in the figure) are considered. It was found that for speech signals less time and greater accuracy accrued when listening to signals in the right ear than when listening to signals in the left ear. For sonar signals the exact opposite was true. This verifies a contention of Kimura (1961) that verbal material should be better identified on the right, and nonverbal materials on the left.

The second point of interest has to do with the response time (and accuracy) when the short-duration signal was the pertinent one versus when the long signal was pertinent. The short signals took a significantly longer time for response than the long ones, and more errors were made. This would tend to support the interference with the trace theory of short-term memory (or forgetting); that is, no decisions could be made on the short- or the long-duration signals until the short one was finished. If the long one was pertinent, there it was for a half-second in the clear to be voted on. If the short one was pertinent, it had to be recalled from memory in the presence of the now irrelevant long signal. And as stated, better scores in less time accrued to the longer signal.

If the information transmission rate is calculated for each dimension for both signals, it turns out that for the speech signal the rate is highest when frequency is the orienting dimension (about 4.5 bits per second) followed by duration, quality, source, and inflection (about 2 bits per second). For sonar the order is source (about 2.2 bits per second) and quality followed by duration, frequency, and inflection (the last three being essentially equal at about 1.3 bits per second). Since the ordering of dimensions within the different kinds of signals is not the same, the physical properties of the signals are not the only determiners of information transmission rate.

References

Bartlett, F. C. Remembering: A study in experimental and social psychology. Cambridge, Eng.: Univer. Press, 1932.

Broadbent, D. E. The role of auditory localization in attention and memory span. J. exp. Psychol., 1954, 47, 191-196.

Egan, J. P., Carterette, E. C., and Thwing, E. J. Some factors in multi-channel listening. J. acoust. Soc. Amer., 1954, 26, 774-782.

Kimura, D. Cerebral dominance and the perception of verbal stimuli. Canad. J. Psychol., 1961, 15, 166-171.

Spieth, W., Curtis, J. F., and Webster, J. C. Responding to one of two simultaneous messages. J. acoust. Soc. Amer., 1954, 26, 391-396.

Spieth, W., and Webster, J. C. Listening to differentially filtered competing voice messages. J. acoust. Soc. Amer., 1955, 27, 866-871.

Treisman, A. M. Attention and speech. Unpublished doctoral thesis, University of Oxford, 1961.

Webster, J. C. Information in simple multidimensional speech messages. J. acoust. Soc. Amer., 1961, 33, 940-944.

Underwood, B. J. An evaluation of the Gibson theory of verbal learning. In C. N. Cofer, (Ed.), Verbal learning and verbal behavior. New York: McGraw Hill, 1961.

THE SPECTRAL SHAPE IN THE F2-F3 REGION

Osamu Fujimura
Speech Transmission Laboratory
Royal Institute of Technology (KTH)
Stockholm, Sweden, and
University of Electro-Communications
Chofu, Japan

For a long time many speech workers have felt that vowels are characterized by two spectral peaks. Some synthesis experiments seem to support this hypothesis, but it appears that these two peaks do not exactly correspond to the first and second formants. In close front vowels, in particular, listeners usually prefer a sound with a second peak that is located at a higher frequency than the second formant observed in natural utterances.

A question is raised: Can there be in the higher frequency range an effective single peak that (together with the lower peak) determines the vowel quality? Before answering this question, one should ask: What is meant by a peak? The definition must be made clear. There can be various spectral shapes even within a category of a single peak. Particularly, it has to be realized that a shift of a formant in frequency, in the case of real vowel sounds, is necessarily accompanied by readjustments of the spectral levels not only of the peak itself, but also in all other, especially higher, frequency regions. Thus it is not meaningful to discuss the effect of the frequency of the peak, unless we specify how the peak is made and how the levels in other frequency ranges are determined.

One way of clarifying what we are doing is to limit the sounds to be tested into the frame of naturally producible vowel sounds, or to make it a little broader and more practical, sounds produced by a series-type terminal analog (POVO). By doing so, we can define the frequency of a peak as that of a formant, or of a cluster of formants in a certain way. A high naturalness of the synthesized sounds can be expected, if we select the range of formant locations and the bandwidths carefully.

Speakers of Swedish have an advantage as subjects for this kind of testing. This language has three close front vowels, and these have very similar frequencies for the first formant. The fourth formant is also comparatively fixed. Typical frequencies for the lowest four formants, according to Fant's measurements of sustained articulations (by male speakers) are (in cps):

Table 1. Typical Formant Frequencies

	F_1	F_2	F_3	F_4
/i/	256	2,066	2,960	3,400
/y/	257	1,928	2,421	3,300
/ʉ/	283	1,633	2,140	3,314

Experimental Procedure

In Figure 1, a block diagram is given for our synthesis procedure. As an average for the three vowels, a fixed F_1 was located at 270 cps (bandwidth 60 cps). Similarly F_4 was set at 3,300 cps (bandwidth 145 cps). We used a fixed effective F_5 and a higher pole correction circuit designed for 4,000 cps. The frequencies and bandwidths of the second and third formants were varied in a systematic way. In view of the behavior of human perception in the frequency range of interest, stimuli were prepared in such a way that the formant frequencies varied evenly in the logarithmic scale.

A series of listening tests has been designed. In a vowel identification test, which shall be discussed here in some detail, two independent variables determined F_2 and F_3. One was the (geometrical) mean of the two formant frequencies, and this had eight (logarithmically) equally spaced values ranging from 1,600 to 3,000 cps. This set of conditions

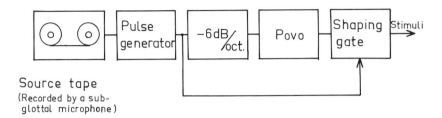

Source tape
(Recorded by a sub-
glottal microphone)

Fig. 1. Block diagram of the experimental scheme for generating
the vowel stimuli.

was labeled 1 (the highest) to 8 (the lowest). The second variable was
the separation between the two formants. In terms of a quarter tone
unit, this was selected at one of four values 3, 5, 7, and 9, labeled
here I, II, III, and IV, respectively. The bandwidths for the two
formants were set always at the quarter tone interval of the formant
frequency, ranging from 45 to 90 cps depending on the formant location.

A listening tape contained, in a random order, all combinations of
these two variables, except III-1, IV-1, III-8, and IV-8, which had
extreme values of either F_2 or F_3. In addition to these stimuli, the
tape contained similarly synthesized samples for which F_1, F_2, F_3,
and F_4 were set at values copied from measured data (cf. Table 1).
These will be labeled $\boxed{i}$, $\boxed{y}$, and $\boxed{u}$. Three different source
signals were used to trigger the pulse generator, for each of the
formant conditions, and each formant condition appeared in six test
items. The subjects were asked to identify each item as one of the
three vowels.

In consideration of dialectical or personal differences in the
criteria, a short similar test was run immediately preceding the main
test. This preliminary test contained only three formant conditions,
viz., $\boxed{i}$, $\boxed{y}$, and $\boxed{u}$. The result of the preliminary test showed
that the synthesized sounds were mostly identified as the intended
vowel by our subjects. About one half of the subjects, in particular,
gave all "correct" answers. There was a tendency, however, that the
sounds intended as /y/ were sometimes perceived as /u/. This
tendency depended heavily on particular subjects, and those who gave
"correct" answers for less than two thirds of these stimuli were
excluded in counting the data reported here. There were 2 out of 11
such subjects. Subjects with some experience in speech research did

not show this tendency within this short test, even though they did show it in the following main test, where the samples were mixed with other more extreme sounds.

Results

The result of the main identification test is shown in Figure 2. The boxes along a row had the same mean frequency. Those along a column had the same value of separation.

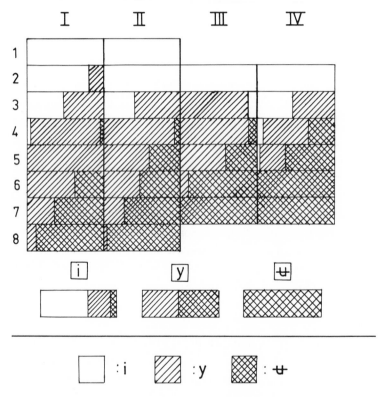

Fig. 2. Distribution of the response as a function of mean frequency (ordinate) and separation (abscissa).

It is seen that for each of the vowels, there is at least one condition of formants which gave rise to a unanimous judgment. The conditions are IV-2 (F_2 = 2,400 cps, F_3 = 3,108 cps) and others for /i/, I-5 (F_2 = 2,019 cps, F_3 = 2,201 cps) for /y/, and IV-6 (F_2 = 1,699 cps, F_3 = 2,201 cps) and others for /ʉ/. The conditions [i] and [y] seem to have failed to convince the subjects. This point will be discussed later.

It can be seen that the <u>mean</u> does not constitute by itself a consistent criterion for the vowel identification. Along the row 5 for example, the judgment varied from a unanimous /y/ to a majority /ʉ/ as the separation increased. The same type of change is seen in the next lower row. Some other simple criteria may be tested: if we take F_2 alone as the criterion, we have a counterproof: for the same F_2 (2,078 cps), the condition [i] gives a majority /i/ whereas III-4 a predominant /y/. Similarly, the third formant as the criterion is refuted by some comparisons: for the same F_3 (2,852 cps), I-2 gives a predominant /i/ but IV-3 gives a majority /y/; also for another fixed value of F_3 (2,201 cps), I-5 gives a unanimous /y/, whereas IV-6 gives a unanimous /ʉ/.

As a matter of fact, any linear combination of F_2 and F_3 with positive fixed coefficients would be refuted by a comparison of I-6 with IV-5, because both have the same F_2 (1,852 cps), and I-6 which gives a majority /y/ judgment has a lower F_3 (2,019 cps) than IV-5 (F_3 = 2,400 cps) which gives a majority /ʉ/.

Discussion

It seems in Figure 2 that the supposedly representative values of the <u>mean</u> for /i/ and /y/, namely the <u>means</u> of the conditions [i] and [y] , are slightly too low compared to the optimum locations in the present test situation. (As for the values of F_2 and F_3, [i] should be located to the right of IV-3 in Figure 2, [y] should be at a point between the columns III and IV and slightly above the row 5.) One possible explanation is that there is a contrast effect. Particularly for the /i/ judgments, there are some extreme conditions which can not be effected by the usual speech organs of average male speakers, but may be taken as an extrapolation of the /i/ characteristics. Some of the stimuli are probably within the actualizable range, though shifted from the quoted data. In the presence of these stimuli, the frame of judgments of our subjects may have been somewhat shifted. This interpretation conforms with our finding that the same stimuli in our short preliminary test acquired all correct judgments from many of the same subjects. This effect may have been enhanced by the comparatively high fundamental frequency which happened to be used in this experiment. If we had quoted slightly higher formant frequencies that would be valid for somewhat shorter vocal tracts and that would suit the fundamental, this disagreement might have been largely corrected.

The distribution in our space of representation of the optimum conditions for the /y/ judgment forms a peculiar narrow strip which shifts slightly upwards toward the right in Figure 2. This shape of the distribution probably can be better explained in terms of the articulatory condition. The vowel in question, a rounded front close vowel, can have a real single peak consisting of F_2 and F_3 in natural utterances. This can be demonstrated by a recording of a continuous frequency response curve of the vocal tract, obtained by use of an external excitation. (A peak of this nature observed by us was located at 1,950 cps.) This F_2-F_3 proximity is probably a uniqueness of the articulation which can only occur within the category of the phoneme/y/ (for Swedish). It would then be quite conceivable that a formant condition like I-5 is unmistakably responded to as a /y/ judgment, even if a more usual condition for the phoneme may exist in a slightly shifted articulatory position. The highly nonlinear relation between the articulatory variables and the formant frequencies in this particular range of articulatory conditions presumably is responsible for an appreciable change in the separation but a rather limited shift in the mean corresponding to a slight shift of the tongue position. The response to conditions with a more usually encountered value of the separation may be affected partly by the existence of a more extreme /y/-like sound. It is probably reasonable to conclude from our data that the degree of separation plays a role in the distinction between /y/ and /ʉ/ in a rather complex way. Results of quality judgment tests with a control of both the separation and the damping of the formants seem to support this point.

Finally, we may point out that even though our synthesized sounds are quite humanlike, they still seem to fail to satisfy Swedish subjects as isolated utterances of the single long-vowel syllables. This is probably due to a diphthongization and a frication which are unmistakably heard towards the end of natural utterances of /ʉ/ and /i/ syllables. Our experiment deals only with the stationary aspect of the vowel quality. Within this aspect, we may conclude in particular that we do need to specify some detail of the "higher peak." It may well be said, however, that even though we can hear slight differences in the spectral envelope as relevant features of phonemic distinctions, and we do hear them in certain environments such as this experiment, still a dynamic mode of speech perception may be something substantially different.

CONTRIBUTED PAPERS III

The Role of Experience in Visual Perception

Chairman: Richard M. Held
Department of Psychology
Massachusetts Institute of Technology
Cambridge, Massachusetts

PREFACE TO THE SESSION [1]

Among the many ways of attempting to gain insight into perceptual processes, the appeal to experience has played a traditional role. At the same time, counterarguments, denying a significant place to experience, have been made with equal vehemence. In the background lurks the question: Do we admit of something called perceptual learning? And, if so, what do we mean by this concept? How is it to be distinguished from the learning of specific responses and, more generally, from changes in the sensory control of overt behavior? Recent years have witnessed a sharpening of these issues and the growth of experimental techniques that promise to yield answers to questions which have produced little more than polemics in the past. The following papers represent a small sample of the types of research going on in this field.

Experience, as a factor in experiments, can be categorized in terms of type and duration. The former may range from carefully structured training to free exposure in natural environments. The latter may, accordingly, vary from short periods of intensive training to substantial fractions of a lifetime. Two of the following papers — those of Whitman and of Henneman and Mathews — deal with the effects of relatively short periods of training on the recall and identification of forms. Whitman questions the alleged alteration of stimulus processing caused by varying degrees of learning and arrives at a negative

---

[1] This preface has been edited from Professor Held's remarks made at the time of the symposium and consequently prior to any revisions by the authors.

conclusion. Henneman and Matthews are concerned with the interaction of stimulus cue and response bias.

The papers of Dodwell and of Held and Hein deal with adaptation to
optical distortions of the visible world. An adaptive process compen-
sates for distortion, to a significant degree, when human subjects are
exposed under natural conditions for periods of time lasting from
minutes to many hours. Dodwell proposes a model of the adaptive
process designed to reestablish that conformal transformation which
correctly relates the retinal image to the visual field. Held and Hein
argue from observations of adaptive change in form perception that
certain aspects of form discrimination are acquired in very young
animals. They propose a distinction between types of form discrimination having different sequences of development in the young animal.

One method of determining the role of experience in development
consists in testing infants shortly after birth. To the extent that
perceptual discrimination can be demonstrated at that time it must
obviously antedate experience. Subsequent effects of experience must
then be interpreted either as altering capacities present in the neonate
or as influencing different processes. To this end, Hershenson, Kessen,
and Munsinger, using highly sophisticated techniques, have examined
the pattern and brightness preferences of newborn infants. Their
results show some indication of considerable individual differences
and preferences. The authors point out the difficult methodological
problems in studies of this type.

Stages of the development of perception in children extend over a
significant fraction of the human life span. Fisher reports two experiments designed to test ideas of Piaget and Revesz. The author
distinguishes textural from spatial cues for identification of shape
in haptic perception. From the results of an experiment, he concludes
that Piaget's report of progression in the child's development from
a topological to a Euclidean system of spatial coordinates is the result
of verbal response bias.

Gregory reports on his attempts to solve the problem of figural
illusions by showing them to be related to mechanisms of size
constancy. It is not yet clear whether these mechanisms depend in
part upon a history of exposure to the environment during the life of
an individual. Finally, Howarth discusses the problem of distinguishing
the effects of training animals to make discriminations from their
actual capacities to discriminate.

Taken together, these papers raise many more questions than they answer. However, they do reflect the increasing sophistication of workers in this field. Neither experience nor endogenous factors are any longer conceived in an all-or-none fashion. The role of response in studies of perception is given considerable attention both on (a) methodological grounds and (b) as a determinant, together with the sensory feedback accompanying movement, of the development of perceptual structures. As a group these papers illustrate some of the diverse difficulties of solving the puzzle of pattern perception. In this respect they resemble most of the contributions to this symposium.

Richard Held

THE DEVELOPMENT OF VISUAL AND TACTILE-KINESTHETIC PERCEPTION

Gerald H. Fisher
Department of Psychology
University of Newcastle upon Tyne
Newcastle upon Tyne, England

An increasingly large number of experimental studies are being conducted in the field of perceptual development. Implied in those due to Piaget and Inhelder (1956) and Révész (1950) are two important suggestions concerned with the nature of developmental features of shape perception and spatial operations. These are referred to as (a) the "non-manipulation" paradox and (b) the "topological-primacy" hypothesis.

The "Non-manipulation" Paradox

Both Piaget and Révész have observed that what might be called "passive touch" appears to be an early stage in the development of tactile-kinesthetic or haptic perception. Révész describes this as the "static tactile process" in which stage, when objects or shapes are presented to child-subjects for tactile examination only, no attempt is made to maximize the available spatial information relating to their configurations. Paradoxically, they are, nevertheless, able to identify by touch cues alone many objects with extremely complex spatial

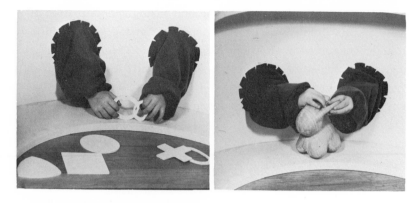

Fig. 1. Objects in the hands of children.

configurations with a high frequency of accuracy. It seems difficult, however, to understand how this can be the case if cues to the shapes of such objects are afforded only by such chance stimuli as the accidental pushing of a finger through a hole or into an indentation in the shape or object, as is argued by Piaget. Accordingly, an experiment has been conducted in which consideration is given to the possibility of the perceptual mechanisms underlying spatial identification in situations of this kind being other than spatial. The results of this experiment suggest strongly that, at this stage of development and in situations of the kind used, the most important cues for identification are textural rather than spatial.

Fig. 2. Examples of "linear" and "topological" shapes.

The "Topological-primacy" Hypothesis

A good deal of the work of Piaget has been concerned with identifying stages and substages of a variety of features of development. In considering spatial development he argues forcibly that the achievement of a spatial co-ordinate system, which is essentially linear, is not complete until the age of about 8 or 9 years. He interprets the findings of his haptic perception type experiments as indicating a general development from using "primitive" topological relationships to using linear or Euclidean relationships based upon a vertical-horizontal co-ordinate system. This development is not complete until the age of 8 or 9 years. A number of other studies including those of Page (1957, 1959) have substantiated these findings in their essentials. This hypothesis has been considered in an experimental situation similar to that used by Piaget but within the framework of an entirely different experimental design. The most important feature of this was that the subset of verbal responses available in the situation was controlled in such a way that the probability of a response being available to each of the shape categories "linear" and "topological" was equal. In this way a further examination of the influence of linguistic categories upon perceptual categories was made (Fisher, 1962). The results of this experiment appear to indicate that, when a response is available equally to each of the two shape groups under consideration, the hypothesis of "topological-primacy" requires to be replaced by one of "linear-primacy."

Detailed scale drawings and photographs of the apparatus prepared specially for these experiments are available in book form (Fisher, 1963a) and developments of this research are indicated in "The Spatial Senses" (Fisher, 1963b) and "Perceptual Development" (Fisher, 1964; Fisher, 1965).

References

Fisher, G. H. Phenomenal causality in conditions of intrasensory and intersensory stimulation. Amer. J. Psychol., 1962, 75, 321-323.

Fisher, G. H. Objects, models and two-dimensional shapes for use in visual and tactile-kinaesthetic shape perception experiments. Newcastle upon Tyne, Eng.: Inst. of Educ., Univer. of Durham, 1963. (a)

Fisher, G. H. (Ed.) The spatial senses. Dep. Psychol., King's College, Newcastle upon Tyne, Eng., Res. Bull., 1963, No. 1. (b)

Fisher, G. H. (Ed.) Perceptual development. Dep. Psychol., Univer. Newcastle upon Tyne, Eng., Res. Bull., 1964, No. 2.

Fisher, G. H. Developmental features of behaviour and perception: 1. Visual and tactile-kinaesthetic shape perception. Brit. J. educ. Psychol., 1965, 35, 69-78.

Page, E. I. Haptic perception. Dep. Educ., Univer. Birmingham, Eng., 1957.

Page, E. I. Haptic perception. Educ. Rev., 1959, 11, 115-124.

Piaget, J., and Inhelder, B. The child's conception of space. London: Routledge and Kegan Paul, 1956.

Révész, G. Psychology and art of the blind. London: Longmans, 1950.

A MODEL FOR ADAPTATION TO DISTORTIONS OF THE VISUAL FIELD

P. C. Dodwell
Department of Psychology
Queen's University
Kingston, Ontario, Canada

Introduction

A great deal of interest has been generated in recent years by demonstration of the ability of humans to adapt to distortions of vision induced by prisms and other optical devices (e.g., Held, 1962; Held and Bossom, 1961; Kohler, 1951; Taylor and Papert, 1956). It is generally conceded (Hochberg, 1957) that some criterion of "structure," "orderliness," or "stability" is required to explain how such adaptation occurs, and why it always tends toward the re-establishment of the "normal" visual world. However, precise hypotheses about how adaptation is mediated have been rare. The two most explicit attempts to explain adaptation to pattern and movement distortion have been made by Taylor (Taylor, 1962; Taylor and Papert, 1956) and by Andrews (1964). Neither of these theories is very satisfactory, although for different reasons in the two cases. The model to be proposed here is an error-correcting system similar in general principle to that of Andrews, but one which collates visual input with other sensory input, particularly in the tactile-kinesthetic mode. In this sense it shares similarities with Taylor's theory, but uses a quite different principle of error correction.

The optical distortions under consideration — displacement, rotation, inversion, regular distension, and contraction over the field which produces curvature changes — can be related to "normal" visual input by a single type of transform, namely, a conformal transformation. A conformal transformation, or mapping, is given by a relation such as $w = f(z) = \dfrac{ax + biy}{cx + diy}$, where $z = x + iy$. In the geometry of complex planes, each point on the z plane (considered as the normal visual field) is mapped onto one or more points in the w plane. A converse transformation maps points in w on to z. The transforms of interest here are biuniform, so that a one-to-one relation holds in each direction.

The Geometrical Interpretation of a Complex Number

The usual geometrical representation of a complex number, $z = x + iy$, is shown in Figure 1, and is called the "Argand diagram." The ordered pair (r, θ) could equally well be used to specify z. If z is a function of

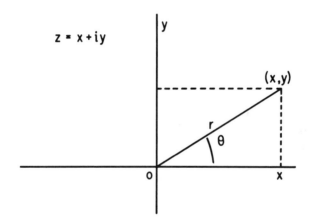

Fig. 1. The representation of a complex number z geometrically. $z = x + iy$. (Alternatively, z may be defined in terms of $[r, \theta]$.)

(x,y) then corresponding to the locus of z in the z plane there will be a different locus, given by $w = \phi(u, v)$ in the w plane, where u and v have the same interpretation in the w plane as have x and y in the z plane. This locus will be completely specified by $w = f(z)$ and in general u and v will each be functions of both x and y [say, $u = f_1(x,y)$, $v = f_2(x,y)$]. Such a conformal transformation maps straight lines or smooth curves in the z plane into either straight lines or smooth curves in the w plane. However, the important "local property" of equiangular intersection for pairs of lines (curves) is preserved. That is to say, if two lines intersect at an angle α in z, their transforms in w will intersect at the same angle α.

About the simplest possible conformal transformation is a <u>translation</u>. Translation along the "real" (x) axis is represented by z ± A, on the "imaginary" (y) axis by z ± iB, where A and B are real numbers. <u>Inversion</u> in one of the axes is attained by reversing the sign of either the real or the imaginary parts of z. Figure 2 shows how the pattern on the right-hand side is reflected in the y axis by the transformation w = -x +iy (w = $-\bar{z}$, where $\bar{z}$ is the "complex conjugate" of z; $\bar{z}$ = x - iy). Much more complex inversions, for example in a circle centered at the origin, can be expressed conformally, but do not appear to correspond with any of the optical distortions readily producible. <u>Rotation</u> about the origin is demonstrated in Figure 3; in this case w = $ze^{i\phi}$,

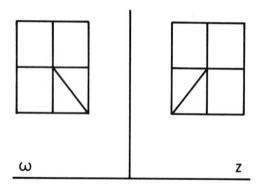

Fig. 2. Mapping of points in the z plane (right-hand side of figure) into the w plane (left-hand side, here superimposed on z plane) specified by w = $-\bar{z}$ (= -x +iy).

where ϕ is the angle of rotation. Figure 4 is an example of mapping straight lines into straight lines and curves, maintaining equiangular intersection. Only the w plane is shown, and the pattern is the transform of the right-hand side of Figure 2. In this case w = antilog z, since the transform w = log z maps a polar net of circles concentric with the origin, and their diameters, in the z plane, into a cartesian net of straight lines parallel to the u and v axes in the w plane.

A conformal transformation can consist of a sequence of transformations (e.g., a translation plus a rotation). The shape shown in Figure 5 could be produced by the successive application of a logarithmic transformation, a rotation and a displacement to the

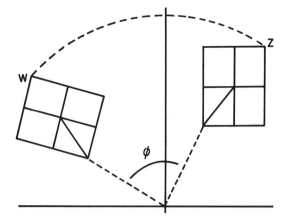

Fig. 3. Rotation of z plane through angle ϕ. $w = ze^{i\phi}$.

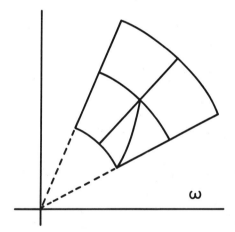

Fig. 4. Logarithmic transformation (w plane only is shown).
(The original shape of Figure 2 is here transformed by
w = antilog z.)

original pattern of Figure 2. This gives a fairly close approximation
to the appearance of the original pattern (Figure 2) as seen through
a wedge prism.

So far it has been shown that the usual "static" distortions studied
can be represented, at least to a good degree of approximation, by
conformal mappings of the original visual input, considered as a plane
projection of the spatial information in the visual field (e.g., as the
image formed on a plane by a pinhole camera). The question of

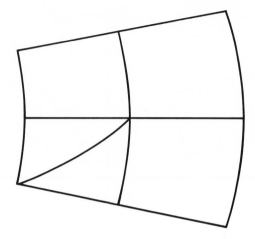

Fig. 5. The original shape of Figure 2 transformed by a logarithmic transformation, followed by rotation and translation.

movement distortions, when the head and eyes move, will be taken up
in the next section.

A Model for the Adapting System

It is postulated that the visual system makes use of conformal
mapping in adapting to optical distortions. This postulate may seem
fanciful at first sight, but in fact it seems that even without the
introduction of artificial distortions the visual system has to operate
such a transformation; the mapping of points on a hemisphere (the
retina) into a plane (the visual field) can be expressed conformally.
Additional points in favor of the postulate will be considered later.

It is proposed that, if the visual-world-to-retina transform function
is expressed as $w = f(z)$, the visual system has to use the (fixed)
inverse transformation, which I shall call $z = f^{-1}(w)$ to "recreate" the
visual field. Introduction of additional steps in the first of these
processes (by prisms, etc.) entails operation of the inverse process
in the visual system to restore the normal visual field. There is
considerable evidence to show that tactile-kinesthetic stimulation
plays an important part in this adaptation process. A possible model
for it is shown in Figure 6.

The operation of the model is straightforward. The normal "fixed"
operation $f^{-1}(w) = z$ is performed by the coder, and the computer
controls the motor system according to its input from the coder. The
comparator looks for differences between z, the visual information,

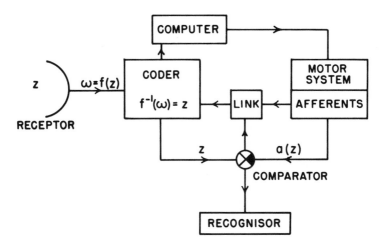

Fig. 6. A model for the adapting visuomotor system (see text).

and a(z) the afferent information which results from action of the coder-computer-motor system. If z is congruent with a(z) — visual and motor afferent information match — the link is inactive, and the coder continues to apply $f^{-1}(w)$ to its input from the retina. If z and a(z) do not match, the comparator activates the link, which causes the coder to change its transform function, and this process continues until z and a(z) again match, and the link is inactivated.

It may be noted that the computations required to find $f^{-1}(w)$, and other similar transforms, could be carried out in any system in which the x and y co-ordinates for each point in the plane can be operated with independently. A general purpose digital computer, given a suitable input system, could certainly be programmed to perform the necessary operations.

Discussion

It may well be asked why one should choose just the class of conformal transformations, since other mathematical expressions may be useful in describing the operation of the visual system. (For a treatment using the theory of Lie groups, see Hoffman [1964, 1966] .) The principle reason for adumbrating a model incorporating conformal mapping is, simply, that the distortions studied can be described by some elementary mappings of this sort. Although no special class having unique properties to fit the adaptation situation can be singled out within the general class of conformal transformations, restricting

the class to conformal transformations does circumscribe quite
clearly the sorts of distortion to which adaptation may be expected to
occur. As far as I know, no case has been reported of full adaptation
to a distortion not expressible conformally.

Conformal transformations preserve the important "local property"
of equiangular intersection, while allowing enormous variability in the
positions of possible corresponding points in two complex planes. This
is important since in a model of the Andrews type, for example, all
adaptations occur "locally"; this is not a restriction that the real
visual system meets. A conformal model is consistent with neurophysiological data: for instance, the "complex fields" of Hubel and
Wiesel (1962) are receptive fields for straight lines in a specific
orientation in the visual field, but such complex fields may cover a
large proportion of the total visual field (up to 30 degrees in the cat).
This evidence is not strong, since it could be explained by a set of
fixed connections within the visual system just as well as by a transformation on the visual input from different visual directions correcting
for distortions produced in the optics of the eye and at the retina.

For a system to operate by conformal transformation of its input,
information from two mutually perpendicular systems must be
preserved independently. This certainly happens in any visual system
where binocular fusion and stereopsis occur, since in such a system,
as is well known, disparities in horizontal visual directions at the two
eyes have very different properties from vertical disparities. The
fact that mapping from a plane to a hemisphere can be expressed
conformally has already been mentioned; there is other evidence that
the visual system operates with such transformations in the absence
of distorting media. When the eyes converge asymmetrically,
particularly if the point of fixation is above or below the line of normal
regard, the images at the two eyes suffer different degrees of magnification and rotation (the latter through cyclotorsion) and yet the images
may fuse perfectly, without introducing anomalous stereoptic effects.
The "reduction" of the two images to a "normal" form may be considered as a pair of conformal transformations applied separately to
the inputs at the two eyes. If, as this suggests, the transformations at
the two eyes may be relatively independent, it would be interesting to
find out whether a subject perfectly adapted to two different conditions,
one for each eye separately, would have normal binocular fusion and
stereopsis when both eyes were exposed simultaneously to visual

stimulation for the first time after adaptation. Should stereopsis occur, it would indicate a real correlate of the apparent changes in visual direction, produced by adaptation, in the system for binocular fusion.

It is well known that adaptation to optical distortions usually occurs gradually, and adaptation to different aspects of the distortion generally occurs at different rates (Hay and Pick, 1963). This is consistent with the point already made, that a conformal transformation may often be considered as a sequence of simple transformations. It would not be too surprising if the components of a total transformation were to adapt at different rates. This is indeed to be expected, in the sense that the different components of the transformation differ in complexity. Translation is expressible as addition/subtraction of the same constant for each point (x, y), rotation by multiplication, again by a constant for each (x, y), inversion by change of sign. All these may be conveniently expressed by matrix operations of addition or multiplication, the transform matrix containing only constants. The correct constants — which reduce visual and afferent stimulation mismatches to zero — must then be found by a series of successive approximations. More complicated inversions may involve matrix multiplication with the values of the argument, x and y, occurring in the transform matrix itself. Other transformations, such as the logarithmic, require still more complicated computations, such as finding $\frac{1}{2} \log (x^2 + y^2)$. This might entail step-functional processes, rather than gradual transitions.

An important point in favor of the conformal transformation model appears when one considers the question of movement distortion. In normal vision the world[1] appears stable as the head and eyes are moved; one may also say that the visual field appears to flow steadily and without distortion as the eyes move uniformly relative to the world. When a distorting device such as a wedge prism is worn, this is no longer true, since there is no stable visual world, and the pattern of "visual flow" is distorted in several ways. It is no longer uniform across the field, and the extent of the distortion depends in a precise way on position within the field. There is a neat analogy between this situation and the hydraulic engineer's study of flow patterns. The flow of a homogeneous fluid in a certain environment may give rise to a complicated flow pattern. The analysis of such patterns is greatly simplified by the fact that, under certain restrictions, the flow pattern

---

[1] "Visual world" and "visual field" are used here in Gibson's (1950) sense.

can be conformally mapped into a parallel rectilinear uniform flow pattern. The condition under which this is possible is that the flow pattern should be irrotational, and this in turn is a necessary and sufficient condition for the pattern to be represented by an analytic function of a complex variable (see Valentine [1959] pp. 139-147). This condition is embodied in the so-called Cauchy-Riemann equations which specify invariant "local properties" of the flow pattern just as in the case of the static counterparts discussed earlier.

The restoration of "uniform visual flow" in the visual field can be attained by an appropriate conformal mapping. This turns out, as one would expect, to be the same mapping that eliminates static distortions. The details are not difficult to work out, but too lengthy to go into here. The fact that both the static and dynamic distortion adaptations fit the same transformation paradigm appears to me to be good evidence that the visual system does make use of some conformal mapping analogue in its adaptation to optically produced distortions. On removal of a distorting device, an opposite distortion (both of pattern and movement) is seen, to the extent that the subject has adapted to the original distortion. This indicates that a transform has been applied to the whole visual input, and is the inverse of the transform of the distorting device.

Finally, a brief comparison with the two other theories mentioned earlier is in order. The present model is similar in principle to that of Andrews, but accounts for a range of phenomena not covered in that model, which considers only properties of the visual metric, such as the classical illusions and figural aftereffects. It is now fairly well-established that the human visual system adapts by collation of information from several sensory modes, and a model of the system must take this into account. This criticism cannot be leveled at Taylor's theory, which rests heavily on the notion of the conditioning of movements to visual stimuli and classes of stimuli. Taken at its face value, it is difficult to see how this theory can account for partial adaptation and reversal effects; for example, if the wearing of a prism of a certain power yields partial adaptation, the degree of adaptation may be measured by looking through a series of prisms of weaker power, to discover which one yields an apparently "normal" visual field. The conditioning process is incomplete in one sense, and yet — paradoxically — "correct" in another. Interestingly enough in Papert's appendix to Taylor's book (1962) the idea of representing distortion and adaptation effects by complex number operations is used for a specific case, but without consideration as to whether this could be used as a general principle for understanding how the visual system operates in this situation.

Conclusion

It has been shown that both the static and movement distortions commonly produced by optical devices such as mirrors and prisms can be represented, to a fair degree of approximation, as conformal mappings of the "normal" visual field. It is proposed that the human visual system adapts to the distortions by finding the inverse transform function, and applying it to the retinal input. A structural model for this process which appears to be able to account for the main facts presently known, is outlined. Without doubt, the model will be found eventually to be an oversimplication of the real system.

References

Andrews, D. P. Error-correcting perceptual mechanisms. Quart. J. exp. Psychol., 1964, 16, 104-115.

Gibson, J. J. The perception of the visual world. Boston: Houghton Mifflin, 1950.

Hay, J. C. and Pick, H. L. Adaptation to prolonged visual distortion of prism spectacles. Paper read at Psychonomic Society, Bryn Mawr, August 1963.

Held, R. Adaptation to rearrangement and visual-spatial aftereffects. Psych. Beitr., 1962, 6, 439-450.

Held, R., and Bossom, J. Neonatal deprivation and adult rearrangement: Complementary techniques for analyzing plastic sensory-motor coordination. J. comp. physiol. Psychol., 1961, 54, 33-37.

Hochberg, J. Effects of the Gestalt Revolution. Psychol. Rev., 1957, 64, 73-84.

Hoffman, W. C. Pattern recognition by the moethod of isoclines: I. A mathematical model for the visual integrative process. Math. Res. Lab., Boeing Scientific Res. Labs, Math. Note 1964, No. 351.

Hoffman, W. C. The Lie algebra of visual perception. J. math. Psychol., 1966, 3, 65-98.

Hubel, D. H., and Wiesel, T. N. Receptive fields, binocular interaction and functional architecture in the cat's visual cortex. J. Physiol., 1962, 160, 105-154.

Kohler, I. Über Aufbau and Wandlungen der Wahrnehmungswelt. S. B. Ost. Akad. Wiss., 1951, 227, 1-118.

Taylor, J. G. The behavioural basis of perception. New Haven: Yale Univer. Press, 1962.

Taylor, J. G., and Papert, S. A theory of perceptual constancy.
Brit. J. Psychol., 1956, 47, 216-221.

Valentine, H. R. Applied hydrodynamics. London: Butterworth,
1959.

DISTORTION OF VISUAL SPACE AS INAPPROPRIATE CONSTANCY SCALING

Richard L. Gregory
Perceptual Laboratory
Department of Psychology
University of Cambridge
Cambridge, England

It is very well-known that certain simple line drawings are seen
incorrectly. One class of such figures distort visual space; certain
lines appear too long or too short, bent or curved, or rotated through
some angle. Best known, are the Muller-Lyer, Ponzo, and Hering
figures. Many suggestions for the origin of these distortions can be
disproved rather easily, but there is one suggestion which has never
received adequate experimental examination. Advanced by R. Tausch
and described by H. L. Teuber, the proposal is one which I have been
investigating for some years: First, the illusion figures are typical
two-dimensional projections of three-dimensional space. That is,
they are skeleton perspective drawings. For example, the Muller-
Lyer arrows give the same retinal images as inside or outside
corners; the Ponzo figure is equivalent to, e.g., railway lines converging with distance; the Hering figure is like a tunnel, and so on for all
these illusions. This generalization was, in fact, made by adherents
of the Perspective Theory in the 1930's, but they did not carry it
further. Second, the important step from here is to suppose that
perspective depth cues (e.g., corners and angles) trigger, or set the
mechanism normally responsible for compensating reduction in retinal
image size with object distance, giving size constancy. I call this
mechanism, which I regard as being an active scaling process, set by
various cues to distance, Constancy Scaling. (It may be noted that this
view of constancy differs from that of Professor J. J. Gibson, as
expounded in his Perception of the Visual World [1950], and I would
suggest that the study of the illusions could prove decisive in deciding
the nature of constancy.)

The difficulty with the theory as it stands is that constancy is thought of as being related directly to apparent distance, as in Emmert's Law for afterimages. If this were always true, it would be impossible to account for the illusions in this way, because they appear as flat. My suggested solution is as follows: although the figures are essentially perspective drawings, the depth is countermanded by competing depth cues, especially the texture of the paper on which they are drawn. This possibility led to experiments using luminous figures arranged to glow in darkness, and viewed with one eye to avoid stereoscopic cues. It turned out that the figures viewed under these conditions typically do appear in depth as indicated by their perspective. It remains true however that perceptual "set" is important; it can modify the apparent depth.

I have now devised a method for obtaining objective measurements of apparent depth. This makes it possible to relate quantitatively the perceived depth with the extent of the illusion, as measured with a standard matching technique. The results are highly satisfactory. Considering the Muller-Lyer illusion, we found extremely high cor- relations (around 0.9) between the extent of the illusion, as determined by the angle of the fins of these arrow figures, and the depth in the figures, as measured with the new technique.[1] The effect goes the right way round for the theory; that is, the illusion is an expansion for those parts of the figure which recede in depth, and a shrinking of those parts which appear nearer. The plotted results go through zero both for depth and illusion for the neutral figure having straight bars at the top and bottom, forming a capital "I." As far as I am aware, no such relation would be expected on any other theory so far considered.

The methods for measuring the depth consist in matching depth given by monocular cues, such as perspective, with binocular depth given by the convergence angle of the eyes. (An alternative method would use binocular disparity, but this we have not yet tried out.) The light from the luminous illusion figures is polarized, and cross- polarized at one eye, while a small dim reference light is introduced optically into the figure with a half-silvered mirror. This light is visible to both eyes, though the illusion figure is visible only to one. This makes it possible to place the reference light, using binocular

---

[1] These results were found in work with Miss Linda Townes in Profes- sor Teuber's Department, at M.I.T., during the summer of 1964, and also in a preliminary experiment in Cambridge, England, with my student Ian Horrell.

vision, to the same position in depth as any selected part of the figure viewed with a single eye. The reference light is attached to a scale, and a graph is built up of subjective depth from the plots obtained in this way which are compared with measures of the same illusion figures, but presented on normal textured paper, with a comparison line adjustable in length and fitted with a scale. Evidence for the theory that the illusions are due to constancy scaling set by perspective features, normally countermanded by texture of the paper, is not limited to this experiment but I believe this to be the strongest evidence at this time, whereas the technique employed seems to have application over a range of perceptual problems.

The theory certainly implies that constancy involves an active scaling process, and that it is not necessarily tied to apparent distance. This has implications which seem worth following up with further experiments and debate.

Reference

Gibson, J. J. Perception of the visual world. Boston: Houghton Mifflin, 1950.

THE ROLE OF TRAINING IN THE IDENTIFICATION OF AMBIGUOUS VISUAL FORMS

R. H. Henneman and S. R. Mathews
Department of Psychology
University of Virginia
Charlottesville, Virginia

This experiment was one in a series of studies investigating stimulus cue utilization and response biasing in learning to identify ambiguous visual forms. Twelve nonsense forms (Boynton's struniforms) provided the stimuli which were rendered ambiguous by systematic distortion of contours. In these experiments the general procedure was as follows: subjects first learned to identify the forms with letters of the alphabet in a paired-associate training session. Differential frequency of paired forms and labels was employed in training to induce biased responding during attempted identification of the ambiguous forms in a subsequent test session. For each of the 12 basic

forms, or "prototypes," variations were constructed and scaled to
provide additional stimuli at three levels of similarity to the originals.
In the identification test session subjects viewed both prototypes and
the variations, thus having to make judgments at four levels of stimulus
ambiguity. Identification errors were analyzed in terms of training
frequencies, i.e., whether the erroneous labels were those which had
been high-frequency or low frequency labels during training, and
whether they were applied to high-frequency or to low-frequency forms.

In previous experiments two principal training and testing procedures
had been employed in the manipulation of variables providing different
opportunities for stimulus cue utilization and frequency biasing to
influence identification responses. These two procedures were: (a) a
separated training-and-test procedure, in which subjects viewed only
the 12 prototype forms during training, and were tested in a subsequent
session on the larger population of prototypes plus distorted variations.
During the test session all stimuli were shown at equal frequencies and
subjects were given no knowledge of results, i.e., did not see the
correct labels following attempted identification; (b) a combined
training-and-test procedure in which subjects were shown both prototypes and variations from the outset, thus having to respond to 12
classes of forms, rather than to the smaller population of 12 basic
forms. Subjects were instructed to begin attempted identification as
quickly as possible and were shown the correct label following each
response. Because of the larger population of stimuli, improvement
in identification success was necessarily slower than in the separated
procedure. Since success of identification was measurable from the
start of training, this procedure provided concurrent training and
testing, hence the descriptive term, combined training-and-test.
Frequency of presentation (of stimulus forms and subsequent labels)
was manipulable equally in both procedures. Differential frequency of
presentation and knowledge of results continued throughout all sessions
of the combined procedure.

In the earlier studies the combined procedure had usually produced
a high-frequency bias in identification errors, whereas the separated procedure had at different times yielded a high-frequency bias, insignificant
bias, and (unexpectedly) a low-frequency bias! In the present experiment a systematic comparison of the two procedures was sought,
holding stimulus material, identification labels, type of stimulus
distortion, and total number of presentations constant. Differential

frequency training in the ratio of five-to-one was also a constant. Four experimental groups were run as follows: Group I, using the separated training-and-test procedure described above; Group II, using the combined training-and-test procedure; Group III, starting with a training session identical to that of Group I, but ending with a test procedure identical with that of Group II; Group IV, starting with the combined training-and-test procedure of Group II, but ending with a test session like that of Group I. Twelve subjects were assigned to each group. The procedure entailed one session, on each of 2 successive days. On Day 1 subjects viewed a total of 288 stimulus presentations, considered as "training." On Day 2 subjects first observed another block of 144 presentations, considered as further training, then sat through a "test" session of 144 presentations. Identification errors on this final block of 144 presentations were analyzed. Experimental comparisons were made among the following variables: (a) training procedure, (b) test procedure, (c) frequency of presentation during training, and (d) level of stimulus distortion (degree of similarity of the variations to the prototypes). These variables were related to (a) total errors, (b) proportion of high-frequency labels used in error, (c) proportion of high-frequency labels applied incorrectly to high-frequency forms and to low-frequency forms, respectively.

The principal results were the following: (a) Total errors were significantly greater following combined training than after separated training (see Figure 1), verifying that subjects were able to learn less about the larger population of stimulus forms in the former procedure. (b) The proportion of high-frequency labels used in error was signifi-

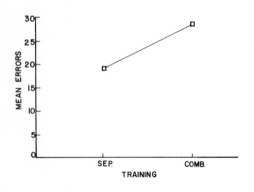

Fig. 1. Errors related to training.

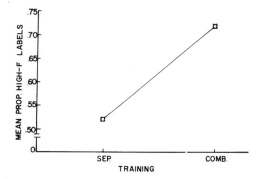

Fig. 2. Label frequency related to training.

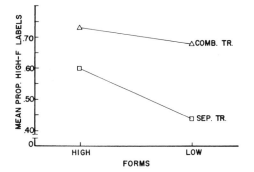

Fig. 3. Label frequency, form frequency, and training.

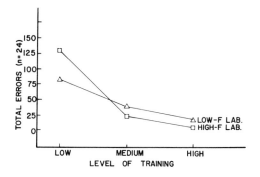

Fig. 4. Analysis of training errors.

cantly higher following the combined training procedure (see Figure 2). This suggests that subjects using this procedure, while learning relatively little about the stimulus forms, did learn to use the 12 labels, and further distinguished between the high-frequency and low-frequency responses, respectively. Presumably, when test stimuli could not be clearly identified subjects responded on the basis of previous probability of occurrence. (c) High-frequency labels were applied with approximately equal frequency to both high-frequency and low-frequency forms by subjects using the <u>combined</u> training procedure (see Figure 3), indicating that they had not learned to distinguish clearly between the high-frequency and low-frequency stimuli during training. On the other hand, subjects using the <u>separated</u> training procedure tended to apply high-frequency labels in error to high-frequency forms and vice versa (Figure 3). This indicates that subjects in the <u>separated</u> training groups had learned to distinguish between high-frequency and low-frequency forms as well as between the two frequency classes of labels. Apparently, these subjects were able to utilize stimulus information to a greater degree than those of the <u>combined</u> training groups, as evidenced by (a) fewer over-all errors, and (b) recognition of stimulus forms as high-frequency or low-frequency, respectively.

In order to account for the absence of a significant frequency bias in the test data of the groups using the <u>separated</u> training procedure, the errors made over the course of training were analyzed with respect to both frequency of label used and frequency of stimulus to which the label had been applied. Definite trends in the type of errors were clearly discernible (see Figure 4). During the early stages of learning (first block of 144 presentations) high-frequency labels predominate, and are applied primarily to high-frequency stimuli. As learning progresses (second block of 144 presentations) errors that are high-frequency labels drop rapidly as the high-frequency associations become learned. Low-frequency labels are now more numerous in the error data, and they are applied almost entirely to low-frequency forms, indicating that the subjects have now come to respond to the low-frequency stimuli as a class, but cannot yet correctly identify the specific members of this class of forms. If training is carried far enough errors of all types approach zero. While not apparent in Figure 4, this result was clearly evident in the last subblock of 36 presentations. At this point of almost complete learning, subjects are using all 12 labels and applying them to forms of both frequencies with approximate equality. Logically, therefore, it seems apparent that the <u>separated</u> training procedure may be expected to produce a high-frequency bias, a low-frequency bias, or no bias, depending upon the degree of paired-associate learning that has taken place prior to the identification test. No parallel trends were found in the error scores of subjects using the <u>combined</u> training procedure.

EFFECT OF OVERLEARNING STIMULI ON THE LATER FREE RECALL OF THESE IN A LARGER SET OF STIMULI

James R. Whitman
Research Services
Veterans Administration Hospital
American Lake, Washington

Garner's analysis of free-recall learning relates learning difficulty to characteristics of sets of stimuli rather than to characteristics of individual stimuli. These characteristics of sets of stimuli are produced by the variables which describe the stimuli as the subject perceives these.

The purpose of this study was to determine, for the free-recall learning of complex visual figures, whether or not the stimulus variables were modified (and hence the internal structure changed) when a substantial part of the set of stimuli in a free-recall learning task has been overlearned by subjects, prior to practice.

Method

Four groups of subjects were required to learn by free recall a set of eight visual figures shown to them one at a time. Practice continued for ten trials or until all correct responses were given by the subject on two consecutive trials. The subjects were not told how many of their responses were correct until the foregoing criterion was met.

Prior to this, three experimental groups learned by free recall, four of the above stimuli, One group learned these to the criterion of all correct responses on two consecutive trials. A second group received additional practice in copying and reproducing the four stimuli from memory. A third group received all of the above training then additional practice in the free-ordered recall of the stimuli. All subjects in the experimental groups were tested individually, and they did not know whether or not the four figures they had learned were included in the larger set of eight stimuli. A control group received as preliminary training, repeated practice in drawing random sets of four different figures after having been shown a sample. These subjects were tested in a group situation.

After practice on the eight figures, the subjects in the experimental groups were required to recall the four figures which they had pre-

viously learned, and the subjects in the control group were required to
reproduce any four different figures.

The subjects were students in college extension courses. Thirty-
nine subjects were assigned at random, and in equal numbers, to one
of the three experimental groups. An entire class of 15 constituted the
control group.

The stimuli were geometric figures differing in four characteristics,
each with two values (see Figure 1). From the total set of the 16
figures representing all of the possible combinations of these variables,
a set of 8 was selected. Within this set of eight, the interrelationship

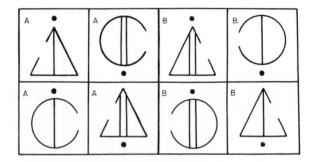

Fig. 1. The eight stimuli used. (The letters denote those in
Parts A and B.)

between the variables (i.e., internal structure) was in the form of an
interaction. The set of eight figures was divided into two parts each
of four figures (Parts A and B). The parts were selected so that the
four figures in each represented all values of all of the characteristics
with equal frequency. The internal structure of each part was in the
form of simple contingencies between variables. The experimental
groups learned one of these parts (Part A) prior to practice on the
larger set of eight figures (Part A plus Part B).

Results and Discussion

The control group provided the basis for testing differences between
groups; "t" tests and the 0.05 level were used. The correct responses
of the control group were equally divided between Parts A and B of the
set of eight stimuli.

The experimental groups were first compared with the control group
then considered individually. The first comparison of the groups was

on the basis of the number of Part A responses appearing during the learning trials with the eight stimuli. On the first trial, the experimental group, which had learned Part A to the criterion of two trials with all correct responses, did not give significantly more Part A responses than did the control group. The other two experimental groups which had received the additional practice did. By the fifth trial, however, there were no significant differences between the groups; and this was also the case on the last practice trial. On no trial did all of the subjects in any of the experimental groups recall all of the stimuli in Part A.

After practice on the larger set of eight stimuli, subjects in the experimental groups were asked to recall the Part A figures previously learned. The subjects in the control group produced any four figures. The experimental group which had learned Part A to the criterion of two perfect trials only, did not recall more Part A figures than those produced by the control group. The other two experimental groups which received the additional practice (overlearning) with Part A, did not differ significantly from each other in the number of Part A figures recalled, and these two groups recalled a greater percentage of Part A figures than the control group.

Learning curves for the groups suggest that the effect of the overlearning of stimuli on the later free recall of these in a larger set of stimuli is one of increasing the probability that the overlearned stimuli will be recalled early in practice only. It is therefore concluded that the stimulus variables were not modified by the overlearning provided in this study.

Finally, the two groups which had overlearned Part A gave a greater percentage of correct responses (Part A and Part B figures) during the ten trials with the larger set of eight figures than did either of the other two groups which did not differ from each other. However, less than half of the subjects in three of the four groups had reached the criterion on this learning task at the end of the learning trials provided.

PATTERN PERCEPTION IN THE HUMAN NEWBORN: A CLOSE LOOK AT SOME POSITIVE AND NEGATIVE RESULTS

Maurice Hershenson
Department of Psychology
University of Wisconsin
Madison, Wisconsin

William Kessen
Department of Psychology
Yale University
New Haven, Connecticut

Harry Munsinger [1]
Department of Psychology
University of Illinois
Urbana, Illinois

Our attempt to evaluate the perceptual abilities of the newborn reflects our interst in the nature of the processes which underlie perceptual development. It further reflects our belief that speculation as to the nature of such mechanisms based on data obtained from adults — or from children — is risky, at best, and that the newborn can be studied if the proper techniques are applied.

Our particular methodological posture derives from the conviction that the study of perceptual development in nature will be fruitful only when perceptually mediated responses — "perceptual indices" as they have been called — are somehow related to organization or structure in the stimulus field. That is to say, a theory of perceptual development must be based on an analysis of perceptible stimulus structure. Otherwise, generalization to classes or orders of stimulus elements is impossible, whether it be in terms of dimensions of stimulation or attributes of objects as we know them, or some organization of the stimulus array with which we are not familiar. We say not familiar because one may not assume that the newborn is sensitive to perceptual arrays similar to those to which adults respond, and we should be prepared for this contingency. At any rate, unless this analysis is accomplished, it is difficult to see the gain from speculation about mechanism.

Thus the problem resolves itself to one of detecting perceptible dimensions for a nonverbal, essentially immobile organism when stimulus

---

[1] Now at the Department of Psychology, University of California, San Diego, California

prepotency cannot be assumed. How, then, to begin? Fortunately, Stevens, in the very first chapter of the Handbook (1951), supplies us with part of the answer: The minimum information necessary to establish a linearly ordered set involves an analysis of relations among at least three elements. That is, if a response, ocular orientation, for example, could be interpreted to indicate how three stimuli are "related" to one another, then we might have a basis for establishment of a scale. The requirements which a system must satisfy if it is to be classed as ordered are given by Huntington's postulates. These demands are as follows:

1. If $a \neq b$, then either $a < b$ or $b < a$.
2. If $a < b$, then $a \neq b$.
3. If $a < b$ and $b < c$, then $a < c$.

The properties asymmetric, transitive, connected, and irreflexive are implied by these postulates.

Now in order to apply the postulates of serial order to our problem a definition of the relations is necessary in terms of observable responses. Let $a \neq b$ denote the relation of inequality when "a is fixated for a significantly different number of frames than b," and let $a < b$ denote the relation of order when "a is fixated for fewer number of frames than b." (We may abbreviate the latter relation by saying "b is preferred to a.") The relation "preferred" may now be measured by means of ocular orientation and if an ordered set can be derived, then we may index perception in the newborn by means of precisely this operation while at the same time proposing that the ordered set obtained represents a perceptible dimension. Thus we can assume discriminable stimulus structure if, and only if, a serially ordered set of responses obtains. The task of determining the aspects of stimulus structure which correlate with those of the ordered response set can be simplified by using unidimensional stimuli with any given set of responses.

There are, of course, further problems relating to the organism being studied and also to specific stimuli. We shall return to these later. For the present, let us briefly describe the method and then plunge into an analysis of the results.

Babies were seen in the second, third, or fourth day of life in a small room on the Maternity Service of Grace-New Haven Community Hospital. The relevant apparatus and procedures have been described in detail elsewhere (Hershenson, 1964). We should indicate, perhaps,

that in each of the studies three points on a single dimension were
selected as stimuli to be presented in a paired-comparison procedure
and that photographs of eye fixations served as the basic measure.

Homogeneous Stimuli

In the study of homogeneous stimuli (Hershenson 1964), light from
the projector lamps was reduced by achromatic filters to produce three
levels of illumination at the stimulus screens. Twenty newborns each
saw six pairs of stimuli. The scale scores of orientation are shown
in Figure 1. The medium intensity was more often fixated than either

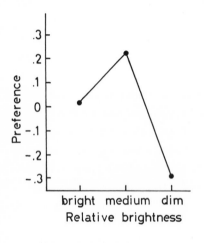

Fig. 1. Scaled brightness
preferences.

the bright or the dim, and the bright stimulus was more often fixated
than the dim one. All comparisons were significant over the entire
group of babies. Moreover, child-by-child analysis shows a large
number of infants with significant individual differential fixations.
These data, then, meet the demands of Huntington's postulates and we
may conclude that newborn humans can perceive brightness.

Patterned Stimuli

Sixteen infants were observed in a study of "complexity" defined as
number of brightness transitions (Hershenson, 1964). This dimension
correlates with the perimeter of solid figures. The stimuli used were
checkerboards of 4, 16, and 144 alternately blackened squares. As
can be seen from Figure 2, the differences in scale scores are much
smaller than for brightness and, in fact, only the difference between

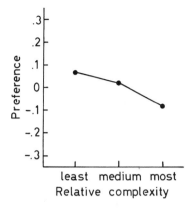

Fig. 2. Scaled complexity preferences.

the least complex and the most complex stimuli was statistically stable. We should also note that an apparently inordinate number of babies showed, individually, a texture of significant preferences.

For the group, transitivity was not demonstrated; only the superiority in number of fixations of one of the stimuli. Although one might be inclined to conclude, on such data, that the two stimuli have been discriminated — that the responses were related to the dimension on which the two stimuli are points — this conclusion is clearly unwarranted. All that has been demonstrated in this case is that the infants attend to one of the stimuli; the other stimulus may not be available to them at all but may be part of the background. Recall, if you will, our earlier argument essentially emphasizing the importance of just this differentiation — between "They discriminate A from B" on the one hand and "They attend to A" on the other — between discrimination on the one hand and attention tropisms on the other.

The second pattern study, of 20 infants, is the hardest to name and we have oscillated between calling it "organization" and "faceness." As can be seen in Figure 3, the stimuli show Joan Crawford in nature and in two states of facial disorder. The scale scores shown in Figure 4 indicate no differences in preference among the stimuli; the differences for the group are indeed small or nonexistent. But again we must note the very large number of infants who, considered individually, show significant preferences. For the group, there is no transitivity, no single preferred stimulus.

In a third study of patterned stimuli, the "turns" study, 17 babies were presented with solid black figures which differed in the number of independent turns (Hershenson, Munsinger, and Kessen, 1965). This

a. Real face.

b. Distorted face.

Fig. 3. Stimuli in
"organization" or
"faceness" experiment.

c. Scrambled face.

dimension approximates information value. Although the scaled preferences produced the interesting pattern shown in Figure 5, once again only one comparison was significant while a great many babies showed individual preferences.

Pattern of Scores; Random Baby; Random-constrained Baby

Of the summary data presented for four studies, only in the case of brightness could unequivocal interpretation be suggested. For this reason it was felt that a finer analysis of the grain of individual preference might clarify the results. To this end, a tabulation of the number of preferences for each comparison was carried out on an individual subject basis. This tabulation clearly shows that for a

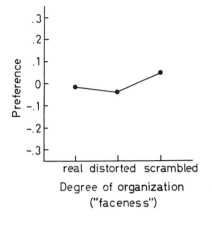

Fig. 4. Scaled "faceness" preferences.

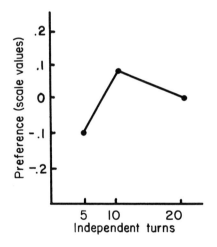

Fig. 5. Scaled "turns" preferences.

significant over-all pair preference to be exhibited, either the preferences (strong and weak) of most of the subjects must be in the same direction, or strong preferences by a few of the subjects must be in the same direction, or both. The former is the case in the brightness study and the single significant preference of the complexity study; the latter case describes the single significant pair in the turns study. On the other hand, many strong preferences were shown in the other comparisons but these were about equal and opposite in direction and therefore canceled each other. Thus while it is possible for an over-all result to be positive when only a few strong preferences favor a given direction, it is likewise possible to get a negative over-all result, i.e., no preference, while still obtaining a relatively large number of strong individual preferences. Thus the relationship between the relative number of strong preferences and the over-all result is not clear.

Moreover, we must cope now with the problem of interpreting strong individual preferences when the combined data are inconsistent, namely, if over-all preference is not significant, does a significant individual preference indicate "perception" on the part of the individuals? This question can be clarified by reporting the results of two more studies — ones in which no live babies were tested — nevertheless, two studies in which the exact same procedures of stimulus presentation were followed. The first study involved 15 randomly responding subjects who had to meet the same response criteria as the live subjects, i.e., they were required to respond at least 10 times. An upper limit of less than 60 responses was also set so that the response patterns would mimic those of the "live" studies as closely as possible. The total number of responses for each stimulus pair was randomly determined within these limits. The results are as expected: no significant preferences overall; no significant individual preferences. There is only one score greater than one SD from the mean, and the scale scores are close to zero.

In a second study, 15 random babies were again run in the same stimulus situation except that they were constrained in their side preferences. Specifically, each of the subjects in this study was assigned the over-all side preference of a baby in the brightness study. To ensure the same total over-all preferences, he was further assigned the stimulus-pair totals but these were now randomly assigned to pairs. Within these constraints the subject was free to respond randomly. These results indicate that merely imposing a side-preference structure on the data forces individual stimulus preferences to emerge but that over-all (i.e., group) stimulus preferences remain negligible.

Perhaps we are now in a better position to say something about the individual preferences shown and indeed about the over-all preferences. First, it appears that position preference imposed upon random looking is not sufficient to explain group preference. This suggests that the individual preferences are artifact of position preference. Precisely how this operates is not clear but it seems to imply that the usual experimental controls and even our attempt at statistical control may not have been adequate. Second, our view that the over-all preferences

are not artifact but represent some real stimulus-contingent responding
is reinforced. And third, we should, perhaps, look to further refine-
ments of methodology to help us avoid some of the problems of interpretation.

Conclusion

Now the problem is "Where do we go from here?" Do we continue
using a methodology based on unidimensionality until, by chance, we hit
upon a perceptible dimension, or would it be more profitable to turn
immediately to a multidimensional approach? We feel certain you
would be easily convinced that the solution is not apparent if we had
time to discuss in detail some of the ramifications of these studies
which bear directly on this problem. We have learned a good deal about
the behavior of the newborn including those things we like to talk about,
as, for example, his ability to fixate and to move his eyes in a co-
ordinated fashion; and those we would prefer to ignore, such as his
tendency to prefer looking to one side, or his tendency to manifest
behavioral extremes which severely limit his workday and in effect
restrict his usefulness as a subject in complex designs.

We have also been forced to learn more about the stimulus materials
which present themselves as possible candidates in unidimensional
studies and perhaps what we have learned is that they are multidimensional. At any rate, the list of possible dimensions is growing
so rapidly that we are tempted to let the newborn himself supply the
structure. This consideration forces us closer and closer to large
matrix designs.

These, then, are the main counterforces with which we are presently
grappling. We hope to attack the former by being able to obtain
measurements of relative states of wakefulness and to use many babies
as one subject. We hope to attack the latter by applying multidimensional scaling techniques with appropriate modifications to accom-
modate the newborn.

In summary, then, it would appear that for models of perceptual
development to advance beyond the stage of speculation, the exciting
first glances into the "perceptorium" of the human infant must be
succeeded by parametric analysis and the use of conventional psychophysical procedures in somewhat more sophisticated designs.

References

Hershenson, M. Visual discrimination in the human newborn.
J. comp. physiol. Psychol., 1964, 58, 270-276.

Hershenson, M., Munsinger, H., and Kessen, W. Preference for
shapes of intermediate variability in the newborn human. Science,
1965, 147, 630-631.

Stevens, S. S. Mathematics, measurement, and psychophysics.
In S. S. Stevens (Ed.), Handbook of experimental psychology. New
York: Wiley, 1951. Pp. 1-49

THE METHODOLOGY OF EXPERIMENTS IN PATTERN RECOGNITION

C. I. Howarth
Department of Psychology
University of Nottingham
Nottingham, England

This paper is an expression of dissatisfaction with the present state
of theorizing about pattern recognition. It will be argued that our
theories are inadequate because they have been very poorly related
to the experimental evidence, and that in general, experiments in this
field have been inadequate to carry the theoretical weight which has
been put upon them. Some minimal criteria are suggested, by which
past and future experiments may be evaluated.

Most theoretical work on pattern recognition has been concentrated
on the problem of stimulus classification, and indeed this is the most
interesting problem in this area. Animals with reasonably acute sense
organs can discriminate an enormous number of different stimuli.
In spite of this, in very many circumstances, animals will make the
same response to a large number of obviously different stimuli,
stimuli which they can easily discriminate if necessary. For example,
an animal trained to respond positively to a triangle and negatively to
a circle will transfer its positive response to a much larger or a much
smaller triangle. This transfer of response could be considered the
equivalent of a simple failure to discriminate. But this explanation
seems unconvincing because the same animals can be trained very
easily indeed to discriminate large and small triangles. Perhaps the
most striking feature of this behavior is how little it surprises us.

Our reaction to these patterns is clearly very similar to the animals, since we call all the hypothetically positive stimuli, triangles, while we have no difficulty in describing some as large and others as small.

Theoretical work on the problem of stimulus classification has been concentrated on two distinct but related issues. First, many attempts have been made to invent systems which will classify stimuli into the same categories as are used by humans or animals. Second, there has been much controversy about the effect of experience on the classificatory mechanisms. Are they organized largely by hereditary influences or do they develop as a result of experience?

These two issues are related, since those who subscribe to the view that perception is learnt tend to devise models of perception out of simple elements which are initially randomly connected, but whose connections are ordered by experience. Possibly, with suitable learning postulates, any kind of classificatory system might develop in this way, but since there is a tendency to assume that only the very simplest learning postulates are admissible, these models have not, so far, born any resemblance whatsoever to the models suggested by those who are less concerned with the effects of learning on perception. In fact, existing theories of perception bear so little resemblance to one another, that experiments aimed at testing any one of them are unlikely to have much relevance to most of the others. Economy of effort might be achieved if we could classify theories into different types, and then try to devise experiments which will enable us to discriminate between different types of theory.

I should like to suggest that the central problem in all approaches to perception is the role of learning in the perceptual process, and in particular the relative importance of long-term and short-term learning. In teaching an animal to approach a black circle but not a black triangle or a white circle, no one seriously doubts that the appropriate conjunctive concept has to be learned. But we are in considerable doubt about the nature of the "simple" concepts that are put together to produce the complex concept. To put this problem in another way, we do not know the basic units, or stimulus analyzers, on which short-term perceptual learning operates. To discover the nature of these "simple" concepts is one of the two major issues in perception theory. The other major problem concerns the effect of early and long-term learning on these "simple" concepts. Are they themselves merely overlearned complex concepts, or are they the result of the operation of innate stimulus analyzing mechanisms? To solve both problems it would seem necessary to devise experimental methods for isolating these "simple" concepts or single stimulus analyzing mechanisms, and then, having done so, to investigate their nature and also the effect on them of early experience. As yet, no satisfactory method has been devised for isolating these "simple" concepts, although some suggested methods for doing so will be discussed later. Fortunately the function of early experience may be investigated, reasonably adequately, by experiments which do not isolate these "simple" concepts. But, in spite of this, the appropriate experiments do not appear to have been done.

The logical way to test the effect of experience on stimulus classification is to do so directly by means of transfer experiments. For example, we know that adult rats, and pigeons which have been reared normally, will, when trained to respond positively to a triangle, transfer that response to other larger or smaller triangles and also in some cases to distorted or rotated triangles. Such transfer experiments provide the only evidence we have about how animals classify stimuli. It would be most interesting to find out whether animals reared in the dark, or in some other perceptually poor environment, would show the same ability to transfer responses. When trained to respond positively to a triangle and negatively to a circle, the animal may be responding to a simple or to a complex concept, so that transfer of the response could reflect the operation of one or more stimulus classifying mechanisms. If perceptually deprived animals transfer in the same way as normal animals, this does not matter, since such a result would indicate that a similar mechanism (or mechanisms) is available to both sophisticated and naïve animals. If the perceptually deprived animals show different transfer behavior, the interpretation would be more difficult. Only if we knew that the transfer reflected the operation of a single mechanism, would we be entitled to assume that experience is essential for the development of "simple" concepts. If the transfer reflected the operation of more than one mechanism, then a difference between naïve and sophisticated animals would tell us only what we already know, i.e., that complex concepts have to be learned.

Many theorists, of whom Hebb is the best known, have suggested that, in the absence of suitable experience, stimulus classification as we know it, would be impossible, and very many experiments have been done to test this idea. Unfortunately none of these experiments has used transfer experiments to indicate the nature of the classification mechanisms. They have all been concerned with the effect of perceptual experience on animals' ability to make perceptual discriminations, whereas none of these theories makes any explicit assumption about the relationship between discrimination and transfer. There seems to be an implicit assumption that discrimination is possible only after the stimuli have been classified. There is no direct evidence for this assumption, nor is it implied by Hebb's theory or indeed by any of the alternative theories of this type. The theories are theories of stimulus classification that are designed to explain why we make the same response to different stimuli. As such, the theories are neutral with respect to discrimination. One could argue that to have learned to put two stimuli into the same category should make them less discriminable. This is not a very strong argument, but it is at least as strong as the one which is implied by those who argue that since perceptual experience seems to improve discrimination, this is evidence in favor of theories such as Hebb's.

The relationship between discrimination and transfer is inadequately understood. Until our understanding improves, discrimination experiments cannot be used as evidence for or against theories of pattern recognition.

I can find only one experiment on the effect of early perceptual experience on transfer. Ironically this experiment was done by Hebb in 1937. He investigated the effect of bringing up rats in the dark on their ability to perform size and brightness transpositions. He found no effect at all. If only he had continued and tested his rats for shape transfer, then a great deal of subsequent theorizing, including his own, would have been on a firmer empirical base, or, possibly, need never have occurred at all.

Now let us consider the experimental evidence concerning the organization of the stimulus classifying mechanisms, neglecting now the question of whether this organization is innate or learned. At present the only behavioral evidence we have concerning these mechanisms comes from transfer experiments. But simple transfer experiments could be very misleading for the following reason. There is some evidence suggesting that both animals and men make use of a number of different classificatory systems, in relation to the same stimulus. We, for example, will classify simple visual stimuli according to their shape, size, and color, and it is not unreasonable to suggest that a different mechanism is involved in each case. Sutherland

has argued that many animals also use more than one stimulus classifying mechanism. If this is the case, then simple transfer experiments may not reveal the properties of any of the systems involved.
Suppose we train an animal to respond positively to a triangle and
negatively to a square. We might then find that the response will transfer to a pentagon when compared with a square but to a rectangle when
compared with a pentagon. If we assume that the same classificatory
mechanism is involved in each case, then we should be forced to conclude that the rectangle is more like the triangle than is the pentagon
and we should then try to construct a model which would arrange the
stimuli in the order triangle, rectangle, pentagon, square. But if more
than one mechanism is involved, this could be a very mistaken
endeavor. Suppose, for example, that there is a complex shape analyzer
and another which simply measures the elongation of the shape. The
transfer from triangle to pentagon might then be due to the shape
mechanism, but if the latter is unable to discriminate between a
rectangle and a pentagon, the animal might then resort to the second
mechanism and choose the rectangle as the more elongated. In this
way the experiments would have specified the characteristics of a
nonexistent mechanism and all attempts to model it would be wasted
effort.

Clearly, before we attempt to build models of perceptual mechanisms,
we need to have more information about whether a particular set of
transfer experiments are homogeneous in the sense that they reflect
the properties of a single system. But are there any satisfactory
criteria of homogeneity? Sutherland has suggested that overtraining
on a discrimination will cause an animal eventually to use only a single
analyzer; presumably the analysis which most effectively makes the
necessary discrimination is preferred to all the others which gradually
drop out. The main evidence for this idea comes from the different
effects of overtraining on the learning of a totally new discrimination
compared with learning the reversal of the initial discrimination.
Overtraining on the initial task impedes the former and assists the
latter. This can be explained by the assumption that overtraining
restricts the animals' attention to a single analyzer and that learning
occurs only in relation to those features of the stimulus situation
which are being attended to. If this idea were correct then we could
be certain that only a single analyzer is being used when overtraining
has no differential effect on reversal and nonreversal shifts.

A second criterion for determining the effect of a single analyzer has also been suggested by Sutherland. He considers that the evidence from transfer experiments in the <u>Octopus</u>, indicates that under the conditions of his experiments, visual shape is an unidimensional quality for the <u>Octopus</u>. The unidimensionality is suggested by the successful transfer which occurs between widely different figures and the fact that the order of preference in a transfer test is independent of the original training shapes. The simplest explanation of the unidimensionality of shape for the <u>Octopus</u> is to assume that the <u>Octopus</u> has only one stimulus analyzing mechanism with a simple quantitative output, so that shape for the <u>Octopus</u> is analogous to our own experience of the size or brightness of stimuli.

These two methods suggest criteria by which the properties of "simple" perceptual concepts, or single stimulus analyzing mechanisms may be isolated. Unfortunately both are new and untried and have not yet received much critical examination, while alternative explanations of both phenomena are possible. Nevertheless, this problem deserves far greater attention than it has yet received, and until it is solved, the construction of perceptual models will continue to be an exercise only tenuously related to experimental evidence.

To summarize:

1. Experiments on the effect of experience on the transfer of responses to visual patterns are needed in order to test whether simple perceptual classifications are learned. Experiments on the effect of experience on visual discrimination are irrelevant to the main theoretical issues.

2. Perception probably involves a number of relatively distinct classificatory devices. Until methods of isolating the performance of one alone have been developed, it is all but impossible to relate experiment to theory in this field.

ON THE MODIFIABILITY OF FORM PERCEPTION

Richard Held and Alan Hein
Psychology Department
Massachusetts Institute of Technology
Cambridge, Massachusetts

Concern with the modifiability of perception has traditionally been associated with questions about its earliest development in animals and men. Logically, there need be no relation between modification in the adult and development in the young, but the association provides a strong hypothesis that has intrigued investigators for centuries. Evidence from three types of research has been brought to bear on the issue:

1. Studies of the performance of neonatal animals including human infants.

2. Experiments involving the rearing of animals under special conditions, usually deprivation, until they are matured to the stage when the full range of sensorially guided behavior may be expected. They include the accidental experiments undergone by humans when circumstances, such as congenital cataract, have eliminated pattern vision prior to surgery.

3. Research dealing with the modifiable sensorimotor co-ordinations of adult animals and humans based on the supposition that such plasticity of co-ordination must obtain during neonatal development as well.

This paper poses the issue, as we currently view it, from the perspective of our own research and that of others. Our work in vision began with studies of the effects of optically displacing the perceiver's view of his environment by means of wedge prisms placed in front of his eyes. The results of these experiments led us to investigate aspects of the earliest development of spatial vision. Taken together, the findings have raised some new questions concerning form perception.

Rearrangement Experiments: Evidence and Implications

Rearrangement experiments utilize prisms and other optical devices to displace or otherwise distort the array of light rays entering the eyes of experimental subjects. Predictable errors in visual-motor co-ordination and perception result from such rearrangement. However, when free to continue their normal activities, human subjects adapt to the rearrangement by showing decreasing amounts of error in measures of their visually guided responses. Furthermore, prolonged wearing of some of the rearranging devices yields full and exact compensation for the initial errors. These results imply the existence and utilization of a source of information generated by the continued interaction of the rearranged subject with his environment. This information must be invariant over the transforms produced by rearrangement to the extent that visual-motor control returns to its originally accurate state. A series of experiments, summarized by Held and Freedman (1963), has convinced us that this source of information is generated by the motor-sensory feedback loop. Self-produced movements of a subject experiencing rearranged vision have been shown to be a sufficient condition for partial adaptation, and they appear to be a necessary condition for full and exact compensation.

Because of the stability of the normal environment, the changes in visual stimulation, accompanying bodily movements, taken together with the signals to the musculature that produce these movements, afford the central nervous system a source of highly correlated information. Full and exact compensation for rearrangement occurs when this correlated information is provided. Adaptation is retarded by decorrelation and normal co-ordination is degraded by prolonged decorrelation (Abplanalp and Held, 1965; Efstathiou and Held, 1963; Held and Freedman, 1963). Since this form of correlated information is available to a mobile neonate, the process responsible for adaptation may, in theory, begin to operate from birth to assure the development and subsequent maintenance of accurate visual control. This speculation has called for experimental test. The type of test we have so far used compares the performances of animals reared either with or without visual feedback contingent upon motor output but with visual inputs equivalent under both conditions.

Motor-Visual Feedback in Development

Riesen and his collaborators (1958) discovered deficits in the vision of animals (cat and chimpanzee) reared either with deprivation of patterned visual stimulation or with deprivation of movement in the presence of objects. Following his lead, we have reared pairs of kittens under conditions equivalent in all respects subject to experimental control except for the source of their movements when in an illuminated environment (Held and Hein, 1963).

An apparatus limited the movements of one kitten (Active) to locomotion around three axes of rotation. By means of a mechanical system, locomotory movements of the Active kitten were transferred to its mate (Passive) held in a gondola. The major movements of both animals around the three axes were, therefore, identical. Symmetry of the experimental environment made the optical situation equivalent for both kittens and assured comparable visual inputs. After many hours of such treatment the Active animal showed normal, visually controlled responses in several tests, including choice of shallow over deep drops on a "visual cliff," but the Passive animal failed to exhibit equivalent behavior. In a second experiment, utilizing a similar technique, individual kittens were reared with one eye open (Active) only during self-produced locomotion in an illuminated surround whereas the other eye (Passive) was open only during passive transport over an equivalent path. After many hours of such exposure, the Active eye was found to mediate normal visually guided behavior although the Passive eye failed to do so. Thus we produced between the use of Active and Passive eyes of one kitten the behavioral difference found between the Active and Passive kittens of the preceding experiment.

This result is important for present purposes because it implicates discrimination of visual direction (egocentric localization) in the response to depth mediated by the normal (Active) eye of the kittens. It is highly likely that the animals using monocular vision can discriminate between the different depths of the cliff solely on the basis of the differing displacements of their retinal images during movement (Walk and Gibson, 1961). The resultant stimulation must then be interpreted by the central nervous system as representing differences in distance from the animal's body in order to produce either approach or avoidance. This interpretation of the retinal stimuli requires the projection of a set of visual direction as if to calculate distance by triangulation. The inability of the Passive eye to mediate the discrimination of depth on the cliff may thus result from a failure to develop egocentric visual directions in the absence of visual feedback contingent upon movement.

The kitten experiments have confirmed our speculation that the information generated by the motor-sensory feedback loop is as important for the development of certain visual-motor co-ordinations

as it is for adaptation to rearrangement. Consequently, we have
tentatively asserted that the two types of experimentation — control
of early experience utilizing the technique of limited exposure to the
environment and rearrangement in the adult — are complementary in
that both influence the process which underlies plastic sensorimotor
coordination.

Adaptation to Spatial Distortion

   In most rearrangement experiments changes in either visually
guided motor responses or in apparent orientations of targets with
respect to the body are measured. An example of the latter is the
altered judgment of the verticality of lines produced by the wearing
of tilting prisms (Mikaelian and Held, 1964). Both types of measure
reveal changes in the perceived directions from the body (egocentric
localizations) of stimulated points on the retina. Such changes imply
modification of form perception when members of the set of visual
directions corresponding to these points are displaced in a nonuniform
manner. Their hypothetical projections to a plane in the visual field
describe forms altered in shape from the nondisplaced condition.
Actually, such modifications in form have been suspected at least
since Wundt (1898) reported gradual reduction of curvature, during
prolonged viewing through wedge prisms, of objectively straight lines
which appear curved because of the prism optics. However, after
Gibson (1933) showed that the mere viewing of a set of uniformly
curved lines will produce a decrement in apparent curvature, the prism-
generated adaptation has been regarded solely (but erroneously as we
shall see) as a consequence of the optically produced curvature.
   When our normal urban environment with its dominant rectilinear
patterning is viewed through a wedge prism, optically curved lines are
bound to appear. Hence Gibson's interpretation is plausible. However,
the possibility that adaptive change in the apparent curvature induced
by prisms could occur, when no curved lines are generated, as a
result of the altered motor-visual feedback produced by the prisms,
has not been tested until recently. We examined the latter possibility
by constructing an artificial environment in which straight lines as
well as statistical approximations to linear order were absent (Held
and Rekosh, 1963). Subjects viewed this visual field (Figure 1) through
wedge prisms under two conditions of movement: Active and Passive.
Before and after exposure the subjects viewed a grating of black and

Fig. 1. The upper pair of scenes are shown as viewed normally, the lower pair as viewed through a wedge prism. The left-hand scene, with its linearly ordered contours, appears curved and distorted by the prism; whereas, the right-hand scene, composed of randomized spots, appears unchanged.

white bars through a variable prism whose power they altered to make the bars appear straight. The results were clear. No curvature after-effect followed exposure with passive movement, although substantial adaptation occurred during comparable amounts of active movement.

The change in curvature represents a modification in form perception attributable to the correlated information generated by motor-sensory feedback. This exposure factor has already been implicated in both adaptation to rearrangement and the developing co-ordination of the neonate. Consequently, the result suggests by analogy that, prior to the availability of sufficient movement-produced visual stimulation, animals that exhibit modifiability in sensorimotor co-ordination should not show the same form discrimination as normally reared animals of the same species. Such discrimination should be abnormal to the extent that it depends upon distinguishing among the sets of visual directions corresponding to the loci of stimulated points on the retina.

Form Discrimination in Neonates

What is the evidence bearing on this supposition? Many of the older experiments on neonatal visual performance and the influence of early deprivation on vision are summarized in a review paper by Epstein (1964). Within the last few years Riesen and his collaborators (1958) have found marked slowing in the normal rate of acquisition of form and motion discrimination by both chimpanzee and cat reared with patterned visual stimulation but with limited motility. However, quite recently Meyers and McCleary (1964) discovered that similarly deprived cats can be trained by the use of electric shock to discriminate between forms, provided that the animals are not required to perform a visually guided response to evidence discrimination. A number of studies of Fantz and his associates (1965) has established the existence of a rudimentary type of form discrimination in neonatal primates including human infants. Hershenson (1964) has replicated some, but not all, of Fantz' work. In neurophysiological investigations, Hubel and Wiesel have discovered that the receptive fields in the visual cortex of the kitten are functional shortly after birth in marked contrast to their failure to function in response to stimulation of an eye that had been deprived (monocularly) of patterned stimulation for several months (Hubel and Wiesel, 1963; Wiesel and Hubel, 1963). These results indicate the caution with which the effects of severe forms of visual deprivation must be interpreted. The receptive-field structures are probably a step along the neural pathway to discriminative responses to form. The fact that they function at birth argues that a necessary condition for discriminative responses to form is present at birth.

The Problem

Juxtaposition of these several findings produces an interesting, if

puzzling, picture. On the one hand, we can make a case for the
importance of motor-sensory feedback in the development of a type of
form perception in primates and cats: that which is dependent upon
the projection of egocentric visual directions. On the other hand,
certain types of form discrimination appear to have been demonstrated
in both neonatal and deprived animals. When may the discrimination of
form depend upon a projected set of egocentric directions? We suggest
two possibilities.

Demonstration that altered motor-visual feedback may change the
apparent curvature of contours led to our initial question about the
development of form perception. Deprived animals apparently discriminate as well as normals among forms dissimilar with respect to
features such as corners and contour breaks. However, they may
show considerably different capabilities in discriminating among
forms that are intertransformable by rearrangement and consequent
adaptation. Perception of these forms, characteristically involving
absolute judgments of circularity, straightness, rectangularity, and
so on, is apparently based, at least in part, on the set of visual directions subtended by the figure. It is these visual directions which are
altered by adaptation to rearrangement and which are apparently not
developed in the movement-deprived animal. Consequently, curves of
generalization along dimensions of form subject to transformation by
adaptation should show very different slopes for normal as compared
to deprived animals.

Object recognition, despite change in perspective, is referred to as
constancy of shape. Perspectival changes in the images of objects
are produced by either movements of the perceiver or of the object.
The spatial orientation of eye to object must be taken into account if
either the various perspectival views are to be perceived as the same
object or identical perspectival views from different objects are to be
discriminated. Information about the orientation — direction and
distance — of the object relative to the eye, taken together with the
perspectival view of the object, is presumed to allow the viewer to
recognize the object despite variations in his view of it. It might be
supposed that the mere availability of the necessary visual stimulation
would suffice for constancy of shape perception in the very young
animal, presuming that his nervous system is sufficiently matured.
However, our results with movement-deprived kittens suggest that it
is not sufficient. Prior to the availability of appropriate motor-sensory

feedback, the kitten fails to relate visual information, correlated with the position of an object, to his egocentric space. This failure is evidenced by the absence, with certain special exceptions, of responses having spatial dimensions related to the direction and distance of the object in space. As a consequence of this failure of orientation to the object, shape constancy dependent upon it may be absent. However, the animal may at the same time be capable of discriminating among visual stimuli that vary with the distance and direction of objects when conditioned by the use of a response which itself bears no spatial relation to the object.

In summary, juxtaposition of evidence for the modifiability of form perception in the adult with the data on form discrimination in neonatal and deprived animals raises the possibility that there may be more than one level of processing for form discrimination in higher mammals. In addition to the built-in analyzers of the retinocortical system, there appears to be a more modifiable mechanism implicating visual feedback from motor output. We have speculated that the latter system operates when orientation of the animal to objects in the environment plays a significant role in form discrimination.

Acknowledgment

Research of this laboratory has been supported by the National Institute of Mental Health (Grant M-7642), the National Science Foundation (Grant GB22728), the U.S. Air Force Office of Scientific Research (AF-AFOSR 354-63), the National Aeronautics and Space Administration (NSG-496), and the Rockefeller Foundation.

References

Abplanalp, P., and Held, R. Effects of de-correlated visual feedback on adaptation to wedge prisms. Paper read at Eastern Psychological Association, Atlantic City, New Jersey, 1965.

Efstathiou, A., and Held, R. Correlated and de-correlated visual feedback in modifying eye-hand coordination. Paper read at Eastern Psychological Association, 1963.

Epstein, W. Experimental investigations of the genesis of visual space perception. Psychol. Bull., 1964, 61, 115-128.

Fantz, R. L. Ontogeny of perception. In A. M. Schrier, H. F. Harlow, and F. Stollnitz (Eds.), Behavior of nonhuman primates: Modern research trends. Vol. 2. New York: Academic, 1965. Pp. 365-403.

Gibson, J. J. Adaptation, after-effect, and contrast in the perception of curved lines. J. exp. Psychol., 1933, 16, 1-31.

Held, R., and Freedman, S. Plasticity in human sensorimotor control, Science, 1963, 142, 455-462.

Held, R., and Hein, A. Movement-produced stimulation in the development of visually-guided behavior. J. comp. physiol. Psychol., 1963, 56, 872-876.

Held, R., and Rekosh, J. Motor-sensory feedback and the geometry of visual space. Science, 1963, 141, 722-723.

Hershenson, M. Visual discrimination in the human newborn. J. comp. physiol. Psychol., 1964, 58, 270-276.

Hubel, D., and Wiesel, T. Receptive fields of cells in striate cortex of very young, visually inexperienced kittens. J. Neurophysiol., 1963, 26, 994-1002.

Meyers, B., and McCleary, R. Interocular transfer of a pattern discrimination in pattern deprived cats. J. comp. physiol. Psychol., 1964, 57, 16-21.

Mikaelian, H., and Held, R. Two types of adaptation to an optically-rotated visual field. Amer. J. Psychol., 1964, 77, 257-263.

Riesen, A. H. Plasticity of behavior: Psychological series. In H. Harlow and C. Woolsey (Eds.), Biological and biochemical bases of behavior. Madison, Wis.: Univer. Wisconsin Press, 1958, Pp. 425-450.

Walk, R. D., and Gibson, Eleanor J. A comparative and analytical study of visual depth perception. Psychol. Monogr., 1961, 75 (15, Whole No. 519).

Wiesel, T., and Hubel, D. Single-cell responses in striate cortex of kittens deprived of vision in one eye. J. Neurophysiol., 1963, 26, 1003-1017.

Wundt, W. Zur Theorie der räumlichen Gesichtswahrnehmungen. Phil. Stud., 1898, 14, 11.

PSYCHOPHYSICS AND PATTERN INTERACTIONS

Hüseyin Yılmaz
Arthur D. Little, Incorporated
Cambridge, Massachusetts

Previous work on psychophysical laws of brightness perception (Yılmaz, 1964) is generalized to include color perception under uniform and nonuniform illuminations. Since a nonuniform illumination is a pattern in the visual field imposed over the existing patterns, the resulting theory is capable of treating the color and light interactions of patterns. The problem treated under the evolutionary requirement gives rise to a number of conclusions which are in harmony with the observed behavior of the human eye. First, we summarize the main points of the previous paper (Yılmaz, 1964). Two fundamental assumptions are made: (a) Perceptual apparatus works as a comparison device. It does not assign sensations S_1, S_2, S_3, ... to objects O_1, O_2, O_3, ... in an absolute sense. Rather, the perceptions are geared to the relationships $(O_1 O_2)$, $(O_2 O_3)$, $(O_1 O_3)$, ... as S_{12}, S_{23}, S_{13}. etc. (b) Evolution requires that when the conditions of perceiving are changed, the associated object perceptions remain unchanged (as much as possible).

Application to brightness perception of the human eye proceeds by requiring that when the illumination I is shifted to a new level $I' = \kappa I$ (without changing the chromatic composition), the associated perceptions be independent of κ. Let, under I, intensities reaching the eye from various objects be i_1, i_2, i_3, ... Under I' they will be $i'_1 = \kappa i_1$, $i'_2 = \kappa i_2$, $i'_3 = \kappa i_3$, ... and we must have

$$S_{12}(i_1, i_2) = S_{12}(\kappa i_1, \kappa i_2). \qquad [1]$$

This can be satisfied if we assume the functional form to be

$$S_{12}(i_1, i_2) = F\left(\frac{i_2}{i_1}\right) \qquad [2]$$

From this it can be shown that if the sensation mechanism in the brain works additively, we have the Weber-Fechner form

$$S_{12} = \alpha \log \left(\frac{i_2}{i_1}\right) \qquad [3]$$

whereas, if the mechanism works multiplicatively, the Stevens form

$$S_{12} = \left(\frac{i_2}{i_1}\right)^{\beta} \qquad [4]$$

is obtained. Thus, as far as the evolutionary constraint is concerned, the brain has freedom in the choice of mechanism. In fact, the mathematical form of the law should give us some hints as to what kind of mechanism is operating in the brain. It is possible that different mechanisms are used in different species or the same mechanism is used for different perceptions. It is also possible that different mechanisms are used for different ranges of the same perceptual variable. It seems that unless some other consideration of an evolutionary nature requires one or the other of such choices, there is really no basic virtue of one law over the other. In fact, the different appearance of the two laws should not deceive us. The difference amounts to a redefinition (calibration) only. If we transform the variables as $i \rightarrow \log i$, the Stevens form becomes identical with the Weber-Fechner form. This shows that as far as the brightness perception is concerned, the general law is Eq. [2]. Weber-Fechner and Stevens forms are only different representations of it. As George Biernson has pointed out[1] another possible representation used in the biological world may be $S_{12} = (i_2 - i_1) / (i_2 + i_1)$. In this connection we may call attention to the fact that Eqs. [3] and [4] are not identical to Weber-Fechner and Stevens laws because i_1 and i_2 refer to different objects. It is only because these functions are separable that the usual Weber-Fechner and Stevens laws can be deduced as $S = \alpha \log i$ or $S = i^\beta$. If the function is not separable as in the case of $S_{12} = (i_1 - i_2)/(i_1 + i_2)$, the usual laws could not be claimed to exist, whereas the general law Eq. [2] allows the case of nonseparable situations.[2]

From our basic assumptions and the form Eq. [2], we can readily draw some important conclusions: (a) If an object in a given scene is black (charcoal), gray (dust), or white (egg), it will retain its appearance when the level of illuminant changes. Under the new illumination charcoal may reflect more light than dust or egg, but it will stay as black as it was before and be identified as charcoal. (b) A television screen looks gray under the room illumination. If we turn on the picture without changing the room illumination, some areas of the screen will look black, although as much light (in fact more) is now reaching the eye from these areas.

These ideas are generalizable to chromatic illuminations. Let i now represent the three color coordinates α, β, and γ of a light sample. Under the chromatic change of the illumination, the scale transformation $i' \rightarrow \kappa i$ will now go over

$$\alpha' = \Omega_{11}\alpha + \Omega_{12}\beta + \Omega_{13}\gamma$$
$$\beta' = \Omega_{21}\alpha + \Omega_{22}\beta + \Omega_{23}\gamma \qquad [5]$$
$$\gamma' = \Omega_{31}\alpha + \Omega_{32}\beta + \Omega_{33}\gamma$$

One can separate this into an intensity change and a chromatic change, $\Omega \rightarrow \kappa\Omega$. Since we have already studied the effect of κ, we may set it equal to unity and study only the chromatic change. The formula Eq. [1] now can be written formally

$$S_{12}(i_1, i_2) = S_{12}(\Omega i_1, \Omega i_2) \qquad [6]$$

---

[1] Personal communication.

[2] A separable set of possible psychophysical laws are also deduced from a different principle by R. D. Luce (1959).

where Ω is a matrix which must have an inverse and satisfy[3]

$$\det \; \left\| \, \Omega \, \right\| \; = 1 \quad , \; \Omega^{-1} = \alpha \, \Omega^{\dagger} \alpha \qquad [7]$$

It is then evident that the evolutionary requirement is equivalent to a transformation on a metric space α, β, γ. This was indeed the conclusion drawn earlier (Yılmaz, 1962) in the author's theory of color perception, where the elements of the matrix Ω were actually deduced. It was also shown that the transformations predict the over-all effects of (a) object-color invariance, (b) color illusion, (c) color contrast, and (d) two-color projections (Land, 1959 a, b).

It was explicitly pointed out that the foregoing formula accounts for the over-all effects but the local effects due to proximity of colors in space and in time of viewing are not included. These can be introduced by noticing that illumination can be nonuniform. A rock which is partly under the shadow of the leaves and partly in sunlight is non-uniformly illuminated. The requirement that even under a nonuniform illumination object-colors tend to remain invariant leads to the conclusion that transformations are applicable to portions of the visual field as well as to the totality. In other words, portions of the retina can act independently of other portions and set up co-ordinate transformations. This means that the transformation matrix is, in general, a function of the position in the visual field; that is, the field of illumination I (x, y, t) sets up a field of transformation

$$\Omega_{ik} = \Omega_{ik} \, (x, \, y, \, t) \qquad [8]$$

This generalization is entirely within the spirit of the earlier consideration and can be similarly worked out.

The following conclusions can be readily drawn: (a) Transformation of colors can take place independently in different regions or in one region within another. In the words of Edwin Land [1959a, p. 120] "multiple color universes can coexist side by side, or one within another". (b) Color contrast is strongest between nearby colors. Areas remote from each other act more independently. (c) Color illusions can manifest locally as well as in an over-all, global sense. (d) Successive contrast is the time counterpart of simultaneous contrast.

---

[3] In other words, the Ω-matrix should leave the scalar product $P = i_1$, i_2 invariant. The matrix α is diagonal and $\alpha_{ii} = +1$ for a positive signature and $\alpha_{ii} = -1$ for a negative signature.

Acknowledgment

This work was sponsored by the Office of Naval Research under Contract #4406(00).

References

Land, E. H. Color vision and the natural image. Proc. nat. Acad. Sci., 1959, 45, 115-129; 636-644. (a)

Land, E. H. Experiments in color vision. Sci. Amer., 1959, 200(5), 84-99. (b)

Luce, R. D. On the possible psychophysical laws. Psychol. Rev., 1959, 66, 81-95.

Yılmaz, H. On color vision and a new approach to general perception. In E. E. Bernard and M. R. Kare (Eds.), Biological prototypes and synthetic systems. Vol. 1. New York: Plenum, 1962. Pp. 126-141.

Yılmaz, H. On the laws of psychophysics. Bull. math. Biophys., 1964, 26, 235-237.

CONTRIBUTED PAPERS IV

Perceptual Organization in Speech

Chairman: Arthur S. House
Department of Audiology and Speech Sciences
Purdue University
Lafayette, Indiana

ON THE MOTOR THEORY OF SPEECH PERCEPTION

Peter B. Denes
Bell Telephone Laboratories, Incorporated
Murray Hill, New Jersey

Years ago, speech recognition was thought to be a simple process, in which, distinct and unique acoustic-auditory features are interpreted as specific phonemes. Modern technology enabled us to check these theories by incorporating them into models of the speech recognition process. The first models failed to recognize speech successfully, showing that our theories were inadequate. As the years passed, our ideas about speech recognition — and the models built to implement them — became more and more sophisticated, and yet, the results are still very unsatisfactory. As matters stand today, we have on the one hand, the human being, who can recognize speech with ease even under conditions of severe noise and distortion, and on the other hand, models of the speech recognition process which take into account all we know about human speech recognition and yet are able to deal only with fewer than a dozen or so words and only when spoken in isolation. It is only natural therefore that new theories should be continuously proposed about various aspects of speech perception. One of these is the motor theory of speech perception. The motor theory proposes that, during speech recognition, we do not directly associate the sound qualities we perceive with linguistic units, the phonemes, words, etc., but that, instead, we first interpret our auditory percepts in terms of the articulatory movements needed to produce these sounds and, in a second stage, we recognize the language units by association with these articulatory movements. A corollary of this theory is that an essential part of the process of learning to <u>recognize</u> speech is training in <u>producing</u> speech ourselves. The purpose of the experiment to be described in this paper was to observe how far being able to listen to our own voice, and thereby getting a chance of associating our articulatory movements with the sounds produced by these movements, makes learning to recognize speech easier.

In order to carry out the experiment, a method was needed for making naturally produced speech sounds sufficiently unlike normal speech that it could not be recognized without learning. At the same time, the sounds had to retain enough information about articulatory movement to make them learnable. This was achieved by modifying an 11-channel vocoder to compress the spectrum of speech in the ratio of roughly 3 to 1. The system is explained in Figure 1. The 180 to 4,500 cps wide speech spectrum is split into 11 bands; the energy from each band controls the output of 11 synthesizing channels which, between them cover the frequency band of 50 to 1,600 cps. The pitch of the speech input is also monitored and is used to control the frequency of the buzz source applied to the synthesizing filters. Again, the pitch of the output,

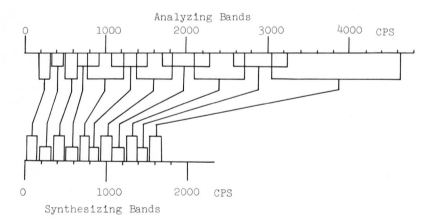

Fig. 1. Frequency transposition performed by test equipment.

compared with that of the original speech input, is reduced in the ratio of about 3 to 1. The speech input could be obtained either from a prerecorded magnetic tape or from a microphone. The output could be heard over earphones.

Ten subjects were used in the experiment. Each session consisted of a 20 minute training period followed by a 5-minute test. The speech material used was taken from a library of 150 words. The words were pronounced in isolation, by one speaker, prerecorded on magnetic tape and rerandomized every time they were used. During the training period, the subjects listened to the processed words over earphones and, at the same time, they had a printed list of the words in front of them. In this way, they could associate the sounds they heard with the words they represented. During the test period, a different list of words was used, the subjects still heard the processed speech, but they did not have the printed list and instead had to write down the words they could recognize.

The subjects were divided into two groups: the so-called "listeners" and the "speakers." During the training period, the listeners could learn solely by associating the processed sounds of the one, prerecorded speaker with the words on their printed list. The "speakers" on the other hand, in addition, had a microphone. They first listened to the prerecorded voice and then had to repeat the word into their microphone. Their voice was processed by the identical device as the voice of the prerecorded speaker and they heard the processed version of their own voice over their earphones. In this way, they could learn to relate (a) the words shown on the printed list, (b) the associated articulatory movements they themselves made when they pronounced these words, and, (c) the processed sounds which they heard as a result of their articulatory movements. The 5-minute test which followed each training period was, of course, the same for "speakers" and for "listeners." The test lists consisted of 50 randomized words and the proportion of words recognized correctly was taken as a measure of the learning achieved. A comparison of the learning progress of the two groups was considered as an indication of the value, in recognizing speech, of the articulatory associations available to the "speakers" only and thereby furnish an indication of the validity of the motor theory. The learning progress observed in 15 consecutive training periods by "speakers" and by "listeners" is shown in Figure 2. No clear-cut difference between the two groups is evident: both curves rise from roughly a 40 percent word recognition score to about 70 percent. The results therefore do not support the motor theory of speech perception. Just the same, a comparison of the speakers' and of the listeners' learning curves show certain dissimilarities thay may indicate that the speakers'

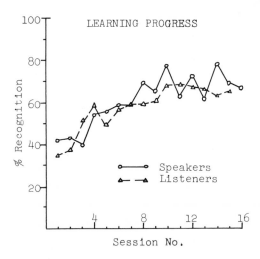

Fig. 2. Test results obtained with the two groups of subjects.

learning progress <u>was</u> influenced by the sound of their own articulations. There are, for example, the marked oscillations in the
speakers' curve as compared with the relative smoothness of the
listeners' curve. This may be the effect of the more variable sounds
heard by the "speakers" as compared with the "listeners." The listeners always heard the same recording of only one speaker, while the
speakers may well have varied their pronunciation as their learning
progressed, producing a feedback type oscillation in their results.
Also — perish the thought — some equipment failure cannot be dis-
regarded. The test equipment was basically a vocoder and pitch
detectors of vocoders are notorious for making errors under certain
combinations of speaker's voice, vowel quality, and voice pitch. While
this could be controlled for the one prerecorded voice, pitch detector
errors were observed for some of the other voices.

Further analysis of the recognition scores showed that almost three
times as many errors were owing to place-of-articulation than to manner-
of-articulation confusions. This, of course, is quite consistent with
the very rough quantization of the spectrum by the analyzing filters:
the second formant region — so important for identifying the place of
articulation of consonants — was divided into just four bands, each
about 450 cps wide, so that only the really strong formant transitions
were at all noticeable in the spectrum of the output. It may, in fact,
have been more reasonable to have used a <u>formant</u> vocoder-based
system rather than the channel vocoder actually used. This approach

would have produced test signals that were still unlike normal speech yet richer in distinctive information about articulatory activity, making the learning of articulatory-auditory associations easier.

Was the output of the present system, in fact, distinctive enough to be learnable? On re-examination, the data showed definite evidence of the learnability of our nonspeechlike test sounds. The recognition scores obtained for certain key words after the first three learning periods were compared with the scores for the same words after the 9th, 10th, and 11th learning periods. It was found that while at the start of the learning period confusions were as high as 50 percent or more; by the end of the 11th learning period, they were down to a very small value. The evident learnability of these processed "speech" signals is important not only theoretically but it also furnishes a guide to the promise of certain frequency-compression hearing aids. Unfortunately, we have no time to discuss these hearing aids and the associated problems of relearning in this paper.

In conclusion then, it can be said that the tests have produced no firm evidence to support the motor theory of speech perception. The results have, however, shown some differences in the learning behavior of "listeners" and of "speakers," indicating that longer learning periods or perhaps more learnable signals might confirm the motor theory after all. The results have also shown that some, at least, of the frequency transposed signals were learnable, an interesting result in itself.

It is, of course, disappointing that this experiment has not produced definite evidence in favor of the motor theory. After all, the idea of speech perception by reference to articulation would provide a framework of unifying simplicity for much of what we know about speech perception. In assessing the results of this experiment therefore two additional factors ought to be considered. First, perhaps the speech learning performed by adults, such as the subjects in this experiment, is different from what takes place when a child learns speech. Second, just as with many others kinds of human activity, there is probably more than one method by which speech perception can be achieved and normally we may well use several different methods simultaneously. If, however, for any reason one of the methods fails, there are the other methods to take its place. The existence of such a multiple system is probably the reason why satisfactory speech perception can be achieved under so many adverse conditions. If such a multiple system does exist, then the learning process based on articulatory experiences which was investigated in our experiment may have been masked by the operation of some of the other methods available for speech perception. The inconclusive results may therefore just indicate the fundamental variety of ways in which speech perception can be achieved rather than that articulatory experiences do not play an important part in the process.

INTONATION AND THE SYNTACTIC PROCESSING OF SPEECH

Philip Lieberman
Data Sciences Laboratory
Air Force Cambridge Research Laboratories
Bedford, Massachusetts

Intonation has often been treated as a peripheral element in the perception of speech. It has been commonly assumed that intonation conveys only the speaker's emotions or his attitude toward the words of his sentences. The model for intonation discussed in this summary proposes that intonation has a central role in the transformational recognition routines that the listener must use for syntactic analysis. Intonation provides acoustic cues that segment the speech signal into linguistic units suitable for syntactic analysis. These acoustic cues also may, in concert with the total ensemble of acoustic information, provide the phonological basis for morphemes which are relevant in the semantic interpretation of the sentence.

Analysis of Intonation

The information bearing elements of intonation must be divided into several categories. Intonation first transmits information that identifies the utterances of a particular speaker. Intonation also transmits the speaker's emotional state, whether he is happy, sad, angry, etc. Darwin (1872) and Bell (1848) discussed these aspects of intonation which they believed derived from the innate expression of the speaker's emotional state. Both of these attributes of intonation, though important, are secondary to the linguistic function of intonation in speech.

Many analyses of intonation have noted that the words of a given

sentence will often have a different "meaning" when the intonation of
the sentence is changed. Some analyses have tried to find pitch
"phonemes" which form "morphemes" that have specific meanings.
Several studies have concentrated on the problem of differentiating
subtle shades of meaning in individual isolated sentences. These
studies have resulted in large lists of pitch "morphemes." However,
the morphemes in these lists do not have specific variant meanings.
It is difficult to isolate any meanings that seem to belong to the
morphemes themselves, since the supposed morphemes generally have
different meanings when they occur in sentences that have different
words. These studies[1], in general, did not critically examine the
problem of how the acoustic signal is segmented into sentences (or
semisentences) during connected speech.

The model for the linguistic aspects of intonation that is discussed in
this summary proposes that meaning is not conveyed by the presence
of specific, highly differentiated pitch morphemes. Long lists of
distinct, unique pitch morphemes do not appear to have any real basis.
Instead we believe that the primary linguistic[2] function of intonation
is to furnish acoustic cues that allow the listener to segment speech
into blocks for syntactic processing.

A syntactic recognition routine is the prerequisite for the semantic
interpretation of the speech signal. The listener must derive an
underlying phrase marker (see Katz and Postal, 1964) starting with
the acoustic signal and his knowledge of the grammar of the language.
The underlying phrase marker is the input to the semantic component
of the grammar. Intonation furnishes acoustic cues that tell the
listener when he has a block of speech that constitutes a satisfactory
input to his syntactic recognition routines. Intonation can furnish
different meanings to utterances that have the same words by grouping
the words into different blocks which direct the listeners' recognition
routines toward one underlying phrase marker rather than another.

---

[1] Daniel Jones (1932) and Armstrong and Ward (1926) have, of course,
considered this problem and they have not been led into the trap of
postulating endless lists of arbitrary, emphemeral pitch morphemes.

[2] The emotional aspects of intonation are extralinguistic since the
listener must know the behavior patterns of a particular talker in order
to decode correctly the acoustic signal. One talker may signal anger
by speaking in a quiet, low-pitched voice, whereas another may speak
in a loud, high-pitched voice. The listener's knowledge of the grammar
of English is not relevant to this decoding problem.

The Elementary Acoustic Elements of Intonation Contours

The psychoacoustic dimension of pitch has as its primary acoustic correlate fundamental frequency. The fundamental frequency of phonation is the frequency at which the vocal cords vibrate. Languages are always characterized, in part, by the fact that certain patterns of muscular activity form the basis of phonemic distinctions in one language while similar, but distinct, gestures form the basis of other phonemic distinctions in another language. Thus English has the vowels /i/ and /u/ while French has these vowels in addition to nasalized /ĩ/ and /ũ/.

We believe that languages are also characterized by particular, normal, "breath groups." We will define a "breath group" to be the acoustic output that results from the synchronized activity of the chest, abdominal and laryngeal muscles during the course of a single expiration. The normal breath groups of different languages are, of course, dissimilar. To a great degree, speaking without an "accent" involves using the appropriate normal breath group and the appropriate modifications of the normal breath group. However, we can make certain generalizations about the breath groups of all languages.

The fundamental frequency and amplitude contours of the normal breath group of American English are plotted in Figure 1. Note that

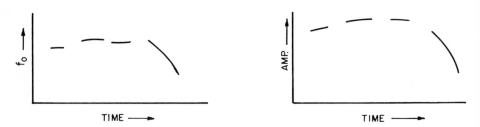

Fig. 1. Fundamental frequency and amplitude contours of the normal breath group of American English.

fundamental frequency and amplitude both fall at the end of the contour. This is a natural consequence of the fact that the frequency at which the human vocal cords vibrate is directly proportional to both the tension of certain laryngeal muscles and the subglottal air pressure. At the end of an expiration the subglottal air pressure must fall as the air supply in the lungs is depleted. The fundamental frequency will fall if the tension of the laryngeal muscles does not increase so as to compensate for this falling air pressure. Different languages are marked by different synchronized patterns of muscular activity which result in slightly different fundamental frequency and amplitude contours for their normal breath groups. However, for virtually all languages the normal breath group ends with falling fundamental frequency and falling amplitude. This seems to be a consequence of a condition of least muscular effort. The talker does not have to tension his laryngeal muscles to compensate for the falling air pressure at the end of an expiration. These normal breath groups are used to mark the limits of complete declarative sentences where we define the sentence[3] to be a unit of speech that contains all the words necessary to transmit a single thought or a group of closely related thoughts as, for example, Joe went home, or The boy who went home has a red coat. The normal breath group is used to segment this block of speech from the words that follow or precede it in the pattern of speech activity. This segmentation is necessary for the syntactic analysis that is part of the process of decoding the information contained in the speech signal. When we hear the utterance: I like red coats the boy who went home has a red coat he also has ... we must delimit the sentence. The boy who went home has a red coat. The speaker therefore unites these words by uttering them on a single breath group. Consider the problem of trying to decide, in 2 seconds, what the following sequence of words meant: ... coats the boy who went to school has a red....

Long sentences that can not be spoken on a single expiration are linked together by tensioning the laryngeal muscles so that the fundamental frequency does not fall at the end of the nonterminating breath group. The increased tension of the laryngeal muscles, which we shall denote by the feature (+rise) results in the acoustic correlate of a breath group marked by a not-falling fundamental frequency at its end. The general interpretation of a breath group marked by the feature (+rise) is that the message has not concluded, that more is to follow. Under certain conditions questions can also end with a breath group marked by (+rise). The interpretation of (+rise) under these conditions is similar, more to follow. However, for a question more is to follow from the person to whom the question is addressed.

---

[3] These sentences correspond to spoken grammatical sentences or semisentences.

We can relate the concept of questioning to a Q morpheme (see Katz
and Postal, 1964) which appears in the underlying phrase marker. It
is important that we do not directly equate the feature (+rise) with the
concept of question. The not-falling intonation that results from (+rise)
is a phonetic sign that is related to Q through phrase structure and
transformation rules. Through a variety of means Q can be signaled
in the speech signal. Special words, e.g., the interrogative pronouns
who, were, etc. can result from the transformations that operate on Q.
In some languages particles, e.g., li in Russian, can signal the presence
of Q. In general, intonation is used to signal the presence of Q when
special morphemes or words are not used for this purpose.

The well-known properties of intonation with regard to making the
"meaning" of the words clearer can also be regarded as examples of
intonation compensating for the absence of words that would make the
underlying phrase marker (hence the meaning) of the sentence clear.
The sentence, I hit the man with the stick, for example, can mean
either (a) I hit the man who had the stick, or (b) The man was hit with
a stick by me. Intonation can indicate either (a) or (b) by manifesting
those aspects of the surface structure that differentiate the two underlying phrase markers. The schematized intonation contours of the two
sentences are presented in Figure 2.

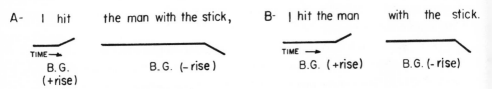

Fig. 2. An example of breath groups "changing" the meaning of
the words of a sentence.

We will be able to make slight mention only of other aspects of
intonation. The speaker can also produce momentary rises in fundamental frequency by producing a pulse of subglottal air pressure at
any part of the breath group. We will use the notation (+P) for these
momentary subglottal air pressure pulses. The speaker can make
any part of a sentence more "prominent" by marking it with (+P). If
the transfer function of the vocal tract were constant during speech
then (+P) would always result in an increase in the acoustic sound
pressure level. However, the transfer function of the vocal tract is
constantly changing during connected speech as the speaker moves

his lips, jaw, tongue, and velum to articulate the segmental phonemes of the speech signal. The primary acoustic correlate of (+P) is therefore an increase in the fundamental frequency of the speech signal. When a listener hears a speech signal and hears a fundamental frequency rise he often has no way of telling whether the rise was due to the activity of the laryngeal or the chest and abdominal muscles. The results of psychoacoustic experiments and phonetic analysis suggest that listeners interpret intonation contours in terms of fixed schema. Not-falling fundamental frequency transitions at the end of the contour are always interpreted as manifestations of (+rise) while local prominences of fundamental frequency elsewhere in the contour are interpreted as manifestations of (+P). Local prominences can be used by the talker to focus attention on any of the words of a sentence.

Some speakers apparently always employ a pulse of subglottal air pressure in addition to tensioning their laryngeal muscles at the end of a breath group where they wish to signal (+rise). Their efforts are nonetheless interpreted by other listeners as normal not-falling intonations. The perception of these elementary "phonetic" entities is based on the listener's knowledge of the basic patterns of muscular activity for the normal unmodified breath group of his language. Even at this level perception is a function of the listener's knowledge of the basic constructs and grammar of his language.

References

Armstrong, L. E., and Ward, I. Handbook of English intonation Leipzig: Teubner, 1926.

Bell, C. The anatomy and philosophy of expression as connected with the fine arts. (9th ed.) London: J. Murray, 1848.

Darwin, C. The expression of emotion in man and the animals. London: J. Murray, 1872.

Jones, D. An outline of English phonetics. New York: Dutton, 1932.

Katz, J. J., and Postal, P. M. An integrated theory of linguistic descriptions. Cambridge: M.I.T. Press, 1964.

SPEECH, PERCEPTS, AND LINGUISTIC FORMS

A. Cohen
Instituut voor Perceptie Onderzoek
Eindhoven, Netherlands

In presenting ideas and observations that may lead to a model of speech perception we will understand by model the distillation of knowledge acquired by empirical and experimental means, which should have some additional power of leading to the presentation of queries and hypotheses not explicitly accounted for in the original construction of the model. In this specific case it will be necessary to distinguish the following notions all implied in the terms speech perception and assumed to be constantly present. The next section will give experimental evidence, and the concluding section will contain suggestions towards a model of speech perception.

Assumptions

Speech (1) itself, in spite of its etymological link to the notion of speaking, involves both a speaker and a hearer together taking part in the process of communication (2). Our main emphasis will be on perception (3) which is dependent on some form of interior mapping based on the language conventions structuring speech into linguistic signs (4). This "mapping" can only be turned to effect after a prolonged period of language acquisition (5). The learning process itself is set in a situation in which prospective language users learn to operate with the signs put at their disposal to implement a pragmatic drive (6).

1. Speech can be seen as the acoustic manifestation of learned language structures which, in principle, can be described linguistically in terms of a system of rules characteristic for each particular language and known in some form or other to both speaker and hearer, who can make contact in the act of communication.

2. The act of communication through speech comes about by means of acoustically manifest linguistic signs, words, which enable the participants to reach beyond the narrow confines of a world of mere sensations. The words, the linguistic signs as such, mediate between things, concepts, and emotions, as well as their interrelations in the world of the speaker and those of the hearer. This intricate network as embodied in the linguistic signs will

provide the participants with the possibility of contacting each
other and of understanding what the speech act is all about. The
knowledge of the linguistic structures used is a necessary prerequisite for the hearer in interpreting the air vibrations reaching
his ear.

3. Perception will come about once the particular language conventions have been properly assimilated. This assimilation will
come as the result of years of arduous learning.

4. Linguistic signs. The basic discovery to be made by the hearer
is that certain sound shapes are invested with a certain meaning
as laid down both in the lexicon and the grammar of the language,
involving, respectively, lexical and grammatical meaning. These
linguistic signs can be described as structured on at least three
different levels. We call these levels the first, second, and third
levels of linguistic structuring.

The first structuring is constituted by the way the continuum of
the empirical world is conceptualized in discrete terms, words,
each with its own immanent and manifest aspects, viz., its conceptual contents and its acoustic shape.

The second structuring is provided by the linguistic marshalling
of these words according to the programming rules of a particular
language involving the possibility of words with an interior structure, the intraword alignment into smaller linguistic units,
described in the morphology of the language, morphemes, which
may be compared with syllables in writing. On a par with it is
the alignment of words into larger structural wholes according
to the syntagmatic rules which, together with the morphological
arrangements, make up the grammatical system of the language.

The third structuring refers to the arrangement of linguistic
forms into discrete units, phonemes, comparable to the letters
of the alphabet.

5. Language acquisition. Right from the start the child is exposed
to speech utterances, being the manifest aspect of the linguistic
signs with which he has to learn to operate. In this operation
speaking and hearing go hand in hand. In fact, several feedback
loops are generally accepted, both exteroceptive, via the auditory
pathway, and enteroceptive, via kinesthesis. To this may be
added the postulated motor coupling in hearing (cf. the shadowing
experiments by Cherry [1962, p. 57] and the work of Liberman,

Cooper, Harris, MacNeilage, and Studdert-Kennedy [1967] at Haskins).

Whenever hearing is defective huge difficulties arise in learning how to handle the linguistic principles as becomes apparent from the rudimentary language capacity frequently found in severely deaf children. Once the linguistic conventions have been assimilated it is possible for the child to produce and interpret completely new structures.

This creation of fresh utterances not previously heard or produced, is going on apace, but even before a high degree of proficiency has been achieved playful new forms may be generated and understood not necessarily all in accord with the adults' conventions (witness children's secret languages). All through the learning stage there should be enough motivation to keep going and improving. This is afforded by:

6. the pragmatic drive, the urge to get things done, to appeal to and interest others, and to give vent to one's expressive needs.

Experimental Evidence for the Assumptions

In all experiments to be reported on here, listeners were instructed to pay attention to the sound shape of linguistic signs or parts of signs. This, in fact, appeals to the faculty assumed in language users of knowing that there is always an acoustic shape at issue which can be perceived as such and identified. Thus we were able to make subjects complete partial word forms, spoken and tape recorded CV combinations. The results show a clear relationship with the frequency of word forms containing the original structure: the favorite completion frame turned out to be CVC which is indeed the favorite word structure in Dutch.

The recognition of nonsense words of the CVC-type, e.g., shows that there is a bare, semiautomatic type of perception where no situational, contextual, or semantic cues are present.

A study of errors in speaking reveals the existence of a rigorous set of rules according to which speech forms have to be programmed; interference of subsequent forms may show up prematurely in the shape of errors of anticipation; preceding speech forms may give rise to errors of perseveration; finally, errors of permutation may crop up involving the transposition of elements in which one or more phonemes reverse places. Anticipatory errors tend to outnumber by 3 to 1 those of perseveration.

Now these data, together with numerous similar findings attested in the literature, go to show that language users continuously use their knowledge of the outward acoustic shape of linguistic signs.

In more analytic tasks subjects were able to evaluate synthetically generated F1-F2 combinations of varying lengths both as to spectral timbre and to appropriate duration. The results amounted to the conclusion that the assumed built-in patterns can indeed be made manifest in terms of tolerances in the case of vowels.

From these and the following experiments it became clear that time cues, duration as well as rise and decay times of the acoustic fine structure, may play an important part in speech perception.

Though no hard and fast borders can be drawn between speech sounds in the articulatory and acoustic phases of the speech chain, in using the technique of gating, which brings about a demasking effect, we were able to help subjects to listen more analytically and managed to obtain from them judgments about the ending of one segment and the beginning of the next (see 't Hart and Cohen, 1964).

These segments need not always correspond in size to single phonemes, notably in the case of consonants, some of which are hard to identify in isolation. Acoustic cues will therefore have to be considered together with distributional ones.

Discussion

The phonemic framework acts as a screen and enables the listener to interpret the acoustic quasi continuum into a quasi discrete sequence of segments. There is, as yet, no certainty whether the size of these segments should be seen as small as single phonemes or rather in terms of larger units comprising frequent clusters and favorite syllable types. The main clue to the perceptual mechanism is the transformation of continuously varying acoustic parameters into discrete perceptual occurrences in which process time cues are picked up both on a micro- and a macrolevel, i.e., for the identification of single segments as well as for the sequential arrangement.

One mode of perceptual behavior may be attributed to the presence of some mapping device which acts as a convertor on the incoming signals. Such a device must have come about through an active process of speech training.

A different mode would suggest that any signal, received by the ear is actually compared with internally generated patterns stored in the

brain. Such a comparative perceptual process is postulated by Jakobson
and Halle (1956, p. 3) in a situation in which a listener is confronted by
the unknown name Ditter.

It is our contention that both modes would have to be accommodated
in any model of speech perception. Yet, there is an essential difference between them to the effect that in learning, the comparing
process is likely to be predominant, whereas after the completion of
the learning process a kind of filtering would be the more adequate
mode to account for ordinary speech perception.

The former is a much more analytical operation in which an individual may use all his ingenuity to come up with the right solution,
and if any suggested solution turns out to be wrong he will by definition
still be learning. There is more awareness of errors than in the
more synthetical mode. In the latter type of recognition, he will no
longer bother about right or wrong decisions: the mapping device will
enable him to make approximations that will be satisfactory to him
on account of previous experience.

The structure and the interrelations of this mapping device have
been built up in the course of language acquisition and its focal points
may be termed percepts. It is these percepts, each with its own
characteristics measurable in terms of tolerances, that bring the
acoustic signals into fusion with their destination, the word forms in
toto.

If now we assume phonemes to be such percepts it has to be borne
in mind that they may be quite complex and the result of long years
of training. All attempts at defining phonemes have always had to
account for this complexity; yet in describing the system of phonemes
arranged as terms of oppositions the simplicity of the ultimate
description does not reflect the intricacy of the terms involved any
more.

In any model of speech perception we have to stress that the
knowledge required for the operation of the perceptual mechanism
in terms of phonemic percepts has been secured in a learning process
in which making and hearing sounds have always gone hand in hand.
In fact, language users have learned to come to grips with linguistic
forms so well that a large part of recognition has become semi-
automatized and the phonological structuring may provide the clue
to the role of percepts in a general theory of speech perception.

References

Cherry, C. On listening with both ears. In Congress Report II, Copenhagen: Organization Committee, Fourth International Congress of Acoustics, 1962. Pp. 55-67

't Hart, J., and Cohen, A. Gating techniques as an aid in speech analysis. Language and Speech, 1964, 7, 22-39.

Jakobson, R., and Halle, M. Fundamentals of language. 's-Gravenhage: Mouton, 1956.

Liberman, A. M., Cooper, F. S., Harris, K. S., MacNeilage, P. F., and Studdert-Kennedy, M. Some observations on a model for speech perception. In W. Wathen-Dunn (Ed.), Proceedings of the symposium on models for the perception of speech and visual form. Cambridge: M.I.T. Press, 1967, Pp. 68-87.

A TRANSFORMATIONAL GRAMMAR RECOGNITION PROCEDURE AND ITS ROLE AS A LINGUISTIC PERCEPTUAL MODEL

S. R. Petrick
Data Sciences Laboratory
Air Force Cambridge Research Laboratories
Bedford, Massachusetts

It is beyond the scope of this paper to discuss the considerations which support the choice of a transformational grammar as a means of characterizing linguistic competence. Although we hold that such a grammar is an appropriate device for linguistic description, we must acknowledge that a transformational grammar is not a model for either the speaker or the hearer. It has been described by Chomsky (1965) as "an attempt to characterize in the most neutral possible terms the knowledge of the language that provides the basis for actual use of language by speaker-hearer." In particular, in order to model the hearer a recognition procedure must be given, that is, an effective procedure for computing the structural description(s) of a sentence with respect to a given transformational grammar. This paper describes one possible such procedure and discusses its implications as a model of perception.

The role played by the syntactic component of a grammar is a central one in the transformational theory. This component assigns an underlying deep structure to a sentence, containing all necessary information for interpretation by a semantic component. The deep structure is mapped into corresponding surface structure by the syntactic component. Finally, a third component, the phonological component, maps surface structure into a phonetic realization of the sentence.

The syntactic component then, is composed of two major parts, a base component that assigns deep structure and a transformational component that maps it into surface structure. In the present paper we consider the base component to be a set of context-free phrase structure rules. Thus, deep structure representations are merely trees in which successively more deeply embedded constituent sentences are attached to the symbol COMP of matrix sentences by the rule COMP→ # S #. For example, the deep structure assigned to the sentence, "It is not easy to forget a perfect day," by a grammar used in our recognition studies is given in Figure 1. In this figure the highest level sentence contains the information that something is not easy, namely, as detailed in the next level of embedding, for someone unspecified to forget some kind of a day. The most deeply embedded level qualifies that day to be a perfect one.

The transformational part of the syntactic component consists of an ordered set of rules, each of which maps one tree into another. The rules are applied in a cyclic fashion, first to the lowest level of embedding and then to the next higher level until finally the topmost level has undergone transformation by the set of ordered rules. The resulting tree constitutes the surface structure of the sentence in question. For our example, this tree is given in Figure 2.

In the terms of this model, understanding a sentence is dependent upon determining all of the underlying deep structure trees for interpretation by the semantic component. In this paper we describe a recognition procedure that employs an almost pure analysis strategy in contrast to the analysis-by-synthesis strategy that has heretofore been discussed (Matthews, 1962). Use is made of inverse transformations in determining structure from outer levels of embedding to inner levels. Those inverse transformations that correspond to singular transformations map one sequence of trees into another, and those that correspond to binary transformations map a single sequence of trees into two other sequences.

We begin recognition at the top level by determining whether or not the last ordered transformation could have been applied. Each transformation has a so-called inverse structural index, a sequence of terminal symbols and syntactic types. An inverse transformation

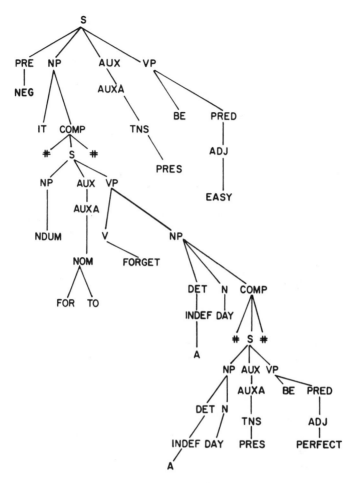

Fig. 1. Deep structure of sentence "It is not easy to forget
a perfect day."

is applicable if it is possible by means of the phrase structure rules
to build up a sequence of trees, whose tips are the terms of the
inverse structural index, from the previously constructed structure.
If the last inverse transformation is applicable, it is carried out, and
the procedure is continued with the next highest ordered transformation. As a separate consideration the inverse transformation is also
not applied.

Continuations of the two sequences of trees resulting from the
application of a binary transformation must be separately considered,
and if both sequences are ultimately identified as sentences, the
structural description of the constituent sentence is attached to the

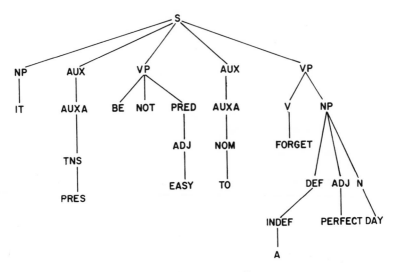

Fig. 2. Surface structure of sentence "It is not easy to forget
a perfect day."

COMP symbol of the matrix sentence structure.

For further details of this recognition procedure and results of
implementing it by means of a LISP computer program see Petrick
(1965).

It must be emphasized that this work was initiated primarily to
obtain structural descriptions for practical purposes and not to propose
a perceptual model. However, it is still reasonable to suggest experiments designed to establish facts that bear on the adequacy as perceptual models of either the present or other recognition procedures
that have been described. In order to evaluate whether a particular
mechanical recognition procedure models certain aspects of human
linguistic perception, it is necessary to determine characteristics
exhibited by the mechanical procedure and to investigate whether or
not these characteristics are also exhibited by the human perceiver
of language. Similarly, it is necessary to determine measurable
characteristics of understanding a sentence that are exhibited by
humans and to investigate whether or not a correspondence is found
in machine recognition. We will consider an example of each of these
evaluative procedures.

The recognition procedure we have presented pieces together any
particular structural description by determining structure from the
top kernel down through successive levels of embedding. It is reasonable

to ask whether this essential order of our recognition procedure is matched by a corresponding temporal ordering of the process of understanding a sentence, i.e., do we understand relationships reflected in higher structure prior to understanding those reflected by lower levels of embedding? This might be tested by asking subjects questions about sentences whose complete comprehension is made difficult, perhaps by assigning extraneous simultaneous tasks. If a plausible method could be devised for stopping the process of understanding "in the middle" somehow, and if, in addition, biases related to position in the sentence could be determined and allowed for, then we could determine whether humans exhibit the same temporal recognition characteristics as our transformational recognition procedure. We have conducted no such experiments. Bever[1] reports that in a few preliminary experiments he has observed a slight tendency to recall higher level information over lower level information, but some exceptions were noted. For one thing noun phrases containing an adjective modifier were perceived as a unit, and the adjective, which reflects lower level structure, was seldom omitted without concomitant omission of the entire noun phrase. It might be interesting to see if such exceptions to the general higher-to-lower temporal ordering of structure determination correspond to structure given by certain so-called auxiliary rules, which we make use of in our recognition procedure. This would give even these rules some psycholinguistic justification. We are, of course, just speculating and suggesting relevant experiments.

Conversely, looking for human recognition characteristics, we cite a recent paper by Miller and Isard (1964). They compare the intrinsic relative difficulty of subjects to understand such pairs of sentences as:

1. The man that said that the rat was killed by a cat that was chased by the dog is a liar.
2. The man that said that a cat that the dog chased killed the rat is a liar.

They attempt to explain the relative ease of understanding the first sentence in terms of various properties of the surface structure of these two sentences. We would, instead, investigate the relative difficulty experienced by our recognition procedure in obtaining structural descriptions of these two sentences. To do this we wrote a grammar that generated sentences of this type, assigning to the first

---

[1] Personal communication.

the structural description shown in Figure 3, and to the second the
same structure save for omission of the two occurrences of BY PASS.

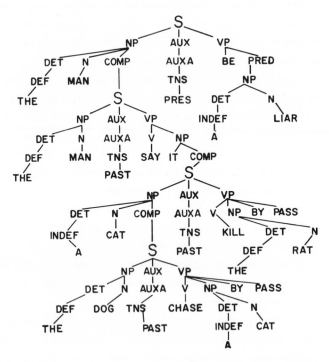

Fig. 3. Deep structure of sentence "The man that said that
the rat was killed by a cat that was chased by the dog is a
liar."

Unfortunately, results depended upon the particular grammar utilized,
but for two grammars considered, the second sentence was recognized
more quickly than was the first sentence. For one grammar the first
sentence took twice as much time to be recognized as the second
sentence, and for the other grammar the factor was one and one-half
times. Hence, our procedure does not reflect human difficulty of
understanding sentences, at least from the standpoint of computational
time required. Other measures such as storage requirements are, of
course, also possible. Finally, we observe that it may well be the
case that people do not find all structural descriptions and then select
one on some basis. Rather, they might find one and see if it "fits"
the situation, going on to find another only if this structural description
is rejected as a possible meaning by a semantic component. If this
were the case, we should look at the time required to find particular

structural descriptions rather than the set of all structural descriptions of a sentence.

Of course, the extent to which our recognition procedure reflects linguistic perception can also be investigated with respect to other observed aspects of linguistic perception. We merely picked one aspect for the purpose of illustration.

We repeat in closing that our purpose in discussing the role our procedure might play as a perceptual model was not to make any claim as to its adequacy. Instead we were concerned merely with assessing factors that might be relevant in evaluating the adequacy of our procedure as a perceptual model and perhaps the adequacy of other models which have been proposed or will be proposed.

References

Chomsky, N. Aspects of the theory of syntax. Cambridge: M.I.T. Press, 1965.

Matthews, G. H. Analysis by synthesis of sentences of natural languages. In Nat. Phys. Lab. Symp. No. 13, 1961 International conf. on machine translation of languages and applied language analysis. Vol. 2. London: H.M.S.O., 1962. Pp. 532-542.

Miller, G. A., and Isard, S. Free recall of self-embedded English sentences. Information and Control, 1964, 7, 292-303.

Petrick, S. A recognition procedure for transformational grammars. Unpublished doctoral thesis, Massachusetts Institute of Technology, 1965.

MODELS AND DATA IN SPEECH PERCEPTION

Mark P. Haggard
Psychological Laboratory
Cambridge University
Cambridge, England

This paper attempts to assess some relationships between different models and between models and data in speech perception; it is, therefore, concerned with the status and relationships of all generalizations about speech perception. As MacKay (1967) has made clear, there is a difference between models designed to account for classificatory behavior and those designed to account for "experience" or noncategorical discriminatory responses. Existing models account only for the former, but it seems in principle possible to incorporate some postulates about mechanisms for identification into explanations of less simple properties of judgments like naturalness, loudness, subjective rate (e.g., Lane, 1962; Osser and Peng, 1964), and some prosodic dimensions.

There are three types of data on speech perception: 1. the findings of experiments correlating particular stimulus features with particular responses, e.g., the Haskins experiments and some experiments on prosodic features (Fry, 1958); 2. a hybrid class of experiments using confusion matrices giving both stimulus response correlations for the set used and an intelligibility index; 3. the intelligibility experiment. The important division in terms of experimental information loss is between the first two types and the intelligibility experiment; the functions of the types are complementary — Types 1 and 2 provide detailed information and Type 3 provides an index of the "importance" of the phenomena, in hand, on a conventional if relative scale.

Particular linkages in Type 1 do not appear to demand psychological explanation, although generalizations about them might (e.g., importance of transitions, relative values, ratios). The behavior of items in confusion matrices (Clarke, 1957) can be accounted for on the theoretical assumptions that two classes of variable affect them and that there are certain restrictions on the way these variables behave (Luce, 1963). There are two predictive systems for intelligibility scores (Licklider, 1959; Stowe, Harris, and Hampton, 1963), only one of which is a model within the conventional sense: however, it is upon the intelligibility experiment that the role of testing the predictions of substantive models falls when stimuli are devised to provide difficulties for the postulated mechanisms of identification (e.g., Miller and Isard, 1963).

Substantive Models

There are essentially two substantive models of human speech recognition — the active and the passive one. Freed of the postulate about the necessity of the individual's own articulations, the "Motor Theory" can be subsumed under the active model. MacKay has shown by an engineering argument (MacKay, 1967) that the important question about these two models is not "which" but "where" and "how much?" Licklider (1952) previously showed for selectivity operations that it was not possible to distinguish formally between an active comparator and a passive filter, however different they might be physiologically

or electronically. But with models of the speech-recognition process
it is possible to generate different predictions of a nonquantitative kind
by applying the models to particular experimental situations.

Broadbent has shown, for example, that an active model and his
passive response availability model (Morton and Broadbent, 1967) can
be made to generate different predictions for the word-frequency effect.
A simple active model might postulate a stronger matching response[1]
in the case of high frequency words and therefore greater discriminability for those words (higher d') while the passive model predicts
that the difference in performance for high and low frequency words
is due merely to a response bias towards the former. The experimental
results (Broadbent, 1967) favor the response availability model. In
accordance with MacKay's observation these results restrict the
generality of an active model rather than disprove its possibility. The
proof of the possibility of an active process might be found with small
known vocabularies where presentations were not equiprobable; the
more probable stimuli should have higher d', their representations
being held ready for active match in limited numbers[2]. There is
some evidence in favor of the possibility of active processes from
other experimental situations (Long, Henneman, and Garvey, 1960;
Sumby, 1962). Although there is not an agreed list of the phenomena
which speech perceptual models have to explain, it is probable that
experiments can determine the generalization ranges of the two
models.

Same Level Explanations

Chomsky and Miller (1963) suggest that speech perception is a
profitable field for study because the structure of the stimulus is
so well worked out. The question arises here whether the explanation
of behavioral data will be a linguistic or a psychological one. It appears
that a number of phenomena in the perception of speech can be given
same-level explanations (cf. Argyle, 1957) from a few general
psychological facts or hypotheses on the basis of linguistic or phonetic

---

[1] Further predictions are (a) lack of response bias and (b) higher d' on
the Type II ROC (see Clarke, Birdsall, and Tanner, 1959).

[2] An errors prediction not a time prediction is appropriate here, any
time difference being easily explained on a passive model. An implication of a positive result would be that only the probable stimuli were
identified "actively," a not unreasonable conclusion.

knowledge that provides a conversion of terms.

For example, different explanations of the Cherry effect[3] have been given. Cherry and Taylor (1954) thought it due to an average perception delay of 1/6 sec causing a lag in the decision to switch attention — a largely psychological explanation. Huggins (1964) demonstrated that the effect was largely due to the recurrence of switch-vulnerable units at the syllabic rate of the speech used — suggesting a structural explanation in terms of consonant-cluster units. However it is possible to account for several parameters of the Cherry effect from some psychological generalizations and some specific facts about speech: (a) switching lag between classes of input is general as to occurrence, variable as to duration (Broadbent and Gregory, 1961); (b) the performance in the attention switching situation is affected by the duration or degree of memory for what has gone before on the ear to which attention is switched and therefore on the total information rate (Cherry and Taylor, 1954); (c) unless relative continuity is provided in one channel it is difficult to keep attention on that channel in face of competition from other channels (Treisman, 1960); (d) consonants carry more information than vowels (Denes, 1963); (e) consonants are characterized by less spectral continuity and shorter duration than vowels and hence greater information per unit time.

The foregoing five premises enable the explanation of the following parameters of the Cherry effect:

1. The effect occurs for switching between mildly frequency-compressed and frequency-expanded versions of the same utterance as well as from ear to ear (unpublished experiment of the writer).

2. In both these situations the critical rate is related to the syllabic rate of the speech.

3. The effect does not emerge unless the subject is loaded with continuous speech[4].

4. Despite containing all the possible information, alternated speech is about equally intelligible with interrupted speech (Huggins, 1964).

5. Intelligibility is improved by adding noise to the silent ear

---

[3] The dip in intelligibility for speech switched from ear to ear at 3 cps.

[4] Personal communication from A. W. F. Huggins, 1964.

(Schubert and Parker, 1955) and therefore encouraging less
frequent switching of attention to the median plane.

Common-sense considerations also encourage this same-level type
of explanation for some speech perceptual phenomena. It is unlikely
that the brain works in fundamentally different ways for different
performances, and it is unlikely that physical or structural differences
between classes of input are not paralleled in perceptual mechanisms.

Perceptual "Unit" Postulates

One large part of perceptual enquiry is directed to discovering perceptual units (Fodor and Bever, 1965; Ladefoged, 1959; Miller and
Isard, 1963). The value of these studies is not merely in what they
conclude to be the unit, but in the description of the sense in which the
unit is meaningfully postulated. Perhaps it is not stretching the
linguistic usage too far to say that language perception is polysystemic
and that description of the operating systems and their relationships
constitutes the basis of a perceptual theory. Thus, when Miller and
Isard (1963) say the decision unit is large, on the scale of the phrase
and Huggins (1964) talks about consonant clusters there is no contradiction intended, only a difference in sense of the term "unit." Saying
that one unit rather than another (cf. Ladefoged, 1959) is the unit is a
conceptual mistake. In the case of the phoneme, the impossibility
of independent sequential decisions is widely acknowledged, but there
is a psychological reality in the phoneme. It is probably correctly
postulated as a perceptual unit in the case of mature perceivers under
noisy or context-reduced situations where an intuitive phonology may
be applied to save overloading the immediate memory, producing
coding forms such as "syllable A plus phoneme X." Psychologically
there is good evidence for this "schema-with-correction" form of
coding in recognition and memory (Woodworth, 1938). In terms of
information rate, syllables are good candidates for schemata, and
phonemes good candidates for differences. Thus, there could be a
phonemic and syllabic system whose relationship was not primarily
hierarchical like the feature-phoneme and feature-syllable relationships.

As the sense of "unit" must at first be restricted to the operations
identifying the unit it is likely that different operations will give
different units. There are at least four possible procedures: (a) the
continuity procedure; (b) the adequacy of synthesis procedure; (c) the

interference procedure; (d) the error distribution procedure.

The continuity procedure was used by Ladefoged and Broadbent (1960) and recently by Fodor and Bever (1965). It consists of reflecting the continuity of the decision processes at a given point by measuring the resistance of that point to subjective location of a superimposed irrelevant sound. This procedure yields a large grammatically based unit; substantively it suggests that the contents of the short-term stores for speech to which attention is paid and for other sounds are separately organized and that there is not in the untrained listener an ability to relate the time scales of the two or to discontinue attention to the continuous speech; also that coding in immediate memory is based on primarily grammatical redundancy.

In the adequacy of synthesis procedure (Sivertsen, 1961) speech synthesis is proposed or practised with various units as base and three criteria are applied with various weightings: (a) economy — the information rate required to transmit speech analyzed in this way; (b) intelligibility; and (c) naturalness. The sense of the unit favored in this procedure is thus further restricted to the criteria of evaluation. For empirical testing of 2 and 3, computer synthesis is required with holding constant of the irrelevant parameters; no comparative studies have been reported yet. However, some preliminary evidence on pre-recorded units is available (Stowe and Hampton, 1961), and calculations of Criterion 1 and predictions of Criteria 2 and 3 favor the conventional units phoneme and syllable as against the units of the same scale diphone and syllable dyad in the sense of units of recognition invariance (Sivertsen, 1961).

The interference procedure was mentioned in connection with Huggins' experiments which showed the consonant cluster to be a unit in an informational sense. The basic assumption is that to maintain communication the "unit" must be uninterrupted or untransformed in the relevant dimensions. Not only the criteria but the form of the distortion can vary. Frequency compression-to-expansion alternation and introduction of silence and time compression-to-expansion alternation have been examined by the writer. For the values tested, these distortions did not produce measurable intelligibility difference while the naturalness criterion favored the syllable rather than the syllable dyad.

The error-distribution procedure might proceed as follows: a large number of representatively or randomly selected words are presented at low signal/noise ratios. It is then seen by which of the units postulated the form of response bias is most economically explained, using distributional and sequential statistics. This procedure has not yet been realized: variations in the result might be expected to follow variations in the material selected or other experimental variables. This technique could be used as one test of the hypothesis offered in the foregoing that phonemic perception is a special tactic for difficult conditions.

The interest in units and their operational definitions is not merely that of creating a perceptual structuralism in the image of a linguistic analysis. The active theory, for example, faces the problem of the scale and form in which the matching process takes place. The implication (Stevens, 1960) is that the matching output is continuous at the acoustical features level, but this creates great problems in the time normalization; it would be more economical for the matching response to operate discretely with steps long compared to the duration of features.

Response Availability Models

The substantive active and passive models are not quantitative as the response-probability models are, but some at least of these quantitative models can be given substantive implication, for example Luce's general equation (1963) and Clarke's constant ratio rule (1957). Luce's expression for $p(r/s)$, the probability of a particular response to a given stimulus, can be thought of in either active or passive terms. In active terminology it is the product of the probabilities of two independent events, that of r being available as a match, and that of s being accepted as a rendering.

Summary

Four types of generalization about speech perception are discussed: the existing substantive models, same-level explanations, "unit" postulates, and response probability models. While there is no promise of an all-embracing framework at present, there are connections between these classes of model and there are ways of making and testing predictions from these models.

References

Argyle, M. The scientific study of social behaviour. London: Methuen, 1957.

Broadbent, D. E. The word-frequency effect and response bias. Psychol. Rev., 1967, 74, in press.

Broadbent, D. E., and Gregory, Margaret. On the recall of stimuli presented alternately to two sense organs. Quart. J. exp. Psychol., 1961, 13, 103-109.

Cherry, E. C., and Taylor, W. K. Some further experiments on the recognition of speech with one and with two ears. J. acoust. Soc. Amer., 1954, 26, 554-559.

Chomsky, N., and Miller, G. A. Introduction to the formal analysis of natural languages. In R. D. Luce, R. R. Bush, and E. Galanter (eds.), Handbook of mathematical psychology. New York: Wiley, 1963.

Clarke, F. R. Constant ratio rule for confusion matrices in speech communication. J. acoust. Soc. Amer., 1957, 29, 715-720.

Clarke, F. R., Birdsall, T. G., and Tanner, W. P., Jr. Two types of ROC curves and definitions of parameters. J. acoust. Soc. Amer., 1959, 31, 629-630.

Denes, P. On the statistics of spoken English. J. acoust. Soc. Amer., 1963, 35, 892-904.

Fodor, J. A., and Bever, T. G. The psychological reality of linguistic segments. J. verb. Learn. and verb. Behav., 1965, 4, 414-420.

Fry, D. B. Experiments in the perception of stresses. Language and Speech, 1958, 1, 126-152.

Huggins, A. W. F. Distortion of the temporal pattern of speech: Interruption and alternation. J. acoust. Soc. Amer., 1964, 36, 1055-1064.

Ladefoged, P. The perception of speech. In Nat. Phys. Lab. Symp. No. 10, 1958, Mechanisation of thought processes. Vol. 1. London: HMSO., 1959. Pp. 397-409.

Ladefoged, P., and Broadbent, D. E. Perception of sequence in auditory events. Quart. J. exp. Psychol., 1960, 12, 162-170.

Lane, H. L. Psychophysical parameters of vowel perception. Psychol. Monogr., 1962, 76 (44, Whole No. 563).

Licklider, J. C. R. On the process of speech perception. J. acoust. Soc. Amer., 1952, 24, 590-594.

Licklider, J. C. R. Three auditory theories. In S. Koch (Ed.), Psychology: A study of a science. Vol. 1. New York: McGraw-Hill, 1959.

Long, E. R., Henneman, R. H., and Garvey, W. D. An experimental analysis of set: The role of sense modality. Amer. J. Psychol., 1960, 73, 563-567.

Luce, R. D. Detection and recognition. In R. D. Luce, R. R. Bush, and E. Galanter (Eds.), Handbook of mathematical psychology. Vol. 1. New York: Wiley, 1963.

MacKay, D. M. Ways of looking at perception. In W. Wathen-Dunn (Ed.), Proceedings of the symposium on models for the perception of speech and visual form. Cambridge: M.I.T. Press, 1967. Pp. 25-43.

Miller, G. A., and Isard, S. Some perceptual consequences of linguistic rules. J. verb. Learn. verb. Behav., 1963, 2, 217-224.

Morton, J., and Broadbent, D. E. Active versus passive recognition models. In W. Wathen-Dunn (Ed.), Proceedings of the symposium on models for the perception of speech and visual form. Cambridge: M.I.T. Press, 1967. Pp. 103-110.

Osser, H., and Peng, F. A cross-cultural study of speech rate. Language and Speech, 1964, 7, 120-125.

Schubert, E. D., and Parker, C. D. Addition to Cherry's findings on switching speech between the two ears. J. acoust.Soc. Amer., 1955, 27, 792-794.

Sivertsen, Eva. Segment inventories for speech synthesis. Language and Speech, 1961, 4, 27-89.

Stevens, K. N. Towards a model for speech recognition. J. acoust. Soc. Amer., 1960, 32, 47-55.

Stowe, A. N., and Hampton, D. B. Speech synthesis with prerecorded syllables and words. J. acoust.Soc. Amer., 1961, 33, 810-811.

Stowe, A. N., Harris, W. P., and Hampton, D. B. Signal and context components of word-recognition behaviour. J. acoust.Soc. Amer., 1963, 35, 639-644.

Sumby, W. H. On the choice of strategy in the identification of spoken words mixed with noise. Language and Speech, 1962, 5, 120-125.

Treisman, Anne M. Contextual cues in selective listening. Quart. J. exp. Psychol., 1960, 12, 242-248.

Woodworth, R. S. Experimental psychology. New York: Holt, 1938.

A MECHANISTIC MODEL FOR THE LIMITS OF AUDITORY PERCEPTION

Edith L. R. Corliss
Sound Section
National Bureau of Standards
Washington, District of Columbia

A number of experiments on hearing may be summarized by setting up a model for the hearing function of the form shown in Figure 1. The figure of merit, "Q," of the selector mechanism, and its least

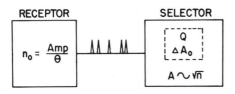

Fig. 1. A model for the hearing function.

count, ΔA_o, are parameters derived from a number of just-noticeable-difference experiments and threshold of hearing determinations.

The equations that permit derivation of "Q" from experiments on noise masking and experiments on difference limens for intensity and frequency are taken from a recent paper on the limits of analyzers (Corliss, 1963). Equations applying these parameters to describe limits of auditory perception are taken from conventional communication theory.

The paper on resolution limits yields the following equations: (The least incremental change in energy detectable, ΔE_o, corresponds to the "least count" ΔA_o. The total energy stored, E, corresponds to the total signal, A, stored in the selector mechanism.)

$$Q = \frac{f_o}{\Delta f} \sqrt{\frac{\Delta E_o/E}{1-\Delta E_o/E}} \qquad [1]$$

$$Q = \frac{\pi^2 \, n_f \, f_o}{W_s} \qquad [2]$$

The relationship in Equation 1, for example, permits derivation of values of Q for the ear from the classic experiments of Riesz (1928) and Shower and Biddulph (1931). With a modification of the definition of ΔE, Equation 1 is also applicable to derive the Q of the ear from data on the masking of a sinusoid by a sinusoid of a different frequency, as for example, from the experiments described by Arnold Small, Jr. (1959). Equation 2 facilitates deriving the Q of the ear from noise masking experiments. Here W_s is the power level of a sinusoid of frequency f_o that is just perceptible against a noise background of n_f power units per cycle per second. The result of applying these equations to derive Q from a number of apparently diverse experiments is shown in Figure 2.

Now, the mechanism illustrated in Figure 1 gives rise to a one-fourth power relationship between functions of perception represented by the oscillatory amplitude, A, of the signal that the selector mechanism stores (it acts like a filter whose figure of merit is Q) and the input power. This relation is readily derived: since the receptor mechanism is considered to emit unit responses whose number per unit time is proportional to the instantaneous amplitude of the input signal, this number of responses is proportional to the square root of the input power. The responses are considered to arrive at random phase in the selector mechanism, so that the energy stored in it is

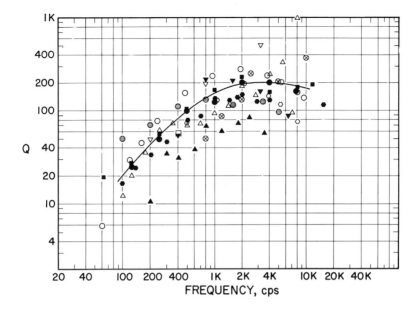

ENERGY & FREQUENCY RESOLUTION
  ■ = RIESZ, SHOWER & BIDDULPH
  ⊜ = V. O. KNUDSEN
  ● = ZWICKER & KAISER
PURE TONE MASKING
  ▲ = WEGEL & LANE
  ▼ = ARNOLD SMALL, JR.
NOISE MASKING OF SINUSOID
  ○ = FLETCHER, OBSERVED
  ● = FLETCHER CRITICAL BAND
  ▽ = SCHAFER, GALES et al
  △ = HAWKINS & STEVENS
  □ = EGAN & HAKE
  ○ = J. D. MILLER
CHANGE OF HEARING THRESHOLD WITH PULSE LENGTH
  ⊗ = PUMPHREY & GOLD

Fig. 2. Values of Q obtained by applying Equations 1 and 2 to various experiments reported in the literature.

proportional to the number of impulses. Thus the amplitude of the circulating signal in it is proportional to the square root of the number of impulses, and hence proportional to the one-fourth power of the level of the input signal.

A detailed discussion of the model is given in a paper, "Mechanistic Aspects of Hearing," which has been prepared for submission to the Journal of the Acoustical Society of America.[1]

---

[1] This will probably appear in 1967.

Communication theory tells us that the "quantum noise" arising from the least count, ΔA_o, can, in general, be considered additive to the count arising from external noise, because the various noise sources would usually be noncoherent. With this background we can look into an experiment conducted by Zerlin and Burnett (1960) on the results of introducing "squared" distortion on the articulation scores obtained on a number of hard-of-hearing subjects.

CNC word-test lists were presented to subjects at 40 dB above their spondee thresholds, via a two-channel tape. One channel contained the "clean" word-test list. The other channel was recorded simultaneously, and consisted of the speech signals passed through a squaring circuit. This process produced intermodulation and harmonic components in a quantitatively predictable ratio. By combining the two channels in known proportions, one observed that various degrees of nonlinear transfer functions could be simulated.

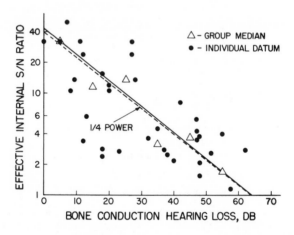

Fig. 3. Effective signal-to-noise ratio as a function of bone-conduction hearing loss.

Taking the drastic assumption that the word-test scores are representative of the probability of detection, we can arrive at a quantitative interpretation of the results. Sensorineural loss without substantial recruitment is represented in this model as a depressed count. Thus the person with a sensorineural loss of this type is working at a lower signal-to-internal noise level, since his loss results in a lower $A/\Delta A_o$ ratio. From this, treating the articulation scores as probabilities of detection, and extracting from the probability an effective signal-to-noise ratio, we should expect the effective signal-to-noise ratio to fall off as the one-fourth power of the bone-conduction hearing loss. This is, indeed, the case, as we can see from Figure 3.

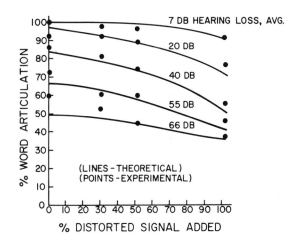

Fig. 4. Comparison of theoretical predictions of articulation scores with grouped averages of experimental data.

Treating the "squared" signal as representing external noise, which may be additively combined with the least-count function, we arrive at a theoretical interpretation of the observations, as shown in Figure 4, where the solid lines represent theoretical predictions of articulation scores, and the dots represent grouped averages.

References

Corliss, E. L. R. Resolution limits of analyzers and oscillatory systems. J. Res. nat. Bur. Stds., Phys. and Chem., 1963, 67A, 461-474.

Riesz, R. R. Differential intensity sensitivity of the ear for pure tones. Phys. Rev., 1928, 31, 867-875.

Shower, R. M., and Biddulph, R. Differential pitch sensitivity of the ear. J. acoust. Soc. Amer., 1931, 3, 275-287.

Small, A., Jr. Pure-tone masking. J. acoust. Soc. Amer., 1959, 31, 1619-1625.

Zerlin, S., and Burnett, E. D. Effects of harmonic and intermodulation distortion on speech intelligibility. J. acoust. Soc. Amer., 1960, 32, 1501. (Abstract)

SEQUENCE LEARNING: PERCEPTUAL IMPLICATIONS IN THE ACQUISITION OF LANGUAGE

Hans G. Furth and James Youniss
Center for Research in Thinking and Language
Catholic University of America
Washington, District of Columbia

Perception of speech cannot be separated from language. Models of speech perception must either explicitly relate nonlinguistic to linguistic factors or implicitly assume as a prerequisite linguistic competence. Developmental observation of normal linguistic learning, and particularly observation of language-deficient children, can provide models for the perception of speech and language, which are both testable and highly pertinent. Natural language is learned by the normal child in a way analogous to other informal learning, such as learning to perceive spatial relationships or social behavior, while hearing-impaired children commonly learn language in a formal way. This difference should be more fully recognized by scientists. The widespread, but largely ignored, failure on the part of deaf children to learn language attests to the difference between such formal and informal learning.

It is proposed that in an investigation of the possible reasons which may impede a child's acquisition of language, apart from hearing sensitivity, one should focus on the perceptual aspect of sound sequences rather than on the conceptual or the symbolic components of language. As evidence for this view it is pointed out that symbolic behavior can be observed or inferred in a variety of ways (dream, art, gesture, play), only one of which is linguistic behavior. Moreover, insofar as language is a system, it manifests the operation of inner, organizing control which is demonstrable in all human activity related to thinking or knowing and is not peculiarly associated with language (Furth, 1964a).

Three closely related perceptual factors deserve to be studied in their own right as peculiar to acquisition of verbal language:

1. Attention. Inhibition (or control) of generalized arousal is a prerequisite to selective responding or attending. Generalized arousal is a behavioral characteristic of infancy, e.g., when an infant "sees" an object, he at the same time tries to move toward it, grasp it, etc. Sound as sense stimulus, in contrast to sight, is unique

in having no temporal permanence and no spatial extension. With regard to this fleeting reality of sound, it may require a notable degree of mature control of generalized mobilization before an infant is ready to attend to sound as potentially meaningful. In this sense, attention as a prerequisite to aural-linguistic perception and learning may be specifically impaired in language-deficient children.

2. Discrimination. It is possible that the difficulty inherent in the discrimination of elementary speech units (phonemic contrast) may be more pronounced than, for instance, in discrimination of visual units. Such implicit auditory discrimination is another prerequisite for acquisition of language.

3. Temporal Sequence. A third and rather unique aspect of speech and language learning is observed in the temporal or sequential presentation of sound units to our ear. Phonemes strike the ear (a) in temporal duration, for example, in the sentence, "Pat can tap," the sounds of the last word come to the ear when the sounds of the first words have ceased to be present; (b) these sequences of sound units, e.g., the phonemes making up the word "Pat," are similar to the ones making up the word "tap." A person has to be capable of distinguishing these combinations of similar units as different sequences. There prevail strong interfering factors of retroactive and proactive inhibitions due to the identity of elements which compose the sequence. Although sequential aspects are present in practically all human activity, it is a characteristic of the reception of oral language that the sequential perception is made more difficult by the absence of easily distinguishable position or overt motor cues. Broadbent (1958, p. 46) and Lashley (1951, pp. 112-136) speculate that a particularly complex neural organization may be needed in the perceptual integration of sequentially perceived material which is made up of a strictly limited number of elementary units presented in various permutations. For instance, the differentiation of the three sequences PAT, APT, and TAP and their association with three distinct responses is a perceptually difficult task and certainly a prerequisite to meaningful speech perception. Mastery of the temporal and combinative aspect in sequences is thus implicit in the perception of language, quite apart from hearing sensitivity or symbolic significance.

A search through the literature failed to produce experimental data
on learning tasks where the correct response had to be directed to the
sequence per se to the exclusion of discrete aspects of the stimulus
situation. Accordingly, a differential response to the sequences AB
and BA is inadequate to infer sequence learning since the response
could conceivably be cued only by the first element of the two sequences.
Three experiments on paired-associate learning of sequences that
required responding to sequences per se are here reported to provide
some developmental information about sequence learning, one with
visual stimuli, another with three types of auditory stimuli, and a
third providing a comparison of the two modalities.

Experiment I: Visual Sequence Learning

Subjects and Procedure. Subjects (N = 64) were normal school
children, aged 7-7 1/2 and 10 1/2-11, evenly divided into groups of
above and below average intelligence. For the sequence learning tasks
four nonsense figures, called here A, B, C, and D were drawn with
black ink on white cards and presented in four different pairs
(sequences). Stimulus presentation for Trials 1 to 8 was: BC, AD,
AC, BD, AD, BD, AC, BC, etc. For Trial 1 the experimenter showed
Stimulus B followed by Stimulus C to which the subject had to learn to
respond by pointing consistently to a response card with Number 4;
similarly, for Trial 2 the presentation of AD required pointing consistently to a response card numbered 3, AC to 1, and BD to 2. After an
initial block of four practice trials, a maximum of 100 trials was given
in a predetermined order unless the subject reached criterion which
was ten consecutive trials with no more than one error. Each element
was shown for 2 sec with an interval of 1 sec between. For successful
subjects there followed a new sequence with a new set of four nonsense
figures and an added fifth stimulus pair DA. The new stimuli were
presented in the initial order: AC, DA, AB, BD, BC. A fifth response
card was added for the sequence DA. If the subject succeeded, a task
with a new set of four nonsense figures generating six, seven, and
finally eight sequences was given, by each time adding one new sequence
and one numbered response card. The final eight-sequence task started
with the following order of sequences: AC, AD, BC, CA, BD, CB, DA,
DB. This task is here called successive sequence (SUC) to differentiate
it from a simultaneous sequence task (SIM) which differed from SUC in
only one way: the stimulus pairs (sequences) were presented simul-

taneously rather than successively, e.g., BC was shown on a white card with B drawn to the left of C and remained in view of the subject until he responded. In all other respects, SIM and SUC were alike.

In addition to these two sequence learning tasks, two control tasks were given, a visual discrete paired-associate task (DPA) and a visual span task (VS). VS, in contrast to SIM or SUC, treated immediate memory, not learning, of a sequence, while DPA demonstrated paired-associate learning without a sequential aspect. In DPA six nonsense figures had to be paired with six different colors; after an initial practice run, 36 trials were given to all subjects. In VS subjects had to reproduce the order in which nonsense figures were shown to them. Starting with three nonsense figures, presented in order ABC, the subject was handed those figures and was required to point out in which order he saw the figures. Any incorrect temporal placement constituted an error. There were two trials each with new sets of 3, 4, 5, 6, 7, and 8 figures, respectively, making a maximum of 66 possible errors.

The four tasks, DPA, VS, SIM, and SUC, were given individually to all subjects during a minimum of two sessions on different days and in four different orders. The learning tasks were consistently reinforced by the experimenter's approval, or if necessary, correction.

Results and Discussion of Experiment I. Task order effects and sex differences were found to be negligible.

In Table 1 results were analyzed for all tasks in terms of mean errors and for the sequential tasks in terms of span or maximum number of sequences on which the subject succeeded. Separate 2 × 2 analyses of

Table 1. Mean Error for All Tasks and Mean Number of Sequences to which Subjects Succeeded

Subjects IQ and Age	SUC Error[1]	SUC Number[2]	SIM Error[1]	SIM Number[2]	VS Error	VS Number	DPA Error
Low 7	39.31	3.75	29.56	4.63	40.56	4.25	22.44
High 7	38.12	3.70	35.85	3.94	35.00	4.69	23.25
Low 10	20.56	4.31	18.31	5.70	32.06	4.75	18.12
High 10	12.62	5.63	15.50	6.00	24.38	6.06	12.81

[1] Only the first task with four sequences is considered, since subjects who failed did not proceed to tasks with more sequences.

[2] This number is somewhat inflated, especially for the younger age group, since subjects failing on four sequences were given a score of three.

variance (Age × IQ) were computed for each column of Table 1. Age yielded reliable F values ($p < 0.01$) in each case, indicating the expected developmental improvement in performance. IQ produced a significant effect for number of sequences in VS. On SUC, Age and IQ interacted such that only the High-10 group succeeded to a notable extent beyond four sequences. This interactive developmental effect suggests that success on learning more than four successive sequences required the maturer intellectual level of the older group. This observation is supported by the analysis of types of errors which argues for a systematic strategy in responding to combinative sequences.

Classification of types of errors for the four-sequence task on SUC and SIM differentiated Recency errors (R) on which the second element was in common (e.g., BC wrongly associated with response to AC), Primacy errors (P) with the first element in common (e.g., BC wrongly associated with response to BD), and Confusion errors (C) where no element was in common (e.g., BC associated with response to AD). Percentage of types of errors was remarkably similar in all four subject groups for both SUC and SIM with R errors ranging in seven instances from 39% to 51% (32% in one instance) of all errors, P and C errors ranging in all eight groups from 30% to 40% and 16% to 28%, respectively.

A comparison, by means of correlated t-tests of the paired span scores of SUC and SIM, indicated that the lower IQ subjects performed reliably better on SIM than on SUC while for the higher IQ subjects the difference was negligible. A similar comparison in terms of error scores on the four-sequence task, however, yielded insignificant t ratios. These somewhat inconclusive results offer insufficient evidence for asserting that SIM was or was not easier than SUC and additional data are presented in Experiment III.

It was expected that the various tasks would be positively correlated, but no remarkable pattern emerged when rank-order correlations of paired error scores were computed. The correlations, based on N = 64, ranged from a low of 0.34 between SIM and DPA to the highest of 0.55 between SIM and SUC.

Experiment II: Three Auditory Sequence Tasks

Subjects and Procedure. Children from Grades 1 and 5, half above and half below average IQ, were evenly divided into three stimulus conditions of 40 subjects each, corresponding to three types of auditory stimulation, pure tone (T), organ sound (O), and spoken vowel (V). A sequence task was used with only two distinct elements, called here A and B, presented in combinations of three. The task started with two sequences and added one new sequence after a determined criterion while leaving the old sequences unchanged. Responses were, as in Experiment I, pointing to numbered cards. Starting with two sequences, BBA→ 1, AAB →2, after a minimum of 6 blocks or criterion within a maximum of 12 blocks, there followed three sequences by adding one new sequence: BBA→1, BAB →3, AAB→ 2. After criterion within a maximum of 12 blocks followed the four-sequence tasks BBA → 1, ABB →4, BAB → 3, AAB→2, then the five-sequence task, and finally the six sequence task: BBA → 1, AAB → 2, ABA →6, BAB → 3, BAA→5, ABB→ 4. Criterion was three blocks of trials with no more than one error.

For V condition, a tape was prepared with vowels spoken in the required combinations, the vowel sound /ɔ/ standing for element A, and the vowel /o/ for element B. For T, pure tones of 250 and 1,000 cps, respectively, were employed; for O two organ notes in the middle range, with an interval of four half tones. The tones and sounds were put on four continuous tapes and connected with a switch which the experimenter controlled. In all three conditions the subject heard the sound combinations at a comfortable sound level via tape recorder and ear phones; each sound element lasting for 1 sec with a 1-sec interval between them.

Results and Discussion of Experiment II. Table 2 summarizes the results for the three auditory conditions in terms of mean number of sequences learned by the subject and also mean error for the 18 trials on the 3-sequence task.

Table 2. Mean Error with Three Sequences and Mean Number of Sequences Learned

Subjects IQ and Age	Pure tone		Organ sound		Vowel	
	Error	Number	Error	Number	Error	Number
Low 6	11.0	2.0	11.5	2.1	9.8	2.2
High 6	7.7	2.4	5.4	3.0	9.7	2.3
Low 11	1.3	3.6	2.7	3.9	3.3	3.9
High 11	0.3	4.2	0.5	4.2	0.6	5.3

Two 3 × 2 × 2 (Auditory Stimuli × Age × IQ) variance analyses were made, one for Errors, the other for Numbers, resulting in significant (p < 0.01) effects for Age and for IQ but not for Types of Auditory Stimuli. It is notable that performance did not vary with auditory condition even though one could have expected that greater familiarity with verbal sequences would facilitate V. The positive effects for Age and IQ, in general, support the developmental findings in Experiment I but a direct comparison of auditory with visual sequence learning seemed appropriate; thus Experiment III was designed.

Experiment III: Visual and Auditory Sequence Learning

Subjects and Procedure. Experiment III had 32 new subjects, evenly divided as in Experiment I, into high and low IQ pupils at CA 7 and 10. With slight modifications they were given the sequence procedure as described in Experiment II. No strict criterion of success was employed and the number of sequences was increased until the subject performed at a near chance level. Discontinued subjects were arbitrarily assigned a chance level error score. Error scores were based only on the first six blocks of the respective sequence tasks. The two auditory stimuli consisted of two easily distinguishable sounds, an organ sound and white noise, taped and presented as in Experiment II. The visual stimuli were two nonsense figures similar to Experiment I. The two tasks were alike apart from using stimuli of two different sense modalities. In addition, subjects were given, as in Experiment I, a comparable simultaneous visual sequence task in order to test for the reliability of SUC-SIM differences.

Results and Discussion of Experiment III. With a maximum chance error score of 90, the mean error for the four groups on the Auditory and Visual Sequence tasks are presented in Table 3.

Table 3. Mean Error over Sequences Two or Six

Subjects IQ and Age	Successive auditory	Successive visual	Simultaneous visual
Low 7	37.13	53.63	49.50
High 7	44.63	54.75	48.62
Low 10	48.63	50.13	42.75
High 10	22.75	31.00	21.25

A mixed factorial analysis of variance with same subjects performing on the successive sequence tasks under auditory and visual condition yielded two reliable effects: auditory was easier than visual modality (p < 0.01) and Age interacted with IQ (p < 0.10). While it was noted in

Experiment II that sequence performance was not affected by varying
the type of auditory stimuli, the greater ease with auditory than with
visual material became evident in this experiment. This facilitation
can be explained by the greater familiarity in dealing with auditory
than with visual sequential stimuli. The interaction of Age and IQ is
consistent with the results of Experiment I in which the High-10 group
was markedly better than the other groups.

Errors were examined in both 6-sequence visual tasks for those
subjects who made less than 15 errors on that task. There were 16
SIM tasks and 8 SUC tasks. As type of errors were similar on SIM
and SUC the data were collapsed for the following analysis. A
symmetrical sequence (e.g., BAB) was more frequently (49%) confused
with the one other symmetrical (ABA) than with any other of the 4
asymmetrical sequences and asymmetrical sequences were more
frequently confused with another asymmetrical sequence. Errors of
the type ABB-response wrongly associated with BAA-stimulus (Element reversal) were 47% of all errors to asymmetrical stimuli.
Errors of the type ABB-response associated with BBA (Sequence
reversal) were 14%, and errors of the type ABB-response associated
with AAB-stimulus were 9%; the remaining 30% of errors were
divided between the 2 symmetrical sequence responses. In errors
involving element reversal, a subject preserves the sequence ("One
simple element, followed by a doubleton of a different element") but
confuses the elements. This attention to sequential ordering is
striking and attests to the processing and organization of sequences
within the organism.

With respect to the SUC-SIM comparison it is clear from Table 3
that the mean scores were quite similar, with the High-10 group performing notably better than the other groups. Thus there seems to
be evidence for similarity in performance level rather than consistent
facilitation of simultaneous over successive perception of a sequence.
This would suggest that the major source of difficulty for learning of
sequences does not simply lie in the memory load resulting from
temporal succession. Rather, the difficulty must stem from the
combinative aspect of sequences in that the same elements generate
differing sequential permutations.

Conclusions and Implications

The three independent studies were consistent in demonstrating three

main conclusions related to stimulus presentation, age and intelligence
which are operative in the perception and learning of sequentially presented stimuli under combinative conditions. The replicated interaction
of age and intelligence in Experiments I and III and the learning
strategies as revealed in types of errors give evidence of some
internal intelligent organization and control, necessary for learning
of sequences. The relatively small difference between successive and
simultaneous sequence learning highlights the difficulty due to the
combinative aspect of sequences and suggests that as far as the CNS is
concerned, there may be not too much difference between these modes
of presentation; in fact, it is known that a strictly simultaneous perception is a physiological impossibility. Finally, although auditory
sense modality was easier than visual it still was a difficult task and
different types of auditory stimuli did not affect performance.
Apparently the processing of sequences takes place at a neurological
level removed from the particular sense receptor.

It is not surprising that the implicit mastery of these types of
sequences during language learning in the first 2 years of human life
proves to be difficult when simulated in an explicit experimental procedure at 10 years of age. In the former case, one observes the
innately complex and maturing capacity of the organism for processing
information, in the latter, one tends to speak of the intelligent employment of learning strategies. These two phenomena, one informal and
the other formal learning, are related, but at the same time obviously
different behavioral processes.

Finally, it is proposed that more explicit research into the developmental processes underlying temporal integration and particularly
mastery of the combinative aspect of sequences could yield specific
clues about the normal and abnormal course of speech and language
learning (Furth 1964b). Auditory sequence learning appears a
promising area of research since it stands midway between hearing
sensitivity and full comprehension of speech and demonstrates the
organization of the hearing capacity in the service of an intelligent,
symbol-producing organism.

Acknowledgment

The research reported in this paper was in part supported by Grant
HD 00219 from the National Institutes of Health to the Hearing and
Speech Center, Children's Hospital of D. C.

References

Broadbent, D. E. Perception and communication. New York: Pergamon Press, 1958.

Furth, H. G. Research with the deaf: Implications for language and cognition. Psychol. Bull., 1964, 62, 145-164. (a)

Furth, H. G. Sequence learning in aphasic and deaf children. J. Speech Hear. Disorder, 1964, 29, 171-177. (b)

Lashley, K. S. The problem of serial order in behavior. In L. A. Jeffress (Ed.), Cerebral mechanisms in behavior. New York: Wiley, 1951.

CONTRIBUTED PAPERS V

Formal Models for Visual Perception

Chairman: Oliver Selfridge
Project MAC
Massachusetts of Technology
Cambridge, Massachusetts

A PROPOSED MODEL FOR VISUAL INFORMATION PROCESSING IN THE BRAIN

Matthew Kabrisky
Air Force Institute of Technology
Wright-Patterson Air Force Base, Ohio

In this paper an attempt is made to show how certain brain structures might perform computations known to be performed by the brain. The model of brain structure and proposed behavior does not include structures or perform computations incompatible with current knowledge of these aspects of the brain.

The facet of brain function considered here is the classification and identification of static, half-tone visual images. Temporal aspects of visual pattern recognition as well as color recognition are excluded; these two factors, especially the temporal make-up of "patterns," will have to be part of any complete model of brain behavior but even the simplified problem considered here is not at all understood. (It is believed that the model suggested in this paper is extensible to these problems, but this not considered.)

Only certain portions of the presently known body of data concerning the human brain and its behavior have to be considered in constructing a model to perform static pattern recognition; these are:

1. The visual input data is in a two-dimensional form as coded in the retina, and this two-dimensional rendering is preserved until it is mapped, homeomorphically, on the two-dimensional surface of the cortex.

2. The subcortical brain structures are capable of only gross assay of the data which they transmit (essentially unreduced in the

human visual channel) to the cortical input areas.

3. The computation performed by the cortex (which is unknown) takes
    place in discrete points in the cortex. Transfer of information
    across the cortical sheet is highly restricted by the orientation
    of axons within the cortex; corticocortical information transfer,
    when required, takes place through axons in the mass of white
    matter (cerebral alba) beneath the cortex.

4. The computation performed by the cortex includes the memory
    function.

5. The results of strychnine neuronography show that the cortico-
    cortical information paths are configured in such a way that they
    might support the computation of general two-dimensional
    crosscorrelation functions of the form:

$$\theta \, (\lambda, \delta \,) = \int_x \int_y \, [P_1 \, (x - \lambda, \, y - \delta) \, {}^*P_2 \, (x, \, y) \,] dy dx \qquad [1]$$

where (*) represents virtually any nonadditive interaction between two-
dimensional patterns $P_1 \, (x, y)$ and $P_2 \, (x, y)$.

Specifically excluded from this model are:

1. Possible mediation of the data by the reticular formation.

2. Possible glial cell function.

3. Possible explanation of EEG phenomonon as a significant trans-
    port medium for large quantities of data.

If one wishes to model a "complete" mammalian information channel
including peripheral sensors, subcortical processing centers, and (at
least input) cortical centers, perhaps the simplest channel to consider
is the foveal-thalamic-cortical pathways in the primate. Anatomical
count of receptors and axonal channels indicate that no peripheral
reduction of data need occur in this unique channel; the number and
grain size of retinal receptors, significantly, matches the optical
capability of the eye. In the foveal region, there are as many axonal
channels in the optic nerve as there are primary receptors (cones),
and there are more than enough thalamic relay centers to provide for
unreduced transfer of data to the cortex. In addition, there are as
many receptor cells (star pyramids in Layer 4a) in cortical Area 17
as there are retinal cones (see von Bonin, 1950). The fact that the
subjective visual resolution on the part of the possessor of such a
system matches the expected optical resolution of the system would
lend credence to the concept of a one-to-one mapping of retinal receptors

through the complete channel from the fovea to the cortex. This is
the assumption made here, namely, that the two-dimensional optical
image on the fovea is essentially replicated unreduced in topological
content and unpreprocessed (except for some sort of automatic gain
control to limit dynamic range of intensity) on the input visual cortex.
The care which is taken to map foveal images homeomorphically and
with full retinal detail would tend to indicate that brain structures in-
ferior to the cortex are incapable of assaying all the pertinent topological information contained in foveal images. Therefore, cortically
extracted information must be responsible for the improved visual
pattern recognition capability in foveal animals compared to the infra-
primates.

One is thereby led to the problem of the cortical computation and its
ability to extract complex pattern information. Two aspects of this
cortical computation concern the model proposed, namely: (a) the type
of calculation that can be performed at local cortical spots in the close
vicinity of afferent axons carrying data to such spots, and (b) the type
of calculation that can be performed corticocortically as a result of
the connection configurations occurring between cortical areas. It is
reasonable to assume that some of the differences between "highly
cortical" mammals and more primitive vertebrates will have to be
accounted for in terms of these two types of computational structures.

Local Cortical Computation

Individual afferent axons to the cortex, for instance those innervating
Area 17 with foveal data, carry information coded in the form of neuron
firing rate. This is analogue-type information, the pulse coding
technique being an expedient to prevent degradation of analogue information in cascaded information processing devices fabricated from
living tissue. The afferent axons ramify and terminate in the cortex
and presumably influence or trigger some operation within the cortex
in a manner dependent on the instantaneous value of the data transmitted. The nature of this cortical computation is unkown as is the
manner in which it is influenced by incoming axonal data; however, the anatomical connections are fairly well known and enable some reasonable
guesses (see Lorente de Nó, 1949) regarding the local computation in
the vicinity of afferent axons.

In the primary visual cortex of man, about 10^5 axons, corresponding
apparently to 10^5 foveal cones, innervate about 2.5 cm^2 of cortex

surface in which are located about 10^5 star pyramids (in Layer 4a).
The star pyramids are particularly large cells and would seem to be
some sort of "input" neuron in view of the fact that their number
matches the number of input axons and they are located in the same
cortical layer in which the input axons ramify. It is tempting, therefore,
to ascribe to the input cortex the function of replicating the cone pattern, cone by cone, of the fovea. If so, it is possible to compute, at
least in the input visual cortex, the dimensions of a "fundamental bit"
of cortical computation equipment; this will be called a basic computation element and hereafter abbreviated, b.c.e. The surface area, S.
of cortex corresponding to one b.c.e. is:

$$S = \frac{2.5 \text{ cm}^2}{10^5} = 2.5 \times 10^{-5} \text{ cm}^2$$

This implies a diameter on the order of 0.05 mm. In the entire human
cortex, there would be about 8×10^7 b.c.e.'s of such dimensions. The
b.c.e. then, is a cylindrical shaped element about 0.05 mm in diameter, about 2.5 mm long (that is, the thickness of the cortex) and contains about 350 neurons (see Figure 1). This seems to be a rather
long, thin element, but a good case can be made for an element of such
a shape because of the very great number of axon paths within the
cortex that are perpendicular to the cortical sheet compared to those
parallel to the sheet; that is, the axon paths within the cortex tend to
organize the cortical sheet into thin vertical columns perpendicular to
the sheet (reminiscent of honeycomb cells). This type of functional
organization was suggested by Lorente de Nó on the basis of histological data at least as early as 1934 and Hubel and Wiesel (1962) reported
just such cylindrical elements functioning as entities in the cat visual
cortex. In the cat, these columns are apparently about 0.5 mm in
diameter. The disparity of this dimension compared to the 0.05 mm
estimated for a foveal animal might be explainable in terms of the
reduced visual acuity (for perception of complex forms) of a cat compared to an animal with a fovea, which is, at least partially, a result of
the retinal preprocessing and reduction of data in the cat area cen-
tralis.

What sort of calculation can be performed by a b.c.e.? Figure 2
shows a schematic representation of a single b.c.e.: This is a simplified and restricted form in that only one input and one output are
allowed (Kabrisky, 1961). While it would seem that the one input is

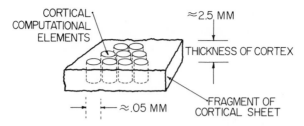

Fig. 1. Schematic representation of b. c. e.'s arrayed in cortex.

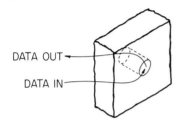

Fig. 2. Schematic representation of the input-output information flow paths in a simplified b. c. e.

correct for b. c. e.'s in the foveal receptor regions of Area 17, the single output for these units is probably wrong; furthermore, consideration of the corticocortical connections required to compute the function in Equation 1 would indicate that in subsequent cortical areas, such as 18, the b. c. e.'s would probably have to have multiple inputs. This might indicate that the 0. 05-mm dimension is in error for such b. c. e.'s.

Although restricted, the model in Figure 1 enables the schematizing of the general calculation that a b. c. e. might perform. The output and input information of such a b. c. e. would be rendered, in an animal, by pulse repetition rate, but will be considered here merely a number. Formally, the behavior of any b. c. e., α, is described by:

$$\theta_\alpha = F_\alpha (I_\alpha, M_\alpha) \qquad [2]$$

where θ_α is the current output, I_α is the current input, and M_α is the current value of a postulated internal memory whose value is postulated to depend on previous inputs. The behavior of a specific b. c. e. is denoted F_α and this is unkown, in vivo. (Note that Figure 1 and its description, Equation 2, subsume the Lorente de No model of local cortical behavior as well as the concept that memory occurs as a result of changes in cortical circuits stemming from usage.) Assuming that there will inevitably be some cross coupling among b. c. e.'s, Equation 2 can be extended by assuming that the b. c. e., α, is embedded in, say, a Cartesian array. If α is placed at an arbitrary point (x, y) in the array, the coupling effects can be formally added to the behavior described in Equation 2:

$$\theta(x, y) = F_{(x, y)} [I(x, y), M(x, y), A(x-1, y),$$

$$A(x, y+1), A(x+1, y), A(x, y-1)] \qquad [3]$$

where A denotes some measure of pertinent activity in the four neighboring b. c. e.'s which affects the behavior of the one at (x, y). Allowing for coupling of neighboring b. c. e.'s enables them to exhibit oscillatory behavior. Depending on the values of A, arrays of b. c. e.'s may show low level scintillation or extremely large oscillations.

Formally, Equation 3 states all that a one input, one output b. c. e. might be expected to do; it does not seem too interesting. A b. c. e. cannot see its neighbors very effectively by means of local coupling and it would seem that arrays of them are not suited to processing two-dimensional patterns which might be mapped on many thousands of such insular units. They do, however, possess an intrinsic memory function having the special property of being activated by the application of an input signal.

Corticocortical Computation

The seemingly limited range of behavior possible in a single b. c. e. raises the problem of determining the functional organization of large quantities of them. Unfortunately, there is very little data relating to the fine structure of corticocortical connections (Fessard, 1962) primarily because of the great experimental difficulty in working with these structures either histologically or functionally. One set of data, however, due to Dusser de Barenne, McCulloch, von Bonin and Bailey (see Bailey, von Bonin, and McCulloch, 1950) may shed some light on the nature of the computation performed in the corticocortical configurations of b. c. e.'s when interpreted within the framework of two-dimensional crosscorrelation. Their experimental data was obtained by the technique of strychnine neuronography in the chimpanzee and showed that single small regions (about 1 mm^2) in Area 17 are connected to a great number of locations in Area 18. It is easy to show (see Kabrisky, 1966) that this sort of connectivity can be the basis for

computing the two-dimensional crosscorrelation function shown in
Equation 1. The two-dimensional crosscorrelation function is an extremely powerful tool for pattern recognition and has been made the
basis for several attempts to build machinery for this purpose. To
illustrate the pertinence of the strychnine experiment results consider
Figure 3.

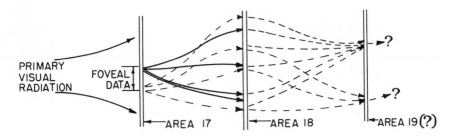

Fig. 3. A schematic representation of corticocortical
pathways.

The solid lines indicate axonal channels configured according to the
strychnine neuronography results. Also shown are dotted lines which
would be reasonably expected in light of the strychnine experiments.
Therefore, b.c.e.'s in Area 17 are considered to be single input,
multiple output units functioning primarily to redistribute input patterns
to many locations in Area 18 wherein are stored known patterns. The
memory mechanism, postulated to be dependent on previous inputs, can
be set up to store patterns which are most frequently applied to the
system. The b.c.e.'s in Area 18, for purposes of this model, would
be, in all probability, multiple input multiple output units as would be
those of subsequent areas. The darkened paths (both solid and dotted)
terminating in Area 19(?) indicate one set of paths which can compute
the crosscorrelation of a pattern, P_1, applied to Area 17 and a pattern,
P_2, stored in Area 18; the approximate value of θ in Equation 1 is
computed by a b.c.e. in Area 19(?) by simple summation and is the
value for $\lambda = \delta = 0$. Values of θ for λ and $\delta \neq 0$ are achieved automatically by eye movement. It is necessary to postulate special ad-
ditional fine structure details of corticocortical connectivity to allow
the model to show, additionally, the moderate invariance to scale change
and angular rotation manifest in the human system. Note that memory
function of Equation 2, if arranged to be related to past inputs serves
as an automatic storage facility which begins to function simply upon

the receipt of data in the data channels.

A certain amount of fine structure has to be interpolated in the coarse results of the strychnine experiments to suit the requirements of two-dimensional crosscorrelation equipment, especially if it has to handle scale changes and rotation of input images. However, the model proposed does not require assumptions incompatible with either the strychnine results or the anatomy of the animal. In this light, it should be stated that corticocortical connections of the type shown in Figure 2 could probably be arranged to compute and operate with the two-dimensional Fourier transforms of patterns with the possible saving of substantial amounts of b. c. e.'s in Area 18 and subsequent areas. Unfortunately, finer details of the corticocortical connections are required to decide the case for either the model proposed or one performing Fourier transforms. Biological experiments are now in progress at the Air Force Institute of Technology to elucidate corticocortical fine structure in the light of the model proposed here. (The system has also been modeled on digital equipment with the good, albeit slow, results that one would expect in a crosscorrelation pattern recognition system.)

References

Bailey, P., von Bonin, G., and McCulloch, W.S. The isocortex of the chimpanzee. Urbana: Univer. Illinois Press, 1950.

Fessard, A. The role of neuronal networks in sensory communications. In W.A. Rosenblith (Ed.), Sensory communication. Cambridge: M.I.T. Press,1962.

Hubel, D.H., and Wiesel, T.N. Receptive fields, binocular interaction and functional architecture in the cat's visual cortex. J. Physiol., 1962, 160, 106-154.

Kabrisky, M. A spatially iterated memory organ patterned after the cerebral cortex. Paper presented at 16th Mtg. of the Association for Computing Machinery, Los Angeles, Sept. 1961. (Paper 2c-3, preprint)

Kabrisky, M. A proposed model for visual information processing in the human brain. Urbana: Univer. Illinois Press, 1966.

Lorente de Nó, R. Cerebral cortex: Architecture, introcotrical connections, motor projections. In J.F. Fulton (Ed.), Physiology of the nervous system. (3rd ed.) London: Oxford Univer. Press, 1949. Pp. 288-315.

von Bonin, G. Essay on the cerebral cortex. Springfield, Ill.: Charles C.Thomas, 1950.

A TRANSFORMATION FOR EXTRACTING NEW DESCRIPTORS OF SHAPE

Harry Blum
Data Sciences Laboratory
Air Force Cambridge Research Laboratories
Bedford, Massachusetts

Introduction

I have approached the problem of shape by assuming that the current mathematical tools were somehow missing essential elements of the problem. For despite more than two millennia of geometry, no formulation which appears natural for the biological problem has emerged. This is not surprising perhaps when one recognizes that geometry has been born of surveying and has grown in close collaboration with physical science and its mensuration problems. A corollary to this position is that there is some central difference between the biological problem that we are trying to deal with and the physical problem that we have been dealing with. Consequently, such an approach requires a restudy of visual function to assess what such a geometry should indeed try to accomplish. Unfortunately, the problem of exploring function is not easy to do in isolation, since the visual world is extremely rich, and hypotheses about visual shapes and their functional value to an organism may reflect the cultural bias of the experimenter to a large degree. I have chosen to enter the problem from the middle by hypothesizing simple shape processing mechanisms, and then exploring together the geometry and visual function that result. One such mechanism is presented in this paper. Since it leads to a drastic reformulation of a number of notions of visual shape, it may be useful to review briefly some of the notions implicit in our views and experiments.

While local attributes of the visual field (intensity, color, edge, angle, motion) and average global properties such as total luminous flux have been subject to progressive experimentation and understanding, the attributes of shape, global properties in which the particular distribution is precisely relevant, are still largely unkown. Yet, shape has been shown to be a particularly stable organization of our visual stimulus by the degree and variety of distortion that are the stock in trade of artists and cartoonists — even being used to enhance recognition. Why, then, has it been so difficult to tease out the properties

of shape? A primary reason is that the number and variety of shapes
are enormous, so that it is impossible within the limits of experiment
to explore more than a small sampling of the variables. Consequently,
one assumes a theory of shape, at least implicitly, in the selection of
experimental stimuli. This reason is compounded by the degree to
which geometry and reading, both synthetic processes, imposed on us
culturally and with considerable difficulty, have biased our view of
shape. As a result, stimuli in even the best animal experiments have
been largely rectilinear or other unnatural geometric shapes presented
in isolation on a uniform field (for example, see Sutherland, 1960).
Except for a limited number of terminated experiments (for example,
Attneave and Arnoult, 1956), quantitative work with humans has been
subject to similar limitations and greater confusion due to the intimate
interaction with cultural artifacts. Consequently, the most primitive
problems of shape vision, segmentation of the field into objects, defining locations and recognition of biologically relevant amorphous shapes,
are implicitly ignored. It is precisely toward these problems that
the process considered here is useful.

If it cannot be assumed that a shape can be isolated and normalized
a priori, or that the wide variety of perturbations that a shape may
take and still be identified, can be exhaustively enumerated, it is
necessary to develop some way of obtaining shape properties without
becoming enmeshed in the huge combinatorics of simple congruence
views. A number of people have proposed to have the shape interact
with itself to accomplish this. The Gestalt school (Koffka, 1935, for
example) used field theoretic notions. Deutsch (1955), and Bitterman,
Krauskopf and Hochberg (1954), have proposed propagation or diffusion models of interaction. Kazmierczak (1960) has used an electric
field analogy and Kirsch, Cahn, Ray and Urban (1958) have used
computer rules on a rectangular grid to allow a wide variety of self-
interactions, including propagation. However, these models failed to
arrive at a set of incisive shape attributes. The present model de-
velops these notions somewhat differently and arrives at a number of
distinct attributes which are useful in two ways: (a) in developing a
physchology of shape for everyday life, and (b) in focusing attention on
some of our biases. The model can be developed in a number of ways.
The propagation scheme used has been chosen for its tutorial ease.
Another view of it, perhaps having more physiological relevance, is
introduced later. A word of warning is important. The model does not

intend to deal with the central perceptual problem in which the entire
history of the organism, its set, and its total stimulus input must be
considered. The output of the transformation merely gives a set of
shape attributes on which the organism can perform selection, using
criteria of usefulness and relevance similar to those used in other
sensory processes.

Definition Using Time

Consider a continuous isotropic plane (an idealization of an active
granular material or a rudimentary neural net) that has the following
properties at each point: (a) excitation — each point can have a value
of either 0 or 1; (b) propagation — each excited point excites an adjacent point with a delay proportional to the distance; and (c) refractory or dead time — once fired, an excited point is not affected by a
second firing for some arbitrary interval of time. A visual stimulus
from which the contours or edges have been extracted, impinges on such
a plane at some fixed time and excites the plane at those points. This
excitation spreads uniformly in all directions but in such a way that
the waves generated do not flow through each other. Figure 1 shows
this process occurring for an input pattern of two points. The waves
start as two expanding circles and merge into a single contour when
these circles intersect. (One can visualize the contours as the front
of a grass fire.) Figure 2 shows the generated wave for a number of
other simple shapes. This wave passes by each point of the space
once and only once. For most points of the space the wave flows by in
a good fashion, each point on the wave front generating a new point on
a new wave front. This is not the case, however, for those places
where corners appear in the wave, or where waves collide with each
other in a frontal or circular manner. The wave front undergoes
cancellation at these places. These places are shown by the dotted
lines in Figures 1 and 2. The two dots of Figure 1 give rise to a line
which starts with an infinite velocity and becomes asymptotic to the
space velocity. From Figure 2, it can be seen that such points occur
only on the inside of an angle or an arc. The corner appears only
after the center of curvature is reached. In the triangle three corners
start propagating and disappear at the center of the largest inscribed
circle. In the case of the ellipse, these points start at the shortest
radius of curvature and disappear at the center of the largest inscribed
circle. Since both of these shapes are convex, they generate no such

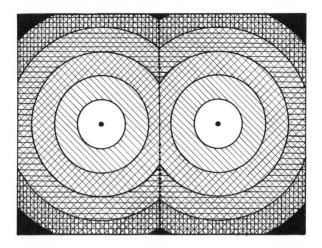

Fig. 1. Wave fronts generated by a two-point grass fire
excitation. (Note the absence of flow-through associated
with propagation of waves in a pond. The mid-line represents the locus of corners in this process.)

Fig. 2. Wave fronts and "corners" generated by some
simple excitations (dotted lines represent locus of "corners").

points outside of themselves. A straight line and a point, since they
are convex and have no inside, have no such points unless a special
definition is used to include them. The circle is a special case whose
description is a single point. The series of dots in a circle is included

to show a closure property of the process. By setting a velocity
threshold (this is equivalent to a smoothness criterion of the wave
front), one sees that it is possible to have these points disappear and
reappear at the center. In this way, a circle and a series of dots in
a circle can be equated. Clearly, under these conditions, the process
is not dimension preserving. Let us examine the process more carefully since these points along with the times or distances associated
with them form an alternate description of a shape.

Figure 3 consists of 2 circular arcs and the tangents connecting
them. A corner does not immediately appear in the wave front since
it is a smooth figure. A corner appears at time t_1, propagates to the
right and disappears at time t_2. Each stage of these expanding waves
represents a figure parallel to the original one. The appearance of
a single corner occurs at the minimum radius of curvature of the
figure. The dissappearance of a corner represents a largest circle
that can be drawn in the figure. All the corner points have a velocity
associated with them that is determined by the angle formed — the
sharper the angle, the faster the velocity. Since the parallel figures
generated in Figure 3 all have the same angle, the velocity along this
central line is a constant. An accelerating point would result from
curvature toward this locus; a decelerating point would result from
curvature away from this locus. The locus of corners will be called
the "medial axis" (MA). When the times of corner occurrence on the
medial axis is included, it will be referred to as the "medial axis
function" (MAF).[1] As long as the MA is a straight line, the figure is
symmetrical. Clearly an arbitrary parameter, such as parallel distance, could be substituted for time.

The transformation from the original pattern to the medial axis
function description is unique and hence invertible. It can be seen
that the original pattern can be described by the envelope of circles of
proper radius (MAF time divided by the space velocity) associated with
each point. This can be done more elegantly by the following inversion
procedure. Excite the space along the MA at a time defined by the
negative of the MAF. Thus, the later points of the function are pre-
excited and allowed to expand by the proper amount before the earlier

---

[1] This locus has also been called the "skeleton" and the function on the
skeleton, the "skeletal function."

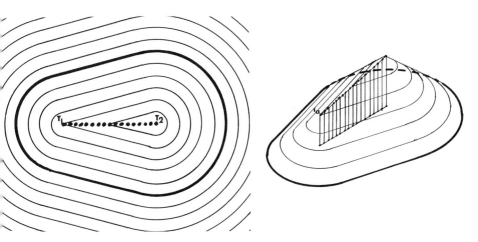

Fig. 3. Generation of new contour description (medial axis
function) centered on enclosed
space. (t_1 is appearance of
corner, t_2 is disappearance.
The locus of points and their
times are required.)

Fig. 4. A three-dimensional
static alternative to the two-
dimensional kinetic view of
the process. (The MAF is the
ridge formed where the union
of cones on the input contour
intersect each other.)

points of the function are excited. This procedure uses a reciprocity
property like that of electromagnetic theory.

Alternate Definitions

There are a number of alternate ways of looking at the transformation, each of which sheds a somewhat different light on the process.
Consequently, it is worth describing them. Figure 4 shows a formulation proposed by Kotelly (1963) in applying an earlier version of this
process to the problem of pattern masking (metacontrast). Here,
vertical distance is substituted for time. Instead of a propagating
wave, one obtains a representation as a surface which is the envelope
of cones whose apexes sit on the original contour. The MAF is then
the locus of discontinuities in this surface. Still another way of looking
at the process is from the viewpoint of field theory. The wave can
be considered as a "nearest distance" field. The MAF is then the
locus of discontinuities in the derivative of that field. Such a field
departs sharply and in important ways from the conventional fields of
physics and psychology, in which the value at a point is an integral of
a distance function to the total input. Still one more, and I feel
particularly interesting definition of it, is gotten from an equidistance

viewpoint. Consider the (minimum) distance from each point of the
plane to the stimulus shape. For most points this distance is unique
to one point on the shape. For points on the MA, however, this distance
is not unique to one point on the stimulus. Consequently, the MA is the
locus of points equidistant from the pattern and in this sense represents
a line of symmetry of the pattern. The MAF can be considered a
symmetrical central description of the space whose boundary is the
stimulus contour. It has been particularly satisfying to me to find that
the process can be expressed in so simple a geometric notion. If one
considers contours as coming from a world of objects, then these
original contours are extremities of objects or transition points between objects. For even so simple a notion as location of an object,
the contour or perimeter description is particularly poor.

Properties

Let us see what kind of categorizations are natural to such a process
by considering a number of smooth, simply connected closed curves.
The MAF of the circle and the ellipse were shown in Figure 2. Figure
5 shows the MAFs for a number of more undulating curves. The
"pinch" in the upper left figure generates a double set of MA points
which propagate in opposite directions. The pinches in the lower left
"3-bulb" do the same. The outward moving points disappear, indicating
closure; the inward points form a triple branch indicative of the three-
sided structure of the figure. That the "3-star" on the lower right
has such a triple structure is again shown by this three branch. At
this point, it can be seen heuristically that by use of the directed graph
of the MAF, it is possible to specify a generic 3-bulb, for example.
This leads to a geometry whose character lies between topology, which
is too general for shape categorization, and the "hard" congruent
geometries such as Euclidean and projective geometry. Figure 6 shows
such a geometry at work in describing an anthropomorphic outline and a
gross distortion of it. It should be pointed out that since these figures
are not convex, they have MAF points which lie outside themselves.
The outside MAFs are generated only by the points of the contours that
are not on the convex hull of the contours.

Since the contour and the MAF description are equivalent and invertible there is no information lost or gained in the transformation.
It is clear, then, that this categorization could have been done on the
contour itself. What then is the virtue of the new description? I believe

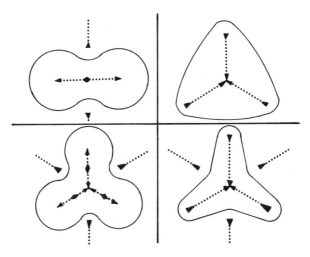

Fig. 5. Representation of simple shape properties by directed graph structure of the MAF.

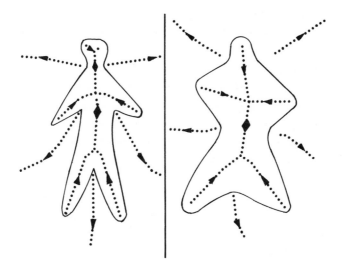

Fig. 6. Two anthropomorphs and their MAFs.

it to be in defining natural shape properties on the new primitive descriptors. It could be argued that the properties I have discussed in the last paragraph could be gotten by such simple contour properties as counting the inflection points and the total curvature of the shape.

Figure 7 shows a case where <u>simple</u> equivalent descriptors cannot be found on the boundary. The upper and lower figures can be arranged to have the same number of inflexion points and the same total curvature; yet they are quite different visual figures. What is different about the figures has to do with the distance across the enclosed space. Carrying along such a distance function to all sorts of other points <u>across</u> the contour as one moves <u>along</u> the contour is a formidable task indeed. To try to deal with such properties from a boundary description such as the intrinsic co-ordinates, for example, implies that one cannot describe a swan's neck until one has gone completely around the swan. This point is illustrated in a different way in Figure 8. The upper figure shows a rectangle and its MAF. The heavy dots indicate points which represent parallel lines and so occur at the same time (infinite velocity). The middle figure shows this rectangle distorted perspectively. It can be seen that the velocity of the central element, a local property, becomes the cue to perspective angle if one assumes one is looking at a rectangle. The lowest figure has been included to emphasize that all is not roses with this theory. For extreme distortions, the MAF structure stays the same but the perspective cue changes. Note that in going from the top to the bottom figure, one passes through a degenerate state when the figure can be circumscribed about a circle. It is an interesting conjecture, that with proper constraints, the MAF structure cannot change without going through such a degenerate state.

An interesting question of continuity is raised in Figure 9. In both parts of this figure the outside shape is continuously transformed to the circle, but by different paths. The intermediate shapes lead to distinctly different MAs. In the upper figure, the MA is continuously deformed from that of the original figure to that of the circle, the central dot. In the lower figure, however, the limiting MA is a radius of the circle. The velocity of the lower MAF, however, becomes asymptotic to the space velocity. Consequently, a viable notion of

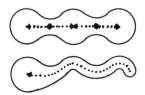

Fig. 7. The width measure of the shape as a primitive property.

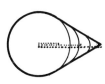

Fig. 8. The MAF for a rectangle
"full face" and in perspective.

Fig. 9. Dependency of MAF
limit on path of curve perturbation.

continuity must include the velocity dimension. This dimension is also
important for the closure property introduced in the circle of dots in
Figure 2 and in the completing of masked figures discussed later.

Figure 10 illustrates the process considered as a co-ordinate transformation. The upper and middle figures depict symmetrical contours
and so have a straight-line MA. The new description consists of the
location of the MA point as a function of time (or length of the normal)
to the MA. Acceleration represents curvature to the axis; decelera-
tion, away from the axis. An explicit formulation can be given for
curvature in terms of velocity and acceleration of the MAF point. The
condition that no branching occurs at a point on the MA generated by
two contours is that the center of curvature of the points mapping into
it do not lie between the MA and those points. (The condition of two
contours is inserted since a third contour may enter for curves with
their centers of curvature on the side opposite the MA such as is
shown in the case of the 3-bulb of Figure 5. The lowest figure shows a
curved MAF. In this case the contours are described by two components, the MAF curvature and the acceleration curvature – one curve

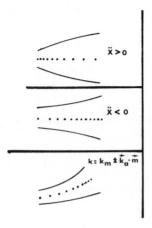

Fig. 10. The MAF as a co-ordinate transformation.

being the sum and the other being the difference when proper components of these curvatures have been taken. Consequently, a curve has
an infinite number of descriptions since it can be described from a
wide variety of MAs, and the location of the MAs is determined by what
else is in the input field. Figure 11 illustrates this. The upper left
figure is a semiellipse, its MA being its evolute continued by the perpendicular bisector of its end points. The upper right figure shows
the change in form of description gotten by completing the ellipse.
The lower left figure shows a descriptor appearing outside the elliptic
arc when space is enclosed there, and the altered description obtained
by putting a barrier line underneath the elliptic arc. These illustrate
clearly the barrier effect of the process. Only the closest contour can
affect the MAF. This guarantees that a description of a shape represents the bounding contour alone. Conventional field theories alter the
relevant description by modifications due to outside contours both far
and near. As such, these and other complete interaction processes,
such as two-dimensional autocorrelation, are certain to become un-
wieldy as the complexity of the input goes up. I feel that this type of
segmentation property is essential to a realistic theory of shape.

Figure 12 shows an abstract generalized input. Except for special
cases, which complicate the description, but not the properties, the
transformation maps each point on the contour into a 2 MAF points,
and each MAF point results from 2 contour points. (To make the
statement general, it is necessary to consider ray paths rather than
contours and MAFs.) Gross properties of the MAF are equivalent to
gross properties of the pattern. Each connected space is represented

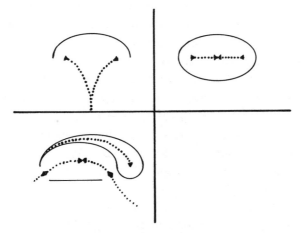

Fig. 11 . Nonsuperposability of partial descriptions and barrier effect.

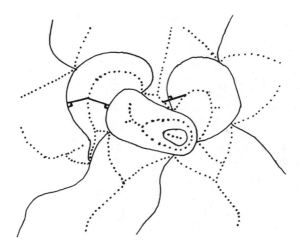

Fig. 12. A generalized input showing MAF as limit of space seen from contour.

by a separate graph piece. A connected space with no holes in it is represented by a "tree, " each hole in a space being represented by a loop. (Topological properties of the space are thus available as primitive properties of the graph.) The order and connection of the expanding spaces is represented by the structure of the directed graph. Since the MA represents discontinuities in the wave, the discontinuities

of the MAF (appearance, disappearance, impulse, and branch points)
can be considered as second-order discontinuities of the process.
These can be categorized by a number pair in which the first number
is the number of MAF points immediately prior to the discontinuity and
the second, the number immediately after the discontinuity. That each
of these represents a particular natural figure property is shown by
Figure 13. A 0,0 represents a circle; a 0,1 a circular arc of less than
180 degrees; a 1,0 a circular arc of greater than 180 degrees; a 2,0 a
double closure such as in an ellipse; a 0,2 a pinch in the contour; a 1,1
a case where the center of curvature lies on the MAF, etc. Simple
constraints of geometry, such as the closest distance between three
points being between two of them, impose a number of constraints on
the possibility of such pairs, which leads to forbidden pairs and pairs
possible only at t = 0. Figure 14 illustrates the equivalent matrix of
the graphical description. Graph discontinuity properties go into the
diagonal, continuous properties into the off diagonal. Each term in
the matrix is a vector, in general. Finding good vectors cannot in
general be done theoretically but must be decided by new experiments
on visual shape. This may be a fruitful area of exploration.

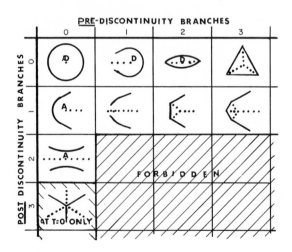

Fig. 13. Shape equivalents of discontinuities on MAF.

Compound Shapes

Thus far we have been considering shapes merely as spaces on a
plane. Figure 15 contains an illustrative example for showing an extension of this process for shapes which are masked by others. In the

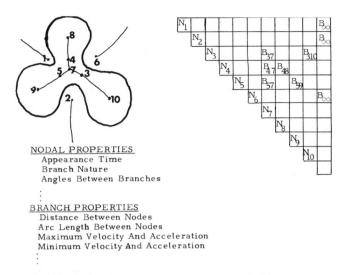

NODAL PROPERTIES
Appearance Time
Branch Nature
Angles Between Branches
⋮

BRANCH PROPERTIES
Distance Between Nodes
Arc Length Between Nodes
Maximum Velocity And Acceleration
Minimum Velocity And Acceleration
⋮

Fig. 14. MAF description allows analysis by matrix of graph.

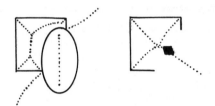

Fig. 15. Extension of MAF to masked shapes.

left-hand figure, an ellipse and partially masked square are shown, the masking considerably complicating the MAF of the square. If the MAF of the ellipse is recognized and its contour removed after its recognition, as shown in the right figure, the representation is considerably simplified. (This can be done from the MAF function by presenting it in negative time so that the ellipse is formed at $t = 0$. If further propagation is stopped, the input can be made refractory at the locations of the ellipse.) The remaining square contour can easily be recognized. In this way, one can attempt to cancel sequentially the entire stimulus contour and equate this cancellation with an acceptable interpretation of it. Clearly, alternate sequences are possible. A number of properties of such a sequential process are particularly interesting. (a) Masking cues are primary outputs of the process. (b) There is an inherent figure-ground effect that comes from matching MAF descriptions rather than the contour itself. (c) There is an

asymmetry of the process with respect to additive and subtractive
noise. Additive noise, such as a masking object, must be explicitly
removed. Subtractive noise, such as a missing contour, is implicitly
filled in. Figure 16 shows a stylized animal behind a tree. If the tree
is recognized by any cues, such as the green of its leaves and brown
of its trunk, its contour can be removed. This facilitates making a
single object of the animal. Such an object completion property may
be an extremely important one to vision; a cat must see through grass,
a monkey through leaves.

Fig. 16. Making a contiguous
world of masked objects.

Psychology and Physiology

Although the transformation has been developed to deal with the
visual problems of everyday life, it is interesting to see how it checks
with the anomalies of vision, the illusions. In Figure 17, I have shown
a number of standard illusions and the MAFs associated with these.
In the right-hand figures, I have accented the faster velocity MAFs.
If one assumes that the visual process tries to line up MAFs, (these
represent the spaces or objects) rather than the contours themselves,
the illusions have a natural meaning. The figures on the left are self-
explanatory, I feel. The MAF opens a new range of processes for explaining the standard illusions. I feel that it goes much deeper than
that, however. The process allows us to take a much broader view of
shape vision. We have been looking at vision as a recognition process,
rather than as a segmentation process. The closure properties suggest that the appearance of a dotted figure as a continuous contoured
one (Figure 2) is an illusion. The process suggests that the whole of
our sensitivity to circles, parallels, and symmetric figures may be an
illusion. If one asks what life and death problem such sensitivities
have emerged to solve, one finds no ready answer. It is suggested
here that these are by-products of an inverting process of the visual
co-ordinates useful for coping with the problems of localization, segmentation, and organization of a world of visual objects.

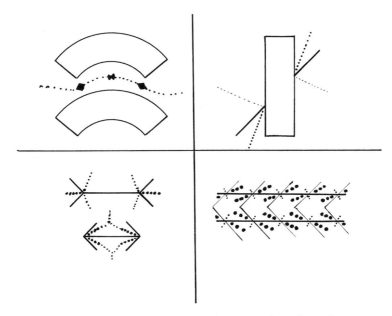

Fig. 17.   The MAF as a source of new explanations for optical illusions.

A word must be said about how such a process relates to the results of Hubel and Wiesel (1962, 1965) on cortical cell responses. This has been abstracted and stylized in Figure 18.   The upper-left figure shows the receptive fields of the "simple cells" that would be fired by a particular contour.   The upper right shows the receptive fields of their "complex cells."   Whereas Hubel and Wiesel have looked at these responses as detectors of lines at particular angles, I am suggesting that they can be looked at as generators of parallel shapes.   The lower left shows the kinds of corners that could be formed from the inter-action of the output of such cells.   The lower right shows a selection of proper "symmetrical corners" obtained by having a cell that re-sponds to a corner at a particular location, but not in an adjacent location.   Such a sequence can perform the transformation without the barrier property.   This requires a further condition.   Unfortunately no one has looked for such a property, as far as I know.

General Comments and Conclusion

A word should also be said about the mathematical implication of the transformation.   (It should be clear that I speak for mathematicians

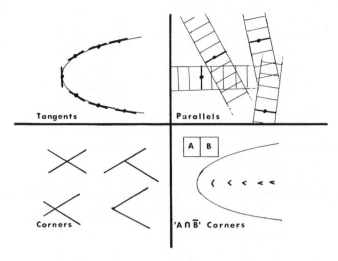

Fig. 18. MAF extraction by idealized properties of visual
cortical cell receptive fields.

here without their permission.) The general Cartesian view of geometry metricizes a space (builds a co-ordinate system) and then describes the curve in that metric in some functional form. Unfortunately, the transformation from geometry to analysis is highly
discontinuous and gives preference to shapes which have easy functional
rather than geometric meaning. The approach introduced here suggests that the co-ordinate system be built on the curve and space be
explored from the curve. The MA is then the boundary of the space
(in some Riemann sense) that must exist if one is to have a good single
valued co-ordinate system. The process indicates that the curve is
then describable from the boundary as the envelope of circles on that
boundary. I have talked hitherto about a Euclidean orthogonal process,
but there is no need to impose such a limitation. This transformation
can be done with non-Euclidean processes, as the spherical visual
mapping may well demand, or it can be done in higher dimensions, as
a three- or four-dimensional world may demand.

Figure 19 shows my first physical embodiment of the process. It
uses a movie projector and camera with high contrast film. These are
symmetrically driven apart from the lens in such a way as to keep a
one to one magnification, but to increase the circle of confusion (defocussing). The lower right inset shows how this dilates the contour.
Corner detection is done separately by a subsequent process. I am
presently building a closed loop electronic system to do both the wave

Fig. 19.   An early opticomechanical device for obtaining
grassfire propagation using photographic defocussing.

generation and corner detection.

In conclusion, I would like to emphasize that our view of vision has
been constrained for too long by problems of physical geometry. Successful methods there have looked at shape as a superposable process
where the total collection of elements is equal to the sum of the parts.
I have tried to depart from this by looking for processes in which the
interaction is precisely the item of interest, without getting into a
conceptual space so rich in possibilities that all things are encompas-
sable in it.

References

Attneave, F., and Arnoult, M. D. The quantitative study of shape
    and pattern perception. Psychol. Bull., 1956, 53, 452-471.

Bitterman, M. E., Krauskopf, J., and Hochberg, J. Threshold for
    visual form: A diffusion model. Amer. J. Psychol., 1954, 67,
    205-219.

Blum, H. An associative machine for dealing with the visual field
    and some of its biological implications. In E. E. Bernard and
    M. R. Kare (Eds.), Biological prototypes and synthetic systems.
    Vol. 1. New York: Plenum, 1962.

Deutsch, J. A. A theory of shape recognition. Brit. J. Psychol.,
1955, 46, 30-37.

Hubel, D. H., and Wiesel, T. N. Receptive fields, binocular interaction and functional architecture in the cat's visual cortex.
J. Physiol., 1962, 160, 106-164.

Hubel, D. H., and Wiesel, T. N. Receptive fields and functional
architecture in two non-striate visual areas (18 and 19) of the cat.
J. Neurophysiol., 1965, 28, 229-289.

Kazmierczak, H. The potential field as an aid to character recognition. In Proceedings international conference on information
processing. London: Butterworth, 1960.

Kirsch, R. A., Cahn, L., Ray, C., and Urban, G. H. Experiments in
processing pictorial information with a digital computer. East.
joint Comp. Conf., 1958, 12, 221-229.

Koffka, K. Principles of Gestalt psychology. New York: Harcourt
Brace, 1935.

Kotelly, J. C. A mathematical model of Blum's theory of pattern
recognition. AFCRL-TR-63-164, USAF Camb. Res. Labs., 1963.

Sutherland, N. S. The methods and findings of experiments on the
visual discrimination of shape by animals. Exp. Psychol.
Monogr. No. 1. Cambridge, Eng.: Heffer, 1960.

LATERAL INHIBITION AS A MECHANISM OF SHAPE RECOGNITION

J. A. Deutsch[1]
Department of Psychology
New York University
New York, New York

Leon Traister[2]
Health Sciences Computing Facility
University of California, Los Angeles
Los Angeles, California

That the mechanism of lateral inhibition could be used to differentiate between different shapes is not a new suggestion. In the present
report our aim is a limited one: namely, to take known results from
behavioral work on shape recognition and known neurophysiological

---

[1]
Now at the Department of Psychology, University of California, San
Diego, La Jolla, California.

[2]
Now at Computer Applications, Incorporated, Los Angeles, California.

results on lateral inhibition and by means of a computer program to see if the neurophysiological mechanism could produce the type of behavioral performance observed. The behavioral data we took were from Sutherland's work on shape discrimination (Sutherland, 1960) and the neurophysiological results were those from the work of Hartline, Ratliff, and Miller (1961). Our hypothesis follows: that in the discrimination of shape a visually primitive animal such as the rat simply took an index of the total amount of lateral inhibition produced by a shape. Different shapes would produce different amounts of lateral inhibition and would accordingly be seen as similar or dissimilar by the animal depending on where they fell on the continuum of lateral inhibition production.

The assumption that rats translate the shapes they see into some kind of continuum is plausible. The most dramatic demonstration of it is by Dodwell.[3] He trained rats to discriminate between interrupted horizontal and vertical stripes. After training the animal to approach the interrupted horizontal stripes and avoid the interrupted vertical stripes, Dodwell then substituted solid horizontal stripes for the interrupted vertical stripes to see which the animals would approach. He found that the rats would now approach the solid horizontal stripes and avoid the interrupted horizontal stripes, treating the stimulus which they had been approaching as negative in the presence of the new stimulus. The same kind of result is obtained with other substitutions of solid bars for the interrupted bars. The solid bars which had never appeared in learning seem more like the interrupted version of the stimulus than the interrupted stimulus itself. It is as if the stimuli were translated into a dimension and the animal learnt to approach that stimulus which was in one direction on the continuum relative to the other presented, and to avoid on a similar principle.

Similarly striking results have been obtained by Sutherland (1960). He found that for rats and octopuses, no matter what two shapes the animals had been taught to discriminate initially, the rank order of transfer of training to other shapes was always highly similar. This suggests that the animal uses the same criterion or dimension whatever two shapes it has to discriminate and that it responds to substitute shapes in a manner simply determined by where such substitute shapes are on this dimension.

---

[3] Personal communication from P. C. Dodwell.

As stated previously, the hypothesis adopted related the dimension used to the sum of lateral inhibition exercised by a shape upon itself and its surround. To find out whether this was true as a first approximation, some of the shapes Sutherland used were investigated (see Sutherland, 1960). The amount of lateral inhibition generated by each was calculated by a computer using the equations found by Hartline and Ratliff (1958) to obtain in the eye of _Limulus_. This was done not because we believe the same relations hold in the brain of the rat, but because it seemed best to try a set of known relations. Of course we did not know the size of the parameters in the rat, such as how far laterally inhibition would extend in relation to our shapes, so we decided to vary such parameters in an effort to obtain a best fit to the known behavioral results of Sutherland.

The technique used in programming the computer, though of no direct significance to the hypothesis under test, is, we feel, of interest. It provides a method of calculating lateral inhibition over a field without the necessity of computing a number of simultaneous linear equations, equal to the number of points which represents that field. As is known, Hartline and Ratliff (1958) have shown that the activity of interacting receptors may be described by a set of simultaneous linear equations, each with n-1 inhibitory terms combined by simple addition. As we wished to use a field consisting of 2,500 points, we would have had to program that number of simultaneous equations. The problem was made more manageable in the following way.

The "usual" field is an array of 50×50 points. The effect of inhibition is carried a distance of, say, five points in each of four directions at which the response is to be calculated. (This is referred to as a five-weight function and is illustrated in Figure 1.)

Now the effect is to be calculated from points in all directions in the plane. So, by symmetry, we get the array shown in Figure 2.

Now if the Point 0 is the (i, j)th point of the visual field, its response is calculated by dividing the points extending up to five points from 0 by the values of W which are directly proportional to the distance from 0.

So:
$$R_{i, j} = A_{i, j} - \sum_{1=0}^{5} \sum_{k=0}^{5} (A_{i \pm k, j \pm 1})/W_{k, 1} \qquad [1]$$

where k, 1 are not zero simultaneously. Here A is the value of each of the field points up to five points and $W_{k, 1}$ is the distance of each point

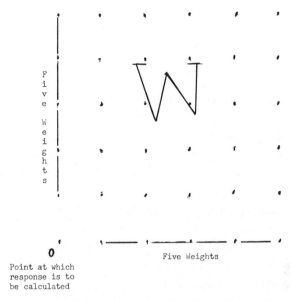

Fig. 1. Illustration of a five-weight function.

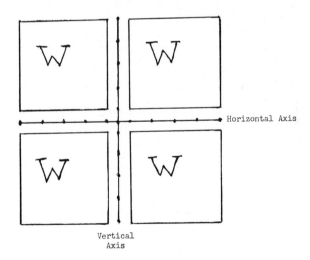

Fig. 2. Array derived by symmetry from the five-weight function shown in Figure 1.

from 0. R is the final response at 0.

By symmetry, the weighting extends over 10×10 off-axis points around 0 plus 20 points on the axes = 120 points. Now a 10-weight function W would extend further out from 0 such that we compute at 20×20

+ 40 = 440 points.   This gives us a factor of four in the times for computation.

Intuitively, the process consists of calculating the distance of all points up to five points (ten points for the ten-weight function) away on the horizontal and vertical axes of one quadrant. By symmetry, the distances in the other quadrants are the same. We lay the weighting function extending over four quadrants so that it is centered at 0. Then we multiply points which "fall on top of each other". The sum of these multiplications is subtracted from the value of the field at 0 to give the new value of the point at 0. Then the whole thing is picked up and moved to the next point in the field and so on.

In the program, the action of thresholds which increase with distance is taken into account by subtracting off the distance dependent threshold from the value of each point around 0 before the computation. A linear threshold increase with distance and a linear decrease in inhibition with distance is assumed.

The final computation algorithm is:

$$R_{i,j} = A_{i,j} - \sum_{1=0}^{N} \sum_{k=0}^{N} \frac{A_{i \pm k, j \pm 1} - K_1 (W_{k,1})}{K_2 (W_{k,1})} \qquad [2]$$

where

$R_{i,j}$ is the response at the point 0: (i, j)

$A_{i,j}$ is the value at 0: (i, j) before the present computation

N is the number of weights in the weighting function (i. e., the extent over which the effect is calculated) (This results in a scope of 2N × 2N + 4N points around 0.)

K_1 is the factor for the increase in threshold with distance

$W_{k,1}$ is the distance from 0: (i, j) of the point (i + k, j + 1)

K_2 is the linear factor for the decrease in inhibition with distance.

As the process of lateral inhibition seems to occur at successive levels in the sensory pathway and as Barlow (1961) has suggested that a repetition of such a process might produce alterations in the image such as fringes, we decided to repeat the process of lateral inhibition three times. This turned out simply to intensify the effect of any lateral inhibition and not to produce any fringes (see Figures 3 and 4).

The rank ordering of shapes used by Sutherland (1960) when some parameters are varied is given in Table 1. A sufficiently large number of variations of parameter has not been tried, but it does appear from

RESPONSE FIELD AFTER II
MAP OF TRUI

RESPONSE FIELD SUM AFTER INHIBITION PASS 3 = 180216.25

CONTRAST FACTOR = 64113.75

Fig. 3. Illustration of the fact that three lateral inhibition passes only intensify the effect of lateral inhibition and do not produce any fringes.

the results that different rank orderings are obtainable. It is therefore conceivable that some combination of parameters would give the type of rank ordering actually found in the behavioral tests on transfer. If this turned out to be the case not only should it be possible to predict the outcome of further behavioral tests, but also to measure the assumed parameters directly in the manner described by Hartline and Ratliff (1958). The mechanism assumed to exist here could easily undergo evolutionary adaptation to produce various types of discrimination. For instance, flattening the shape of the "receptive field" to produce differential amounts of lateral inhibition along the two main visual axes should produce discrimination of the tilt of shapes. Different shapes or tilts of "receptive field" at various stages in the sensory

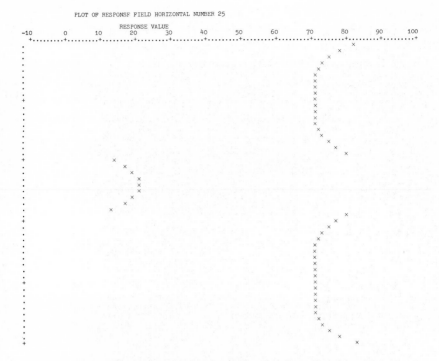

Fig. 4. Plot of response-field values for line Number 25 in
Figure 3.

Table 1. Rank Orders of Shapes According to Amount of
          Lateral Inhibition Generated

Figure set to 30.0		Figure set to 0.0
5 Weights	10 Weights	10 Weights
1. △	1. △	1. △
2. +	2. +	2. □
3. □	3. □	3. +
4. /	4. /	4. ○
5. ○	5. ○	5. /
6. ⊔	6. ⊔	6. ⊔

Note - The cases of "Figure Set to 30.0" allow inhibition
       to act within the figure itself. All surrounding
       fields set to 100.0 initially.

pathway could thus produce many diverse types of classification.

Whatever the truth of the theoretical speculations on shape discrimination may turn out to be, there is one rather practical consequence of the results presented above, and one which should have been obvious even without them. This relates to the techniques used in shape discrimination with animals. When different shapes are used, precautions are often taken to prevent the animal from discriminating simply on the basis of brightness by using shapes of equal area. This is thought to equate stimuli in brightness. Now it is almost certain because of lateral inhibition that two different shapes equal in area will also appear different in brightness, and that discrimination of the two shapes could still be in terms of apparent brightness. In fact, this might be the explanation of the continua which have so far been found. Tests of transfer to different shades of grey might be of interest.

References

Barlow, H. B.   Three points about lateral inhibition.   In W. A. Rosenblith (Ed.), Sensory communication.   New York: M. I. T. Press and Wiley, 1961.   Pp. 782-786.

Hartline, H. K. , and Ratliff, F.   Spatial summation of inhibitory influences in the eye of Limulus and the mutual interaction of receptor units.   J. gen. Physiol., 1958, 41, 1049-1066.

Hartline, H. K. , Ratliff, F. , and Miller, W. H.   Inhibitory interaction in the retina and its significance in vision.   In E. Florey (Ed.), Nervous inhibition.   New York: Pergamon, 1961.   Pp. 241-284.

Sutherland, N. S.   Theories of shape discrimination in Octopus.   Nature, 1960, 186, 840-844.

AN HIERARCHICAL MODEL OF FORM PERCEPTION

M. B. Clowes[1]
Psycholinguistics Research Unit
Medical Research Council
Oxford, England

Introduction

The standpoint adopted here is to regard perception as an informa-tion-processing activity, with a special emphasis upon economy of computation. The model is expressed in terms of a set of algorithms for manipulating and labeling patterns. The algorithms can be real-ized in terms of a limited set of machine operations (macroinstruc-tions); it is this limitation which provides the means for distinguishing this model from other possible models. The model is realized specifically as a set of computer programs called the picture-process-ing program (PPP).

Tests of the model consist in comparing the labeling performance of PPP with the classificatory and descriptive judgments of human subjects when presented with the same patterns. By labeling we mean at least that PPP shall be capable of assigning patterns to classes (e. g. , alphanumeric classes), but more generally we have in mind the human capability for generating descriptions of patterns which do not fall into well-defined classes (e. g. , bubble chamber photographs, maps, etc. ,).

Picture-processing Operations

The picture-processing operations used in PPP fall into three categories: descriptive, addressing, and labeling operations. In each of these categories there is a characteristic limitation upon the type of macroinstruction available.

Description and Addressing. Let us assume that the picture I, physically described as a function $d(r)$, may be completely specified for recognition purposes by a vector P consisting of N binary variables or elements. For the purposes of classifying or distinguishing between the 2^N states of P we could provide a mechanism for evaluating speci-fied Boolean functions of the elements of this N-bit vector. Consider

---

[1] Now with the Computing Research Section, Commonwealth Scientific and Industrial Research Organization, Canberra, Australia.

a simple Boolean function containing terms in "AND" (&) and "AND NOT" ($\sim$) of n variables selected from the total N. There are

$$\sum_{n=1}^{n=N} {}^{N}C_n (2^n) = 3^N$$

such Boolean functions. We may call these n-tuples or descriptors of P: when applied to a picture I their outcome will be a "complete" description of that pattern. If we adopt such descriptors as the basis upon which to decide the identity of the picture I, it will be clear for reasons of economy that only a very limited subset of this 3^N can be evaluated. The selection of a "useful" subset is one of the central problems in Pattern Recognition. In Perceptron (Holmes, Leland, and Muerle, 1962) and other systems (Bledsoe and Browning, 1959; Kamentsky and Liu, 1963) this selection is made in a random fashion. In evaluating the descriptors of a pattern, any computational device must ascertain the state (1/0) of the sets of variables entering into each n-tuple, i.e., it must <u>address</u> the elements of P. In computer terms we might imagine the N variables as stored in the form of an N-bit binary string. In this case, it would clearly be more economic, from the viewpoint of addressing complexity, if the subset of n-tuples chosen was confined to sets of neighboring elements of the string. If specifically we assume that no more than m contiguous elements can enter into any one n-tuple evaluation, then the total number of n-tuples now available is approximately $N3^m$ (i.e., $\ll 3^N$ where $n < m \ll N$). Reinterpreting P not as a binary string but as a two-dimensional binary array, this constraint on n-tuple selection is essentially that adopted by Roberts (1960) in his modified version of the Perceptron (Figure 1). Assigning Cartesian co-ordinates (x, y) to each element of this array, one finds that the i-th n-tuple (for n=3) would be

$$p (x_1, y_1) \ H \ P (x_1 + a, y_1 + b) \ H \ P (x_1 + c, y_1 + d) \cdots \qquad [1]$$

where a, b, c, d are integers and <u>small compared with the total extent of the array</u>. H represents either of the Boolean Operations &, $\sim$. It is important to note that the selection of "local" n-tuples is not primarily concerned with any hypothesis about the properties of I. Essentially this has been postulated as a constraint arising from economies in procedures used to address the elements of P.

   We could assign the elements (x_1, y_1) of the vector S_i the values given by Equation 1; i.e., let

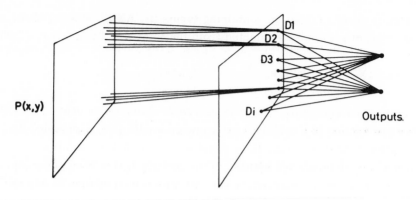

Fig. 1. N-tuples D_1, D_2, D_3...D_i formed by sampling
from among locally defined subsets of the elements of P.

$$S_i \ (x_1, y_1) = P \ (x_1, y_1) \ H \ P \ (x_1 + a, y_1 + b) \ H \ P \ (x_1 + c, y_1 + d)... \quad [1a]$$

Thus far we have not specified how the picture I is mapped into P.
We could visualize as opposite extremes, a random mapping of the
elements of I into P as opposed to an orderly mapping which preserved
the topographical relations between elements of I. In either event, rigid
translation of the picture I, will give rise to a different state of P. If
we now consider some n-tuple $S_i \ (x_1, y_1)$, which is "useful" in the sense
that it reliably predicts some property of patterns I_1, I_2... forming a
class, then if we wish to continue to detect this property under translation of the pattern I we need to select n-tuples whose action with
respect to I will be the same. For a random mapping of the picture
elements onto P the discovery of these sets of corresponding n-tuples
can be made only by trial and error. However, for a mapping which
preserves the geometrical properties of I (specifically a similarity
transformation) sets of corresponding n-tuples are obtained merely by
changing the values of (x_1, y_1) in Equation 1. Such an approach to
n-tuple selection has, in fact, been adopted as the basis of a position-
invariant recognition system (Kamentsky and Liu, 1963). We are
asserting in fact that, given a topographical mapping of the picture I
onto P, we can obtain a generalization of this "useful" descriptor
merely by replicating it across the array.

Assuming that the mapping of I onto P is effected via a similarity
transformation, one observes that it is possible to introduce further
economies in the evaluation of the "replicated" n-tuples $S_i \ (x_1, y_1)$;
$S_i \ (x_2, y_2)$; $S_i \ (x_3, y_3)$... The values of these n-tuples are given by the
states of the elements (x_1, y_1), (x_2, y_2), (x_3, y_3)... of the complete

array S_i (x, y) where

$$S_i \, (x, y) = P \, (x, y) \, H \, P \, (x + a, \, y + b) \, H \, (x + c, y + d) \dots \qquad [2]$$

With certain types of computing facility (Clowes, 1962; McCormick, 1963) it is possible to evaluate S_i in Equation 2 without <u>explicitly</u> addressing the elements (x, y) of P. Thus in the optical system illustrated in Figure 2, P takes the form of a negative transparency. The second term P (x + a, y + b) of Equation 2 is obtained by reimaging. Consequently the resultant light flux transmitted through the negative is an evaluation of P (x, y) & P (x + a, y + b). The displacement (a, b) is achieved optically. The process can be repeated several times in a conventional optical system of this form. If a photographic emulsion is exposed to the subsequent light flux (at L_3) then the resultant developed transparency is a representation of S_i, and may itself be used in further processing. The system essentially addresses all the elements of P (and S) in parallel.

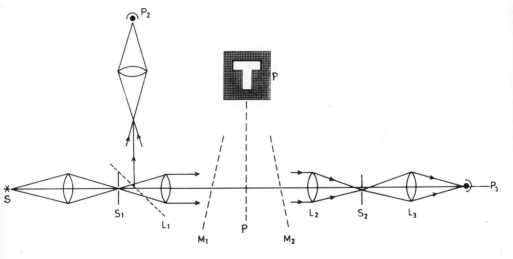

Fig. 2. Collimated light from the source S transilluminates the transparency which is, in effect, the input vector P (x, y). (A half-silvered mirror M_2 reimages P upon the transparency with a "shift" [a, b]. M_1 repeats this operation so as to image in the plane of L_3 the two-dimensional functions S [x, y].)

The PPP evaluates n-tuples in this manner, i.e., <u>it does not ex-</u>
<u>plicitly address elements of V</u> as would be required for an evaluation based upon Equation 1. The representations S_1, S_2 in Figure 3 illustrate this process for two triples (n-tuples with n=3), forming the

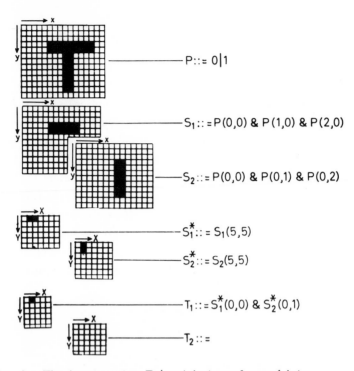

Fig. 3. The input vector P (x, y) is transformed into representations S_1 (x, y), S_2 (x, y). (After compression $S \rightarrow S^*$, the representations S^*_1, S^*_2 are combined to generate T_1 [X, Y], T_2 [X, y]. The rules for deriving these representations are a fragment of a "picture grammar.")

representations S_1, S_2. For convenience the co-ordinate pair (x, y) which is present in all the terms of the n-tuple has been omitted, it being understood that these are <u>picture</u> operations.

Each representation S_1, S_2, ... contains – by definition – information relating only to local properties of P. It is therefore necessary, if PPP is to handle extended patterns, to combine information derived from different S representations: this we may do by constructing n-tuples having the same general form as Equation 2 but containing terms in S_1, S_2... rather than P. The constraints on the magnitude of (a, b) (c, d) etc. would mean, however, that the outcome of such an operation would still reflect only <u>local</u> properties of P. Accordingly S_1, S_2... are <u>compressed</u> to form representations S_1^*, S_2^* so that, for example, the single element S_1^* (0, 0) is an "OR" function of the states of the elements lying between S_1 (0, 0), S_1 (h, 0), S_1 (h, k), and S_1 (0, k), i.e., an $h \times k$ block. If these blocks are nonoverlapping then a compression ratio of h: 1 and k : 1 is achieved. Formally we may represent this step as

$$S_1^* :: = S_1 \ [h, k] \ \ldots \tag{3}$$

etc.

It is upon these compressed representations that the next stage of n-tuple operations is performed, i. e. , by analogy with Equation 2:

$$T_j \ (X, Y) = S_\alpha^* \ (X, Y) \ H \ S_\beta^* \ (X + A, \ Y + B) \ H \ S_\gamma^* \ (X + C, Y + D) \ldots \tag{4}$$

where X = hx and Y = ky.

The effects of these steps (Equations 3 and 4) are illustrated in Figure 3.

The steps by which P is transformed into representations S_1, S_2... and T_1, T_2... are analogous to the rewriting rules found in a phrase structure grammar. We shall refer to the hierarchy of transformations as a picture grammar, noting that the left-right ordering of the elements of a syntactic string has been replaced by the two-dimensional ordering of the elements of a picture.

Labeling. The output vocabulary consists of the symbols appearing in the picture grammar. We hypothesize a mechanism which carries out an ordered exhaustive search of the array of representations T_1, T_2,... S_1, S_2.... The mechanism "prints out" any line of the picture grammar if the representation corresponding to that rule is nonzero. Thus its output in respect of the situation depicted in Figure 3 would be

$$"T_1 \ \{= S_1^* \ (0, 0) \ \& \ S_2^* \ (0, 1)\}; \ S_2 \ \{= P \ (0, 0) \ \& \ P \ (0, 1) \ \& \ P \ (0, 2)\} \ ;$$
$$S_1 \ \{= P \ (0, 0) \ \& \ P(1, 0) \ \& \ P \ (2, 0)\} \ . "$$

Thus the labeling mechanism cannot address individual picture elements of a representation for the purpose of indicating where in a particular representation a nonzero element occurred. This is consistent with the adoption of a processing technique based upon the form of Equation 2 rather than upon that of Equation 1.

Comparison with Physiology.

On the basis of published accounts, some parallels may be drawn between the structural organization, depicted in Figure 1, and physiological functions as revealed by microelectrode recording. These remarks relate largely to the visual system of the cat (Hubel and Wiesel, 1962), but are apparently also true, in part, for the frog

(Lettvin, Maturana, McCulloch, and Pitts, 1959).   Figure 1 agrees, at least up to S^*, with the physiological in the following respects: -

1. There is an orderly mapping of the retina onto the cortex.
2. The mapping is achieved through pattern operations which are local in much the same way as we have indicated.
3. Each picture operation appears to be replicated over the whole retina (at least in the frog).
4. Groups of cells whose sampling areas are confined to a local region of the retina, of extent approximately twice the sampling area, are organized into a single complex unit by an operation identical with the reduction operation $S \rightarrow S^*$ (Hubel and Wiesel, 1962).

Comparison with Psychology.

The output of PPP, as illustrated in the section headed "Labeling," appears consistent with the way in which S's describe pictures of this complexity, i.e., as a hierarchy of spatially related picture properties. Thus we might rewrite the first item of printout as "an S_1 above an S_2" which we can expand to "three horizontal picture points above three vertical picture points." Accepting S_1 and S_2 as rudimentary descriptions of what are conventionally called "horizontal and vertical straight lines," we may compare this printout with the description given by human subjects[2] : "a vertical line bisecting a horizontal cap line." If we accept the organization of PPP as an account of the mechanism underlying such humanly generated descriptions, then we also obtain some understanding of the prevalence of local property descriptors in intuitively designed pattern recognition automata (Stevens, 1961).

The PPP is unable to discriminate between certain types of pattern pairs in a way which can be interpreted as a quantitative prediction of perceptual limitation.   Consider a schematized version (Figure 4) of the pointer and scale used by Hake and Garner (1951).   A picture grammar competent to distinguish between this picture and one in which the pointer (E) has been displaced horizontally, might take the form:-

---

[2] Described by L. Harmon and J.S. Bomba in a Bell Telephone Laboratories internal memorandum, entitled How people describe letters and numbers, not generally available.

Fig. 4. A schematic representation of an ungraduated scale LR and a pointer E.

$$P \; :: \; = \; 0/1$$

$$S_1 \; :: \; = \; P(0,0) \; \& \; P(0,1) \; \& \; P(1,0) \; \& \; P(1,1)$$

$$S_2 \; :: \; = \; P(0,0) \; \& \; P(0,1) \; \& \; P(0,2)$$

$$S_1^* \; :: \; = \; S_1 \, [\, h, k \,]$$

$$S_2^* \; :: \; = \; S_2 \, [\, h, k \,]$$

$$T_1 \; :: \; = \; S_1^* \; (0,0) \; \& \; S_2^* \; (1,0)$$

$$T_2 \; :: \; = \; S_1^* \; (0,0) \; \& \; S_2^* \; (2,0)$$

$$T_9 \; :: \; = \; S_1^* \; (0,0) \; \& \; S_2^* \; (9,0)$$

$$T_A \; :: \; = \; S_1^* \; (0,0) \; \& \; S_2^* \; (A,0)$$

S_1 and S_2 reflect (inessential) differences in the local property structure of E and L, R. Consider two pictures I_1, I_2 in which the distance of the pointer from the nearer end-of-scale (say L) is LE and LE- Δ respectively. For I_1 and I_2 to be labeled differently this must be reflected in a change in the identity of some nonzero T representation. Let G be the maximum value of a, b... A, B. There are two cases: (i) LE $>$ G , (ii) LE $<$ G.

Case (i). I_1 can be labeled in a manner reflecting the relation between L and E by T representations (and not by S representations since LE $>$ a, b, etc.). For I_1 to be labeled in terms of a nonzero T vector, a compression S $\rightarrow$ S* is required given by:

$$LE/_h \; \leqslant \; G.$$

The minimal change in labeling would arise from the "next-nearest" T vector becoming nonzero (e. g. , a change from "T_A" to "T_{A-1}" say). Such a change would be generated when E is displaced through Δ if

$$\frac{\Delta}{h} \; = \; 1$$

but
$$\frac{1}{h} \; \leqslant \; \frac{G}{LE}$$

$$\therefore \; \frac{1}{\Delta} \; \leqslant \; G/_{LE}$$

that is
$$\frac{\Delta}{LE} \; \geqslant \; \frac{1}{G} \qquad\qquad [5]$$

Case (ii). The relation between L and E in I_1 can now be labeled in terms of an S vector, since LE $<$ G. Let us assume that there are LE elements separating L and E in the picture I_1. Then the minimal change in labeling would correspond to a change from "S_{LE}" to "S_{LE-1}"

i.e., $\Delta = 1$

Hence $\dfrac{\Delta}{LE} = \dfrac{1}{LE}$ [6]

The ratio $\dfrac{\Delta}{LE}$ is of course the Weber fraction, and the results, Equations 5 and 6, together constitute a prediction of Weber's law and its departure from constancy (i.e, $\dfrac{1}{G}$) at threshold (Woodworth and Schlosberg, 1955). That is for LE $>$ G the Weber fraction is constant (= $\dfrac{1}{G}$), whereas for LE $<$ G it varies inversely with LE.

The introduction of a fiducial or reference point F into Figure 4 will alter the local property structure of the display advantageously, since if FE $<$ LE, F rather than L can be employed in an appropriate n-tuple. Attempts to use PPP to describe pictures consisting of extended strings of identical digits, e.g., "77777777777," bring out this same limitation in another way. In the absence of a fiducial or pointer it is not possible to define n-tuples which will "select out" (into corresponding representations $S_1 S_2 \dots$ or $T_1 T_2 \dots$) separate digits. It is therefore impossible to "count" such strings with any precision. A moveable pointer can be used to remove this source of ambiguity in PPP in a way which is closely analogous to the use of a pencil point or finger by a human subject performing the same task. A similar though less extreme difficulty is encountered with strings of nonidentical symbols (e.g., words); this may throw some light on so-called specific dyslexia (word blindness).

Discussion

The importance of these results lies in the fact that they do not depend upon predicating a particular picture grammar: only upon the assumption that classes of picture grammar are not available (those with nonlocal n-tuple spans). The problem of discovering picture grammars - like the problem of discovering linguistic grammars - is, of course, of vital importance. It may be approached piecemeal, perhaps, by enquiring as to whether there are classes of picture grammar such as might give rise to familiar perceptual distinctions like position, shape, and texture. It may also be appropriate to speculate here as to the physiological concomitants of the parallel processing operation illustrated physically in Figure 2 and expressed formally in Equation 2. It appears to imply that receptive field units, of say the striate cortex (Hubel and Wiesel, 1962) cannot be addressed individually, but only by type, e. g. , all "vertical detectors," etc. The requirement that subsequent representations S, T, etc. should be two-dimensional provides a new interpretation of the topographical mapping observed at various stages of the visual pathway (Lashley, 1949). A complete identity would be established if we assumed that the labels S_1, $S_2 \ldots T_1$, $T_2 \ldots$ etc. were realized physiologically in some sort of "chemical key" which identified axons by the type of cell from which they proceeded.

Development and application of this model is proceeding via a set of computer programs written for the KDF9 computer. Some results of its use as a pattern recognition device have been obtained through an earlier version (Clayden, Clowes, and Parks, 1967). At present we are studying its performance on handwritten numerals.

Acknowledgments

I should like to acknowledge many valuable discussions, especially with J. R. Parks of the National Physical Laboratory, D. M. Vowles, and N. S. Sutherland.

References

Bledsoe, W. W. , and Browning, I. Pattern recognition and reading by machine. Proc. east. jnt. Comput. Conf. , 1959, 16, 225-232.

Clayden, D. O. , Clowes, M. B. , and Parks, J. R. Letter recognition and the segmentation of running text. J. Info. and Control, 1967, in press.

Clowes, M. B. The use of multiple autocorrelation in character recognition. In G. L. Fischer, Jr. , D. K. Pollock, B. Radek, and Mary E. Stevens (Eds.), Optical character recognition. Washington: Spartan, 1962. Pp. 305-318.

Hake, H. W. , and Garner, W. R. The effect of presenting various numbers of discrete steps on scale reading accuracy. J. exp. Psychol. , 1951, 42, 358-366.

Holmes, W. S. , Leland, H. R. , and Muerle, J. L. Recognition of mixed-font imperfect characters. In G. L. Fischer, Jr. , D. K. Pollock, B. Radek, and Mary E. Stevens (Eds.), Optical character recognition. Washington: Spartan, 1962. Pp. 213-225.

Hubel, D. H. , and Wiesel, T. N. Receptive fields, binocular interaction, and functional architecture in the cat's visual cortex. J. Physiol. , 1962, 160, 106-154.

Kamentsky, L. A. , and Liu, C. N. Computer-automated design of multifont print recognition logic. IBM J. Res. Dev. , 1963, 7, 2-13.

Lashley, K. S.   Persistent problems in the evolution of mind.   Quart.
Rev. Biol., 1949, 24, 24-42.

Lettvin, J. Y., Maturana, H. R., McCulloch, W. S., and Pitts, W. H.
What the frog's eye tells the frog's brain.   Proc. Inst. Rad. Engr.,
1959, 47, 1940-1951.

McCormick, B. H.   The Illinois pattern recognition computer —
ILLIAC III.   IEEE Trans. elect. Comput., 1963, EC-12, 791-813.

Roberts, L. G.   Pattern recognition with an adaptive network.   IRE
int. Conv. Rec., 1960, Pt. 2, 66-70.

Stevens, Mary E.   Automatic character recognition: A state-of-the-
art report.   US Dept. Comm., Off. Tech. Serv., Nat. Bur. Stds.
tech. Note, 1961, No. 112.

Woodworth, R. S., Schlosberg, H.   Experimental psychology.   (Rev.
ed.) New York: Holt, 1955.

A MODEL FOR VISUAL SCENE ANALYSIS

Thomas Marill[1]
Bolt, Beranek and Newman, Incorporated
Cambridge, Massachusetts

Several basic concepts are discussed first.   A "mechanical model"
of a perceptual function is one which actually performs the function
being modelled.   A "learning perceptual model" is one whose performance improves as it accumulates more experience with various visual
inputs.   Models for visual "recognition" are distinguished from models
for visual "scene analysis."   In recognition, the entire content of the
field of view is assigned to one of a prespecified set of categories.   In
scene-analysis, the input may be complex, consisting of many visual
objects in overlapping arrangements on arbitrary backgrounds; the
model must segment the input into individual objects, identify them, and
separate them from the backgrounds.

In the light of these concepts a particular model for the perception
of visual form is discussed.   The model is mechanical, has a capability for scene analysis, but does not learn.   It has been implemented
in a system of computer programs, to which the name "Cyclops-1" has
been given.

---

[1] Now with the Computer Corporation of America, Cambridge, Massachusetts.

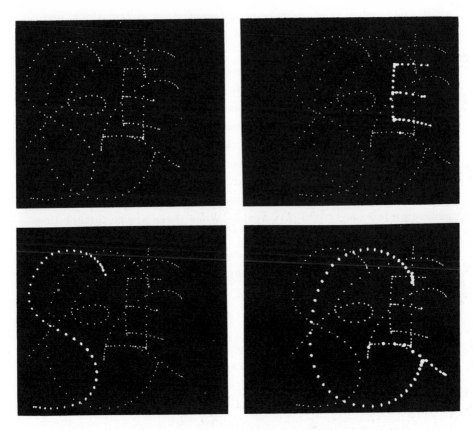

Fig. 1. Photographs of computer scope. (The upper-left frame shows an input to the system. The remaining frames show the results of analysis made by the system. In the upper-right frame, the system indicates its selection of a certain set of points by brightening these points and dimming the others; at the same time the identity ["E"] of this set, and its size and position, are typed out by the computer type-writer. Similarly for the remaining two frames, in which the system has identified an "S" and a "G.")

The system accepts nonvisual inputs which are in the nature of "definitions" of visual objects. Thus, for example, the system has been provided with definitions of the handprinted alphanumeric characters. Visual inputs to the system are drawn on a computer scope by means of a light-pen. Any pattern which may be so drawn is a suitable input to the system. Given a complex input, the system analyzes the scene and attempts to construct from it visual objects of the types that have been defined. Upon finding one, it intensifies the object on the scope and types out the identity, size, and location. In applications to alphanumeric characters, the system analyzes inputs consisting of an arbitrary number of characters of different sizes, orientations, and styles, in overlapping arrangements, and superimposed on arbitrary backgrounds (see Figure 1).

The operation of the system is discussed in terms of three distinct processes: line-forming, hypothesis generation, and hypothesis testing. The line-forming process takes a set of undifferentiated points and organizes it into lines. The hypothesis-generator generates a hypothesis of the type "There is an object named x somewhere in the field of view." The hypothesis tester tests such hypotheses and, if successful, reports which particular lines make up the object. The lines in question are withdrawn from further consideration, and the generator is brought into play again. When there are no further lines or hypotheses, the process ends.

Implications of the model are discussed, as well as possible future extensions to three-dimensional scene analysis, hard copy input, and the ability to learn from examples.

Acknowledgment

The work reported here was supported by Air Force Cambridge Research Laboratories under Contracts 19(628)-227 and 19(628)-4306.

GEOMETRICAL PROBABILITY IN VISUAL PERCEPTION

K. N. Leibovic
Department of Biophysics
State University of New York at Buffalo
Buffalo, New York

A model is presented for visual perception, that makes use of geometrical probability and whose physiological basis is the receptive field and the residual eye movements which remain after fixation of an image point.

If the "language" of the nervous system consists of an "alphabet" represented by nerve impulses and "words" represented by spatial and temporal patterns of nerve impulses, then the mechanism suggested here is one by which the alphabet is formed into words.

The role of the receptive field in visual information processing has been described in a number of papers (Hartline, 1959; Leibovic, 1963;

Lettvin, Maturana, McCulloch, and Pitts, 1959). It may be taken to be a closed, convex figure and, in addition, it can be subdivided into regions of differing stimulus response. Receptive fields have been identified not only in relation to the retinal ganglion cells, but also with respect to cells in the lateral geniculate body and the visual cortex (Hubel, 1963). Therefore, the receptive field is an elementary stimulus structure in information processing and in visual perception. This is not a static stimulus structure, for the receptive field must be presented continually with new stimuli to avoid the fading of a stabilized image. As is well known, the problem of fading is solved by the eye through its voluntary and involuntary movements.

These eye movements can be classified (Ditchburn, 1958) into: (a) a high-frequency tremor, (b) a slow drifting motion, (c) rapid flicks alternating with the drifts.

When these movements are analyzed, it can be shown that the receptive field moves, more or less at random, over the pattern presented to the eye. It is as if the receptive field were a test figure, which generates a statistical input to the optic nerve as a result of these movements. From such statistics, it is possible, in principle, to extract perceptual parameters such as length, area, angle, etc. (Blaschke, 1949). In fact, this has been proposed as a basis for machine pattern recognition (Novikoff, 1962).

It is suggested in this paper that aspects of visual perception, such as perception of form, can be analyzed by means of geometrical probability (Leibovic, 1966). The model put forward for this purpose is, briefly, as follows:

1. The receptive field stimuli are processed by the neural net in the retina to give a measure over a test figure of the visual pattern. This measure is represented in the optic nerve response.

2. Through the combination of eye movements and the different orientations of test figures connected to different optic nerve fibers, a statistical output is produced by sets of optic nerve fibers from a number of test figures and over the pattern presented to the eye.

3. The statistical output from the optic nerve fibers is integrated, in the manner of geometric probability, perhaps in the lateral geniculate body, or in the visual cortex, to yield parameters important in the perception of form.

In using geometric probability, one has to bear in mind that the

measures set up have to be based on the kind of information processing
known to take place in the eye. Moreover, the information contained
in a receptive field stimulus is quite large and only part of this information is required in this model of form perception.

Experiments are suggested to test the model and to lead to further
insight into perceptual processes. These experiments include: (a)
investigation of receptive field positions and orientations and their relation to test figures; (b) analysis of the temporal sequence of single
ganglion cell outputs to identify components which have significance
for geometric probability; (c) analysis of the spatial output from a set
of fibers similarly as in (b); (d) correlation of the input and output of
cells in the lateral geniculate or in the visual cortex, and the possible
use of a computer, whose program is a geometric probability algorithm,
to simulate the input-output relationship.

The value of the proposed model is in providing a possible explanation for perceptual processes, as well as in suggesting experiments to
illuminate the problem further.

References

Blaschke, W. Vorlesungen über integralgeometrie. New York:
    Chelsea, 1949.

Ditchburn, R.W. Eye movements in relation to perception of colour.
    In Nat. Phys. Lab. Symp. No. 8, 1957, Visual problems of colour.
    Vol. 2. London: HMSO, 1958. Pp. 415-428.

Hartline, H.K. Receptor mechanisms and the integration of sensory
    information in the eye. In J. L. Oncley (Ed.), Biophysical
    science — A study program. New York: Wiley, 1959. Pp. 515-523.

Hubel, D.H. Integrative processes in central visual pathways of the
    cat. J. opt. Soc. Amer., 1963, 53, 58-66.

Leibovic, K.N. Information processing organs, mathematical
    mappings and self-organizing systems. Bull. math. Biophys.,
    1963, 25, 189-201.

Leibovic, K.N. A model for information processing with reference
    to vision. J. theoret. Biol., 1966, 11, 112-130.

Lettvin, J.Y., Maturana, H.R., McCulloch, W.S., and Pitts, W.H.
    What the frog's eye tells the frog's brain. Proc. IRE, 1959,
    47, 1940-1951.

Novikoff, A.B.J. Integral geometry as a tool in pattern recognition.
    In H. von Foerster and G.W. Zopf, Jr. (Eds.), Principles of
    self-organization. New York: Pergamon, 1962. Pp. 347-368.

INFORMATION FLOW IN A BIONICS IMAGE RECOGNITION SYSTEM

George Tenery
Astronautics Division
LTV Aerospace Corporation
Dallas, Texas

Introduction

This paper describes a concept for a bionics image recognition system which will, on the basis of shape, learn to distinguish between a set of arbitrary visual forms presented to it in a learning phase. Having once learned a set of images, it will subsequently, in a sorting phase, be able to sort that imagery on the basis of shape independently of the size, orientation, position, and handedness of the imagery as it falls upon the viewing matrix, or retina, of the systems sensory input. The system operates on the basis of two concepts which have been validated: a concept of statistical image transformation (Tenery, 1963, 1964), which determines a statistical organization of the forms falling on the system sensor, and a concept of probability state variable (Lee, 1963) for a system of adaptive transfer functions determined by "rewards" and "punishments" based on the goals of the total system.

The writer refers to the general philosophy of the bionics image recognition system as a philosophy of "feedback of information," that is, there is a steady reduction in bandwidth in the system as information flows from a sensor to the output. The sensory input of the system, a viewing matrix of 400 photosensitive elements, is capable of $2^{400} \simeq 10^{120}$ possible states. Ashby (1963) has called attention to the magnitude of the problem of information reduction called for between the viewing matrix and the output if the output is to classify the input information into a few states corresponding to an operator's perceptual classification of the set of input forms. For specialized input imagery, such as the characters of an alphabet, it would be possible to reduce the magnitude of the problem by special techniques; however, the system to be described has been designed for operation in an arbitrary universe of generalized visual forms.

A Bionics Image Recognition System

The writer's concept of an image recognition system is shown in Figure 1. The system takes the form of the generalized bionics sys-

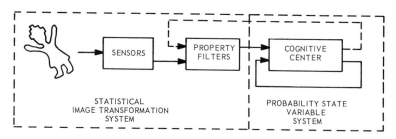

Fig. 1.   Bionics image recognition system.

tem set forth by Butsch and Gwinn (1963).   In Figure 1 the model of the
generalized bionics system is shown to consist of sensors, property
filters, and a cognitive center.   Overlain on the flow diagram are shown
the two concepts used to define the bionics image recognition system:
the statistical image transformation system and the probability state
variable system.   Both concepts have been defined and demonstrated
analytically and reduced to practice with laboratory demonstration
equipment.

As information flows from the input sensors from left to right, we
may imagine an information feedback from right to left taking place
which results in a progressive bandwidth reduction of information until
the output in bits per state more nearly corresponds to the input in bits
per symbol.

The two basic concepts and their combination into the concept for a
bionics image recognition system are described in the following sections.

The Statistical Image Transformation

Basically, a statistical image transformation is a statistical measure
of the organization of an image or visual form relative to a geometrical
element falling randomly in a plane or retina containing the image.   In
a transformation which is concerned with the organization of input information we are reminded of a recent remark by Gerard (1964):   "With
this shift from sink to source is a progressive and remarkable shift,
especially in the more highly organized animals and most dramatically
in man, from concern with the quantity of input, or output, to the organization of pattern of input and output.   In at least one broad sense,
this is what is meant by the term 'information.'"

The general concept of a statistical image transformation has been
defined as:

A probability measure which may be expressed as a quo-

tient of integrals of valid integrand functions with respect
to geometric elements of an invariant measure (Tenery,
1964, p. 20)

The concept is derivative from integral geometry as monographed by
Santalo (1953). Ball (1962) and Novikoff (1962) have discussed applications of integral geometry to pattern recognition.

The writer has developed a specialized statistical image transformation symbolized by P_F (d) and defined as:

The conditional probability that if the origin point A of a
line segment of length d, falling randomly within a retina
entirely containing the image F, falls within the image F,
the terminal point B also falls with the image F (Tenery,
1963; 1964).

It is seen that the $P_F(d)$ transformation of the image F is invariant with
respect to translations, rotations, and reflections about the axis of the
image F. Further, if the scale for measurement of d is chosen such
that the area of the image F is unity in that scale, the transformation
as d varies in invariant with respect to the size of the image F. The
mathematical forms of $P_F(d)$ have been discussed elsewhere (Tenery,
1963; 1964).

An iterative integration of the $P_F(d)$ transformation has been programmed for a computer. A prototype statistical image transformation
generator has been constructed for the transformation general silhou-
etted imagery. The transformation generator employs a parallel
areal integration of the intersections of a stored central image with an
identical image displaced and nutated about the stored central image at
various displacements of the parameter d. Experiments with a wide
variety of imagery, such as airplanes, satellites, Chinese characters,
and submarines have demonstrated that there is sufficient variation
among the transformations for effective discriminations between the
various types of imagery to be made. Generator $P_F(d)$ transformations for two airplanes are displayed in Figure 2.

At the present time, advanced studies for the specification of fast
and effective image transformation generators are in progress. Generalizations of the statistical image transformation concept to the time
domain have been made. Transformation concepts corresponding to
the techniques of spectrazonal photography (Colwell, 1964) are being
studied.

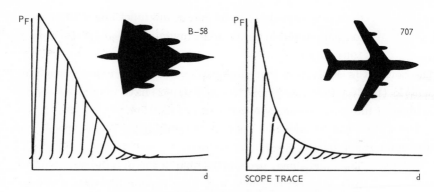

Fig. 2.   Transformation generator input and output.

Probability State Variable

The cognitive center of the bionics image recognition system has been conceived in terms of the concept of probability state variable as developed by Lee (1963) and others.

"The probability state variable device is one approach to the machine intelligence problem...It involves a migration of the statistics of behavior of a machine in the direction of the most satisfactory behavior" (from Lee, 1963). In the bionics image recognition system, probability state variable devices will be used to establish effective values of the parameter $\underline{d}$ to be used in the discrimination of the various transformations of the image input universe.   Thresholds of $P_F(d)$ will be established for the recognition of imagery in a sorting phase.   The physical elements to be used in the cognitive center will be composed of networks of neurotrons (Lee, 1963) which are elements with variable transfer functions in which the transfer functions develop a high probability of a specific value on the basis of "rewards" and "punishments" determined from the system goals.

Operation of the Bionics Image Recognition System

In the bionics image recognition system, the cognitive center will function in a learning phase of operation to achieve an optimal parameterization of the distance parameter $\underline{d}$ for feedback to the property filter when the system is being used in a sorting or recognition mode of operation.   The optimal value of $\underline{d}$ for a two-image input will be that value of $\underline{d}$ which results in the $P_F(d)$ transformations for the two images having a maximum difference.   This maximum value of the difference will enable a high probability of discrimination between the two images by means of threshold values of $P_F(d)$ stored in the cognitive center. This scheme is shown diagrammatically in Figure 3 for two images, their $P_F(d)$ transformations, and the initial and final cumulative probability distributions, $Pr(d)$, for the choice of $\underline{d}$ in the neurotron network.

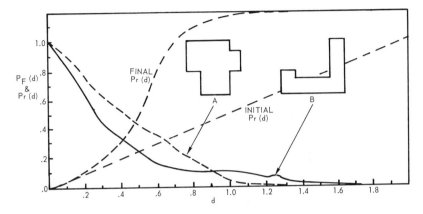

Fig. 3. Initial and final cumulative probability of d, $Pr(d)$, for two images.

In summary, the operation of the bionics image recognition system is as follows:

1. The statistical image transformation system senses the input imagery and performs a preprocessing, essentially a parameterization, of the image input signal resulting in a reduction of bandwidth. A priori image information is not utilized.

2. In a learning mode, the probability state variable system is able to parameterize the property filter of the statistical image transformation system such that a minimal number of optimal parameters will be used in a sorting or recognition mode of operation. Thus, a further bandwidth reduction is effected.

References

Ashby, W. R. Systems and information. IEEE Trans. Mil. Elect., 1963, MIL-7, 94-97.

Ball, G. H. An application of integral geometry to pattern recognition. Project No. 3605, Stanford Research Institute. Contract No. Nonr 3438(00), 1962 (AD-275352).

Butsch, L. M. Jr., and Gwinn, C. W. Bionics - status and plans. IEEE Trans. Mil. Elect., 1963, MIL-7, 261-266.

Colwell, R. N.   Aerial photography - a valuable sensor for the
    scientist.   Amer. Scientist, 1964, 52, 17-49.

Gerard, R. W. Opening address. In Proc. 22nd int. Cong., Int. Union
    physiol. Sci., Leiden, 1962, Vol. 3, R. W. Gerard and J. W. Duyff
    (Eds.), Information processing in the nervous system. Amsterdam:
    Excerpta Medica Found., 1964. Pp. 3-8.

Lee, R. J., Gilstrap, L. O. Jr., Snyder, R. F., and Pedelty, M. J.
    Theory of probability state variable systems - Vol. I - Summary
    and conclusions. Tech. Doc. Rep. No. ASD-TDR-63-664, Con-
    tract No. AF33(657)-7100. Adaptronics, Inc., 1963.

Novikoff, A. B. J. Integral geometry as a tool in pattern recognition.
    In H. von Foerster and G. W. Zopf, Jr. (Eds.), Principles of self-
    organization. New York: Pergamon, 1962. Pp. 347-368.

Santalo, L. A. Introduction to integral geometry. Paris: Hermann
    et Cie., 1953.

Tenery, G. A pattern recognition function of integral geometry.
    IEEE Trans. Mil. Elect., 1963, MIL-7, 196-199.

Tenery, G. Final summary report on the statistical image recog-
    nition concept (OSIRIS). Tech. Rep. No. 00.410, Contract No.
    Nonr 3831(00), LTV Astronautics, 1964.

ON THE CLASSIFICATION OF LINE-DRAWING DATA

Herbert Freeman
Department of Electrical Engineering
New York University
Bronx, New York

The classification of line-drawing data is one of the key problems in
any storage-and-retrieval or pattern recognition scheme involving such
data.   Probably the best-known illustration of this is offered by the
classification of fingerprints.   Other examples can be found in the
various pattern recognition schemes for geographic maps, bubble
chamber photographs of nuclear particle tracks, electrocardiograms,
and handwriting specimens.   The classification of line drawings is a
peculiarly difficult problem because of the inadequacy of our vocabulary
for describing graphical data.   Terms such as "islands," "bays,"
"peninsulas," "inlets," and "turns" are entirely qualitative and their
interpretation is much too subjective.   To devise an effective classification scheme it is necessary first to develop a means for describing
line-drawing data in a quantitative and unambiguous sense.

An individual line conveys information solely through the manner in

which it changes direction as one traces it from end to end. The
changes in direction represent its "curvings," and these may be either
continuous or abrupt. For a line drawing consisting of more than one
line, there are two major ways in which the drawing may convey information. First, the information may be conveyed strictly through the
curvings of the individual lines, in which case we refer to the drawings
as monolineal drawings. Examples of these are electrocardiograms,
highway maps, and handwriting specimens. Second, the information
may be conveyed primarily through the composite effect of many lines
acting together. Drawings of this type will be called polylineal drawings.
Typical examples of the latter are fingerprints, contour maps, and
drawings in which striations are employed to give three-dimensional
effects. Not infrequently one encounters line drawings that exhibit
both monolineal and polylineal characteristics, such as, for example,
a contour map on which a highway is shown.

The process of classification consists of placing each subject to be
classified at a point or within a region in a multidimensional feature
space. Identical subjects must map into the same point or region in
this space. Subjects differ from each other if they differ in one or
more of the features that form the co-ordinate axes of the feature space.
Thus to classify line drawings, one must select a set of features
appropriate to the purpose of the classification and measure each line
drawing with respect to these features. To make this possible for line
drawings given in graphical or pictorial form, it is necessary that the
line drawings be first quantized and encoded. The quantization should
be as coarse as possible to minimize the amount of resultant data, and
yet sufficiently fine so as to preserve the information judged to be
significant.

In the approach described here, the so-called grid-intersection
method (Freeman, 1961 b; 1962) of quantization is employed. In this
method a square mesh is superimposed on the line drawing and the
mesh nodes lying closest to the intersections between curve and the
superimposed mesh are determined. These mesh nodes, called curve
points, then define a straight-line approximation to the given line pattern. The representation may be made as precise as desired by selecting a sufficiently fine mesh. The method is illustrated in Figure 1,
where a continuous curve is quantized in terms of the curve points a,
b, c, d, and e.

Once the curve points are obtained, they may be encoded by utilizing

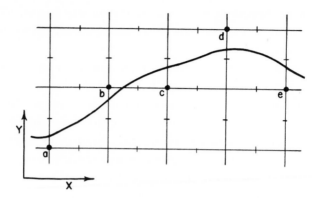

Fig. 1. Grid-intersect quantization.

the so-called chain-encoding scheme (Freeman, 1961a; 1961b). In
tracing out a continuous curve, one finds that for each curve point, the
curve point next in sequence can be only one of the eight mesh nodes
surrounding the given curve point. If one defines an x-y co-ordinate
system as in Figure 1, the mesh points surrounding any given curve
point may be labelled successively from 0 to 7, beginning with the mesh
point located along the positive x axis and proceeding in a counterclockwise sense. This is illustrated in Figure 2. A sequence of curve
points can now be represented by a sequence of digits, 0 through 7.
Thus the curve shown in Figure 1 would be represented by the sequence
1 (a to b), 0 (b to c), 1 (c to d), and 7 (d to e), or simply by 1017.

   Each digit in such a sequence is termed an _element_. It represents –
when multiplied by 45 – the slope in degrees of the line segment connecting adjacent curve points. The total sequence of elements for a
particular curve is referred to as a _chain._ Sections of a chain are

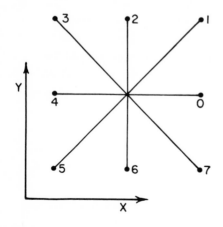

Fig. 2. Curve-point encoding
scheme.

called <u>chainlets</u>. Note that a chain is invariant with translation. To fix a chain in a co-ordinate system, the absolute co-ordinates of at least one point must be given.

Since a typical chain is likely to consist of many thousands of elements, it cannot be used directly for purposes of classification. However, the chain description of a line drawing is in a convenient form for processing by means of a digital computer. With suitable algorithms, a chain may be analyzed for its features. Provided that a sufficiently fine mesh was used to quantize the line drawing, the features of the chain will correspond to the significant features of the line drawing from which the chain was derived.

Simple algorithms have been developed (Freeman, 1961b) to determine some of the gross features of chains such as length, width, height, distance between end points, and – for closed chains – enclosed area as well as area moments about specified axes. In selecting features for classification one finds it is important to know which are orientation invariant and which are scale invariant. Of the foregoing features none are scale invariant and all but width and height are orientation invariant.

For more finely distinguishing features, one must examine the information-bearing curvings directly. If one constructs a smooth interpolation to a chain, one finds that the instantaneous radius of curvature moves alternately from one side to the other. This alternating between "bays" and "peninsulas" occurs at all scale levels, from the very smallest, as determined by only two successive chain elements, up to the largest, as expressed by the totality of all elements.

For each change from a "bay" to a "peninsula" and vice versa, an inflection point can be located on the interpolated chain. The number of inflection points can be arbitrarily restricted by selecting a minimum radius of curvature and a minimum distance between sucessive inflection points. One can then separate the chain into chainlets at inflection points as shown in Figure 3. Each chainlet now represents either a "bay" or a "peninsula." A chain can be reassembled at will by connecting the chainlets in sequence and orienting them in accordance with the inflection-point line (the dashed line in Figure 3).

The features of the bay-peninsula chainlets form a powerful basis for chain classification. Chainlets can be subdivided into "subchainlets" to provide additional levels within a classification hierarchy. Since the bay-peninsula chainlets represent the dominant curvings of a

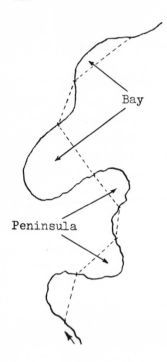

Fig. 3. Separation of a chain into a sequence of bays and peninsulas.

chain, a classification scheme based on them is intimately related to the intrinisic information-conveying features of line drawings and is relatively nonsubjective.

Acknowledgment

The research reported here was part of a study supported by the Air Force Office of Scientific Research, Information Sciences Directorate, under Grant AF-AFOSR-24-64.

References

Freeman, H. On the encoding of arbitrary geometric configurations. IRE Trans. elect. Comput., 1961, EC-10, 260-268. (a)

Freeman, H. Techniques for the digital-computer analysis of chain-encoded arbitrary plane curves. Proc. nat. Elect. Conf., 1961, 17, 421-432. (b)

Freeman, H. On the digital computer classification of geometric line patterns. Proc. nat. Elect. Conf., 1962, 18, 312-324.

CONTRIBUTED PAPERS VI

Statistical Techniques and Acoustic Parameters in Speech Perception

Chairman: Franklin S. Cooper

Haskins Laboratories
New York, New York

A CRITERION FOR THE SELECTION OF SPEECH FEATURES IN SPEECH RECOGNITION BASED ON COMPARISON OF EXPERIMENTS

D. C. Lai [1]
Department of Electrical Engineering
Northeastern University
Boston, Massachusetts

Statistical recognition systems are characterized by the following statements:

1. Data or information about the pattern to be recognized is obtained by measuring a set of its pattern properties.

2. Using the methods of statistical decision theory, the system makes a decision based on the information obtained by measurement.

It is tacitly assumed that the system has learned (estimated) and stored the probability density for each pattern with respect to a predetermined set of pattern properties.

There are a number of papers (Braverman, 1962; Chow, 1957; Marill and Green, 1960; Sebestyen, 1961) on the study of statistical decision systems, but the emphasis in most of these papers is on the methods of making a decision based on the measurement of preselected pattern properties. Experiments must be done in order to learn and to select the relevant pattern features. A number of authors (Chang, Pihl, and Essigman, 1951; David, 1959; Meeker, 1959; Sebestyen, 1961) have used, suggested, or

---

[1] Now at the Electrical Engineering Department, University of Vermont, Burlington, Vermont.

conceived of a large number of relevant speech features in their study of speech recognition systems, but have not emphasized the selection of the most important (informative) features. Typical features of speech as seen in spectrograms are formants, silence, noiselike areas, and the zero-crossings of the speech waveforms. It is desirable and sometimes necessary to select those features which are the most informative. A criterion is proposed in this paper, based on comparison of experiments under the assumption that the Bayes' procedure with a zero-one cost function is used for the decision process. The use of this criterion does not require the cumbersome evaluation of the error probability or the average risk involved.

To set up the mathematical model, let $Z_i (i = 1, 2, \ldots, N)$ be the speech patterns to be recognized and the measurement of one set of features, say the α set, results in the random vector X with components $[x_1, x_2, \ldots, x_k]$. It is assumed that the transition probability densities $p(X|Z_i) = p_i(X)$ have been learned by the machine. The measurement of another set of features, the β set, results in the random vector Y with components $[y_1, y_2, \ldots, y_m]$. The probability densities $q(Y|Z_i) = q_i(Y)$ have also been estimated. We shall first establish the criterion for $N = 2$; i.e., for the two-pattern case.

It is well known that the optimum decision scheme for a given cost function is the Bayes' decision procedure; viz.,

$$\text{if} \qquad L_\alpha(x) = \frac{p_1(x)}{p_2(x)} > \eta, \text{ then the speech sound belongs to } Z_1$$

and

$$\text{if} \qquad L_\alpha(x) \qquad \leq \eta, \text{ then the speech sound belongs to } Z_2,$$

where η is a threshold value which is equal to $(1-\xi)/\xi$ when the cost function is zero-or-one and ξ is the a priori probability that Z_1 occurs. The Bayes' risks involved for the α set and the β set used are

$$R_\alpha = \xi \, P[L_2 \leq \eta | Z_1] + (1-\xi) \, P[L_\alpha > \eta | Z_2],$$

and

$$R_\beta = \xi \, P[L_\beta \leq \eta | Z_1] + (1-\xi) \, P[L_\beta > \eta \, Z_2],$$

respectively. Using the language of comparison of experiments (Blackwell, 1951), we shall say that the pattern feature set α is better or more informative than the other set β, depicted by $\alpha \supset \beta$, in the error probability sense, if

$$R_\alpha \leq R_\beta \; .$$

The set of pattern features may be selected by comparing the risks involved for all ξ. However, R_α and R_β are difficult to compute and cannot be evaluated when ξ is unkown. Hence, some convenient criteria for selecting the appropriate pattern feature set will be very useful. A criterion which yields a simple necessary condition for $R_\alpha \leq R_\beta$ is obtained by using a result obtained by Bradt and Karlin (1956). Their result may be summarized in the following lemma.

<u>Lemma:</u> $R_\alpha \leq R_\beta$ iff

$$E_x[\Phi(\frac{1}{L_\alpha})|Z_1] \geq E_y[\Phi(\frac{1}{L_\beta})|Z_1]$$

for all continuous convex functions $\Phi(\frac{1}{L})$ of $\frac{1}{L}$.

For our purpose, we let, in particular,

$$\Phi(\frac{1}{L}) = -\ln(\frac{1}{L}) = \ln L$$

which is continuous and convex. Then we have

$$E_x[\ln L_\alpha|Z_1] \geq E_y[\ln L_\beta|Z_1].$$

On the other hand, letting $\Phi(\frac{1}{L}) = \frac{1}{L}\ln\frac{1}{L} = -\frac{\ln L}{L}$, we obtain

$$E[\frac{1}{L}\ln\frac{1}{L}|Z_1] = E[-\frac{\ln L}{L}|Z_1] = -E[\ln L|Z_2]$$

and hence

$$-E_x[\ln L_\alpha|Z_2] \geq -E_y[\ln L_\beta|Z_2].$$

The divergence or "distance" between two patterns is defined by

$$J(Z_1, Z_2) = E[\ln L|Z_1] - E[\ln L|Z_2],$$

which has all the properties of "distance" except the triangle inequality property (Kullback, 1959, p.6 and pp.22-26). Therefore, a necessary condition for $R_\alpha \leq R_\beta$ is

$$J_\alpha(Z_1, Z_2) \geq J_\beta(Z_1, Z_2).$$

We shall say that $\alpha \supset \beta$ in the divergence sense if the above inequality is true.

In order to use the Bayes' decision procedure for the multiple pattern case in which $2 < N < \infty$, it is convenient to express the decision rule as a complete preference ordering of pairs of patterns and we write

$$Z_i > Z_j \text{ if } L > \eta$$

and

$$Z_j > Z_i \text{ if } L \leq \eta$$

where $L = \dfrac{p_i(X)}{p_j(X)}$ and $\eta = \dfrac{P(Z_j)}{P(Z_i)}$ for zero-or-one cost function.

The most preferred pattern in the complete ordering is chosen as the pattern to which the speech sound belongs. This procedure is the same as the one which classifies the speech sound to the pattern Z_i with the largest a posteriori probability. The risk involved in discriminating between a pair of patterns from N patterns is

$$R(Z_i, Z_j) = \xi\, P[L \leq \eta | Z_i] + (1-\xi)\, P[L > \eta | Z_j],$$

where $\xi = \dfrac{P(Z_i)}{P(Z_i) + P(Z_j)}$, $L = \dfrac{p_i(X)}{p_j(X)}$, and $\eta = \dfrac{1-\xi}{\xi} = \dfrac{P(Z_j)}{P(Z_i)}$.

If for two feature sets α and β, we have the following inequality for each pair of patterns Z_i and Z_j:

$$R_\alpha(Z_i, Z_j) \leq R_\beta(Z_i, Z_j),$$

then we say that α set is more informative than β set on the basis of pairwise risks and write $\alpha \overset{2}{\supset} \beta$ (Grettenberg, 1963). For $\alpha \supset \beta$, it is necessary that $R_\alpha \leq R_\beta$ for all N patterns. If all the a priori probabilities are concentrated on two patterns, we have seen that the inequality

$$\xi\, P[L_\alpha \leq \eta | Z_i] + (1-\xi)\, P[L_\alpha > \eta | Z_j] \leq \xi\, P[L_\beta \leq \eta | Z_i] + (1-\xi)\, P[L_\beta > \eta | Z_j]$$

is valid for all $0 \leq \xi \leq 1$, where $\xi = P(Z_i)$. Therefore, the above inequality must also hold for all choices of $P(Z_i)$ and $P(Z_j)$ with $0 \leq P(Z_i) \leq 1$ and $0 \leq P(Z_j) \leq 1$. Consequently, we conclude that $\alpha \supset \beta$ implies $\alpha \overset{2}{\supset} \beta$. We are ready to extend the necessary condition obtained previously for the two-pattern case to that for the N-pattern case ($2 < N < \infty$). We say that the feature set α is more informative than the set β (i.e., $\alpha \supset \beta$) if

$$J_\alpha(Z_i, Z_j) \geq J_\beta(Z_i, Z_j)$$

for all choices of pairs of patterns from the N patterns. We may also use the expectation of the divergence which is defined as

$$J_\alpha = \sum_{i}^{N} \sum_{j}^{N} P(Z_i) \, P(Z_j) \, J_\alpha(Z_i, Z_j) \ .$$

If $J_\alpha \geq J_\beta$, then it is said that $\alpha \supset \beta$ in the expected divergence sense. However, the calculation of J_α and J_β requires the knowledge of the a priori probabilities $P(Z_i)$ for $i = 1, 2, \ldots, N$.

In order to show the usefulness of this criterion, further experimental work must be done. The paper has shown the validity and utility of the proposed criterion.

Acknowledgment

This work is sponsored by the Air Force Cambridge Research Laboratories, Bedford, Massachusetts, under Contract No. AF19(628)-3312.

References

Blackwell, D. Comparison of experiments. In The second Berkeley symposium on mathematical statistics and probability. Berkeley, Cal.: Univer. Calif. Press, 1951. Pp. 93-102.

Bradt, R. N., and Karlin, S. On the design and comparison of certain dichotomous experiments. Ann. math. Stat., 1956, 27, 390-409.

Braverman, D. Learning filters for optimum pattern recognition. IRE Trans. Info. Theory, 1962, IT-8, 280-285.

Chang, S. H., Pihl, G. E., and Essigman, M. W. Representation of speech sounds and some of their statistical properties. Proc. IRE., 1951, 39, 147-153.

Chow, C. K. An optimum character recognition system using decision functions. IRE Trans. elect. Comput., 1957, EC-6, 247-254.

David, E. E. Some problems in speech recognition. In W. Wathen-Dunn and L. E. Woods (Eds.), Proceedings of the seminar on speech compression and processing. Vol. 2. Tech. Rep. AFCRC-TR-59-198, Air Force Camb. Res. Ctr., 1959. Paper D5.

Grettenberg, T. L. Signal selection in communication and radar systems. IEEE Trans. Info. Theory, 1963, IT-9, 265-275.

Kullback, S. Information theory and statistics, New York: Wiley, 1959.

Marill, T., and Green, D. M. Statistical recognition functions and the design of pattern recognizers. IRE Trans. elect. Comput., 1960, EC-9, 472-477.

Meeker, W. F. Parametric recognition of speech sounds. In W. Wathen-Dunn and L. E. Woods (Eds.), Proceedings of the seminar on speech compression and processing. Vol. 2. Tech. Rep. AFCRC-TR-59-198, Air Force Camb. Res. Ctr., 1959. Paper D1.

Sebestyen, G. S. Recognition of membership in classes. IRE Trans. Info. Theory, 1961, IT-7, 44-50.

A SIMPLE LINEAR MODEL FOR VOWEL PERCEPTION

Edward C. Carterette
Department of Psychology
University of California, Los Angeles
Los Angeles, California

Introduction

The rise of interest in the perception of complex auditory stimuli stems directly from theoretical and applied research in speech analysis and synthesis. A steady-state vowel is perhaps the simplest speech sound. The workers at Haskins Laboratories showed that the formants are sufficient cues for vowel identification, and that changes in formant position govern perception in certain consonant types (Cooper, Delattre, Liberman, Borst, and Gerstman, 1952). Fant's (1960) acoustic theory of speech production specifies the spectrum of a vowel given only four pairs of numbers: the frequencies and bandwidths of the four lowest formants. The simple physical and psychological structure led me to analyze the perception of vowels distorted by very sharp filtering in order to assess the role of formants in recognition (Carterette and Møller, 1962). Neither of the two similar earlier studies was definitive by itself. French and Steinberg and others (Fletcher, 1953), in their work on the intelligibility of vowels, used consonant-vowel-consonant sounds, whereas Lehiste and Peterson's (1959) filters were not very sharp and the data were too few for stable estimates of confusions.

The work reported here had two major aims. One was to obtain sufficient data to make reliable estimates of confusions among vowels after ideal filtering. The other was to compare the responses of the same listeners to real vowels and their synthetic aliases. Beyond their inherent interest, these data are valuable in assessing vocal analog systems whether as practical devices or as research tools and speech standards. A simple, quantitative model is presented and tested against the perceptual data from real and synthetic talkers.

Procedure

Real vowels. Fourteen Swedish vowels were used. Their IPA symbols, key words, the locus of mean formant frequencies and other relevant data are shown in Figures 1 and 2. Five male Swedish talkers (Stockholm dialect) spoke briefly sustained vowels with constant vocal effort. Each talker recorded 14 lists, each of which had 42 randomly

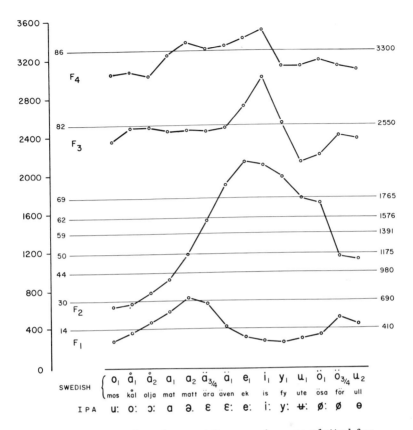

Fig. 1. The first four formant frequencies are plotted for
the 14 Swedish vowels. (IPA symbols and key words are
shown. The horizontal lines locate the low-pass filter cutoff frequencies shown in the right margin. Numbers at the
left end of the lines are mean per cent correct responses.)

arranged vowels (3 samples of each of the 14). This material was
transferred to an identical Ampex 350 magnetic tape recorder through
an electronic gate to give steady-state vowel segments 500 msec in
duration including rise-fall times of 50 msec. Experimental tapes were
prepared by passing the gated vowels through a heterodyne filter designed by Fant (1952). The filter attenuated energy beyond the cutoff
frequency, f_c, at a rate of about 1 db per cps independently of f_c. Nine
low-pass (LP) and eight high-pass (HP) f_c were used. LP (410, 690,
980, 1,175, 1,391, 1,576, 1,765, 2,550, and 3,300 cps) and HP (335, 418,
582, 732, 1,048, 1,358, 1,881, and 3,130 cps).

Synthetic vowels. With use of the values of the formant frequencies
shown in Figure 2 (triangles), gated, shaped vowel segments 500 msec

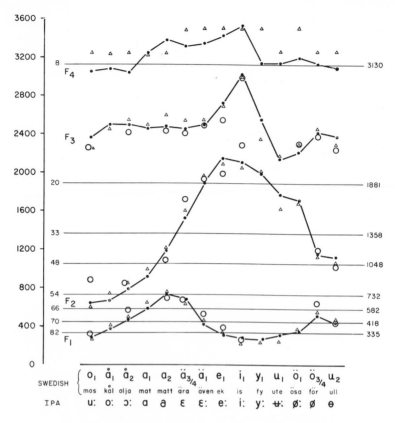

Fig. 2. Same as Figure 1 except for high-pass filtering.
(In addition, the first four formant frequencies are given for
the 14 synthetic vowels [triangles] and for 10 American
English vowels [open circles].)

in duration were prepared with the electrical analog vocal tract, OVE
II, designed by Fant (1960). After gating, vowels were recorded through
the filter system exactly as described for real vowels.

Nine Swedish subjects (six young women and three men) with normal
hearing, between 19 and 28 years of age, listened over binaural tele-
phones. The average total system response was flat within ± 2. 5 db
over the range of filtering. After a single practice tape, listening tests
began. Sounds were heard in random sequence. Subjects were required to respond with one of the 14 vowels after each stimulus by
writing down the key word. Vowels were spoken at a rate of about 10
per minute.

Results

Figure 3 shows for all listeners combined the per cent correct

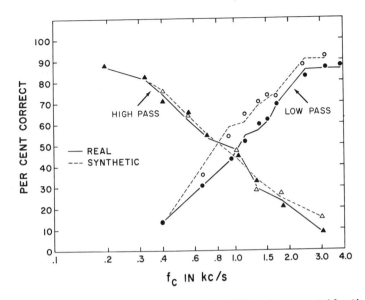

Fig. 3.   Theoretical curves for probability of correct identification versus f_c in c/s, computed from Equation (1) (solid =
real; broken = synthetic). (See text. Solid circles and triangles are real vowel data points, each based on 1,638 observations. Open circles and triangles are synthetic vowel data
points, each based on 378 observations.)

identification as a function of f_c. The cross-over point of the HP and
LP curves is near 1,050 cps, in good agreement with the value of 1,100
cps found in other studies (Fletcher, 1953; Lehiste and Peterson, 1959),
in spite of differences in context, vowel duration, filter sharpness,
language, and number of vowels. To summarize the preliminary report of this work (Carterette and Møller, 1962) it was found that (a)
contrary to the smooth functions obtained earlier (Fletcher, 1953;
Lehiste and Peterson, 1959) of per cent correct identification versus
f_c, discontinuities existed reflecting the nonuniform distribution of
formant frequencies; (b) confusions ensuing when certain formants are
eliminated may be explained by the relationship among those remaining;
(c) real and synthetic vowels behaved much alike; and (d) a simple,
linear regression model describes the data adequately, on the assumption that correct responding will be proportional to the weighted sums
of the number of formants available in a given pass-band.

A plot of correct identifications versus f_c ought to be peculiar to a
given talker, since a distribution of formant frequencies must reflect
the characteristics of the vocal tract from which it arises. The
parameters of a model must take account of this fact. (For generality,

the hearer must be considered too.) Table 1 shows the distribution of the first three formant frequencies for the five talkers. These values were used in the model represented by Equation 1. It is assumed that the probability of a correct response $p_f(C)$ is a linear function of the weighted number of formants that remain after filtering. More precisely,

$$p_{f_c}(C) = W_o + \sum_i^m \sum_j^n W_i \mathscr{F}_{ij} + e \qquad [1]$$

where f_c is a given HP or LP filter condition, m is the number of formants, n is the number of vowels. W_o is a constant, the W_i are weights to be associated with the formants, and e is a normally dis-tributed random variable, $N(0, \sigma^2)$. The number $\mathscr{F}_{ij}$ is a random variable function of F_{ij}, the frequency of the ith formant of the jth vowel, such that

$$\mathscr{F}_{ij} = \begin{array}{l} (1 \ (\text{HP}) \ \text{or} \ 0 \ (\text{LP}), \ \text{if} \ F_{ij} > f_c \\ (0 \ (\text{HP}) \ \text{or} \ 1 \ (\text{LP}), \ \text{if} \ F_{ij} \leq f_c \end{array}$$

The value of $\mathscr{F}_{ij}$ was found from means of formant frequencies mea-sured on Kay sonagrams.

Given the assumption of Equation 1, the problem is to obtain esti-mates of the constants W_0, W_1, W_2, and W_3. The entire statistical analysis is based on the symmetric correlation coefficient matrix P given by

$$P = \begin{bmatrix} 1 & r_{12} & r_{13} \cdots\cdots r_{1N} \\ r_{21} & 1 & r_{23} \cdots\cdots r_{2N} \\ \cdot & & \\ \cdot & & \\ r_{N1} & r_{N2} & \cdots\cdots\cdots 1 \end{bmatrix}$$

where the r_{ij} are the correlation coefficients of the ith and jth variables based on maximum likelihood estimates computed for each pair of variables separately, ignoring all other variables. For a given choice of the r_{ij}, the computer program estimates the regression coefficients and their standard deviations together with the multiple correlation coefficient, the individual correlation coefficients, r_{ij}, and the partial correlation coefficients for each r_{ij} and $p_f(C)$. All estimates are statistically evaluated and their associated probabilities computed. In

Table 1. The distribution of the first three formant frequencies for five talkers. Formant frequencies were measured from broad band (300 cps) spectrograms and are based on three randomly drawn samples from each of the 14 gated vowels.

Model for Vowel Perception

Freq. region (Less than f cps)		SÖ F_1	F_2	F_3	BjL F_1	F_2	F_3	BoL F_1	F_2	F_3	CC F_1	F_2	F_3	UR F_1	F_2	F_3
1	300	2			4			2			3			4		
2	400	5			6			4			3			4		
3	500	3			1			4			2			2		
4	600	1			1			2			4			4	2	
5	700	3	2			1		1	2		1	2				
6	800		1		2	2		1						1	1	
7	1000		1			1		1	2			1			1	
8	1200		1			3			2			3			3	
9	1400		2						1							
10	1600		1												3	
11	1800		2			2			3			1			1	
12	2000		2			3						4		1	3	3
13	2200		2	2		2			3	1		2				7
14	2400			4			5			1			4			1
15	2600			7			6	1		7			7			2
16	3000			1			2			4			2			1
17	3510						1			1			1			
	TOTAL	42			42			42			42			42		

addition, a chi-square test for normality on the e's is made. For a discussion of the mathematical details the reader is referred to Kendall and Stuart (1958 and 1961) and Mood (1950). We caution that interpretations beyond the special conditions of these experiments must be made with care. Naturally we believe that this simple model rests on a sufficiently firm experimental base to warrant exploring its extensions to other vowel systems. But it will become obvious in the discussion to follow that the numerical value of the parameters will be tied very closely to the operations giving rise to the listeners' responses.

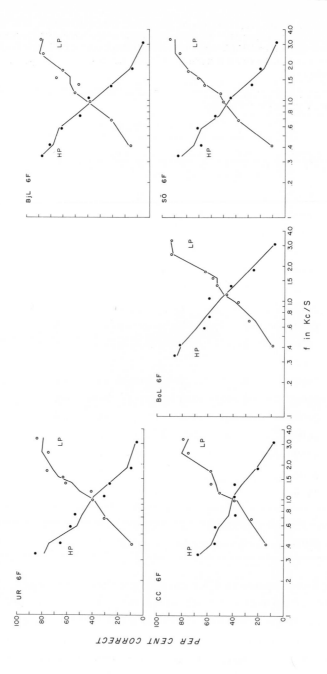

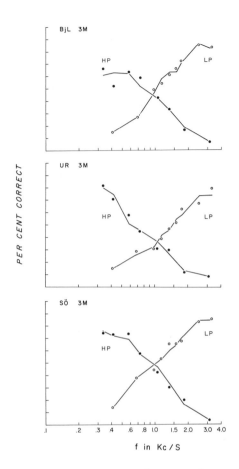

Fig. 5. As in Figure 4, theoretical curves for probability of correct identification versus f_c, computed from Equation 1 for three male listeners: the talkers, B_jL, UR, and SÖ are the same as in Figure 4. (Each data point is based on 126 observations.)

Computations to test the model of Equation 1 for each of the five talkers with that part of the data for the six female listeners was done on the IBM 7094. The solid lines in Figure 4 connect the theoretical points. Open and solid circles are experimental values. Table 2

Fig. 4. Theoretical curves for probability of correct identification versus f_c, computed from Equation 1 for each of five talkers. (Each data point is based on 252 observations.)

gives the multiple correlation coefficient (MCC) and maximum likelihood estimates of the constant W_o and the weights W_i.

Table 2. Multiple correlation coefficients (MCC) and relative
weights for HP and LP functions of Equation 1 for five male
talkers.

	SÖ		CC		BjL		BoL		UR	
	LP	HP	LP	HP	LP	HP	LP	HP	LP	HP
W_o	0	0	0	0	0	0	0	0	0	0
W_1	113	75	0	58	0	70	68	69	0	100
W_2	162	135	205	89	159	179	151	122	153	119
W_3	-25	0	-51	0	0	0	0	0	0	0
MCC	.996	.991	.991	.986	.982	.995	.995	.985	.980	.974

Figure 5 is similar to Figure 4 except that the data shown were obtained for three male listeners who heard a subset of the five talkers
of Figure 4 (BjL, UR, and SÖ). The formant structure of a particular
talker's voice is agains reflected in the listener's responses. The
graphs of data for a given talker show the mild presbycusis for the
older male listeners for HP filtering (e. g., compare UR-6F [Figure 4]
and UR-3M [Figure 5]. Nonetheless, the two UR graphs bear a stronger
family resemblance than do the graphs UR-6F and CC-6F (both in
Figure 4).

The model fits the data well, accounting for 95 per cent of the
variation in the worst case (UR, HP). While the model may be ex-
quisitely simple, it is not wrong, for a wrong model could not give such
high correlations even using the right variables and reliable data. The
solution of the regression equations gives coefficients that may be used,
for example, to adjust parameters of the vocal analog tract. An analysis of the intra-vowel confusions, to be published elsewhere, makes
it clear that by adding a measure of similarity the model may be
generalized to predict particular confusions.

Acknowledgment

This research was supported by the Department of the Navy, Office
of Naval Research, Group Psychology Branch, under Contract Nonr

233(58), and by the Research Committee, University of California, Los
Angeles.

References

Carterette, E. C., and Møller, Å. The perception of real and synthetic vowels after very sharp filtering. In Proceedings of the fourth international congress on acoustics. Copenhagen: Fourth International Congress on Acoustics, 1962.

Cooper, F. S., Delattre, P. C., Liberman, A. M., Borst, J. M., and Gerstman, L. J. Some experiments on the perception of synthetic speech sounds. J. acoust. Soc. Amer., 1952, 24, 597-606.

Fant, G. The heterodyne filter. Proc. Royal Inst. Tech. (Stockholm), 1952, 55, 1-77.

Fant, G. On the predictability of formant levels and spectrum envelopes from formant frequencies. In M. Halle (Ed.), For Roman Jakobson. 's-Gravenhage: Mouton, 1956. Pp. 109-121.

Fant, G. Acoustic theory of speech production. 's-Gravenhage: Mouton, 1960.

Fletcher, H. Speech and hearing in communications. New York: van Nostrand, 1953.

Kendall, M. G., and Stuart, A. The advanced theory of statistics. Vols. 1 and 2. New York: Hafner, 1958 (Vol. 1) and 1961 (Vol. 2)

Lehiste, Ilse, and Peterson, G. The identification of filtered vowels. Phonetica, 1959, 4, 161-177.

Mood, A. M. Introduction to the theory of statistics. New York: McGraw-Hill, 1950.

ACOUSTIC RECOGNITION BY ANALOG FEATURE-ABSTRACTION TECHNIQUES

A. L. Nelson, M. B. Herscher,
T. B. Martin, and H. J. Zadell
Defense Electronics Products
Radio Corporation of America
Camden, New Jersey

J. W. Falter
Air Force Avionics Laboratory
Research and Technology Division
Air Force Systems Command
Wright-Patterson Air Force Base, Ohio

Introduction

A speech-analysis system (Figure 1) is being developed based on the premise that acoustic recognition is a necessary first step, without which the complete machine-recognition of speech is not possible. Acoustic recognition can be considered as the lowest level in a multi-level hierarchy of processes which include the use of language constraints and context, and it is the area which has presented the greatest barrier to progress toward the development of automatic speech-recognition apparatus. The system to be described includes primarily acoustic recognition with a small amount of local context utilized. It is recognized that, in order to extend the system for continuous-speech applications, additional information such as linguistics and context will be necessary.

The experimental investigation is being directed toward the development of the logic required for the acoustic recognition of both vowels and complex consonant sounds using noncontinuous speech samples. The speech samples that have been analyzed consist of isolated CVC sounds with the consonant in initial position followed by each of ten following vowels and the same final consonant /d/ for all sounds. This paper will describe only the results obtained for the fricatives, although comparable results have been obtained for the liquids, semivowels, nasals, vowels, and plosives. For the fricatives, recognition tests have been tabulated for six male speakers.

The processing technique employed has been named analog-threshold-logic (ATL) because of the characteristics of the basic computing element used for most of the logical functions. The ATL element has an output which is linearly proportional to the net sum of excitatory and inhibitory inputs, provided that this net sum is greater than an adjustable

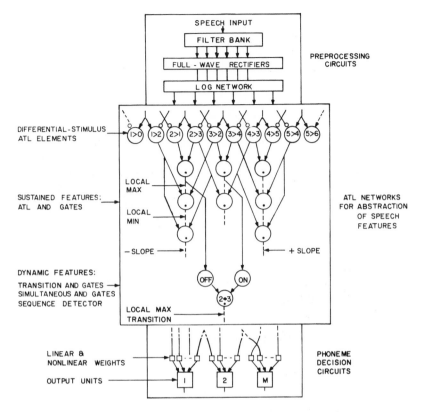

Fig. 1. Simplified block diagram of speech-analysis system.

threshold. The discontinuity in the transfer function (Figure 2) ensures reliable discrimination between quiescence and a minimum output value, thereby avoiding sequential amplification of thermal drifts in cascaded networks. Using networks of ATL elements, one can abstract from the speech signals both the presence and magnitude of significant features. Both relatively sustained and complex dynamic spectral variations can be abstracted.

Technical Approach

For the acoustic recognition of speech, five basic concepts were established.

1. Speech recognition was to be accomplished by the recognition of individual phonemes, the smallest units of speech that distinguish one utterance from another.

2. The method selected for identifying phonemes consists of isolating and recognizing a particular group of features characteristic of

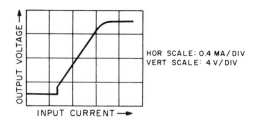

Fig. 2.   ATL-element transfer function.

each phoneme.   These features are fed to phonemic decision
circuits which give weight to them in accordance with their
importance in the identification process.   The method allows for
the fact that the features of each phoneme are significantly modified by the features of the phoneme immediately preceding and
following.

3.   The recognition equipment was designed to follow and to recognize
the most rapid transients that might occur because of the dynamic
nature of speech.

4.   The system was designed to operate in real time.

5.   The logic of the equipment was arranged to perform all feature-
abstraction processes simultaneously.   In addition, particular
attention was given to establishing the logical relationships between neighboring frequency channels (neighborhood logic).

The concept of feature abstraction is based on the realization that a
group of simple observations, judiciously chosen, can convey more
information toward a decision than a single all-encompassing evaluation.
In this approach the identification of phonemes is achieved by combining
several characteristic attributes (i.e., features) of each phoneme.
Consequently, feature abstraction will not permit incidental variations
of the phoneme to dilute the decision process.   Thus, the decisions are
made essentially independently of variations from speaker to speaker
and from utterance to utterance.

When it is realized that not all of the features comprising a particular
phoneme may occur with equal probability, it becomes desirable to
perform logical operations that retain a measure of probability.   Analog-
threshold-logic can maintain a quantitative measurement of probability
throughout all logical operations.   For example, a measurement can
be made of the probability that a transition of speech energy from one
frequency band to another has occurred within a given time interval.

One or more such measurements make up the assurance level of a specific feature. Depending upon the probability that this feature will or will not occur in a particular phoneme, a weighted connection from this feature is combined with other weighted feature measurements to make up the final phonemic decision. It is also important to note that not only is the presence or absence of a feature indicated in the networks, but also the amount to which the feature is present. Retention of this analog measure of quantity has been found to be essential for separation of nearly identical phonemes with overlapping characteristics. The over-all processing efficiency of the networks is therefore greatly enhanced by this capability.

The need to provide a recognition system that can respond to the rapid transients of speech has been determined from speech analysis, speech synthesis, physiology and neurology. Research in speech synthesis has shown that consonants are characterized by the rapid movement of sound energy across the frequency spectrum. The duration of this energy within any one frequency channel (filter) may be as short as 10 msec. For this reason, low-Q resonant circuits become necessary so that a rapid response to the onset and termination of energy in a particular frequency band can be detected. In addition, timing accuracies in the order of 5 msec between adjacent frequency channels have to be maintained.

Subsequent logic operations must also be performed with sufficient speed to maintain the desired timing resolution. The problem is solved with parallel logic, performing all functions simultaneously. The movement of speech energy within the frequency spectrum is recognized in this equipment as a progression of energy through adjacent filter sections. Thus the output from one logic operation is typically determined by the output of one or more neighborhood logic operations.

Another requirement for a speech-recognition system can be derived from the fact that the total dynamic range of speech energy is as much as 62 db over a 200 to 6,000 cps frequency spectrum. Therefore, a fundamental requirement for a speech-processing system is a dynamic range approaching 60 db. A common technique for reducing the dynamic range is the use of agc. However, this introduces an additional time variable which may lead to false conclusions in a study having as its prime purpose the determination of the time-varying features of speech sounds. Through the use of logarithmic compression, the RCA speech-analyzer is capable of abstracting speech features over the entire 60-db dynamic range. An additional advantage of this technique is that the subsequent neighborhood logic operations consist of ratios so that features can be abstracted independent of over-all signal amplitude.

System Description

The major operations involved in the speech processor are shown in the block diagram of Figure 1. Basically, the speech spectra are divided into 19 segments by an overlapping bank of bandpass filters whose outputs are full-wave rectified and integrated. The filter bank is composed of 19 low-Q bandpass filters (Martin, Putzrath, and Talavage, 1962; Martin, Nelson, and Zadell, 1964).

The rectified outputs of each filter are made logarithmic before the various features are derived. This reduces the dynamic range of energy at any one bandpass from 30 to 40 db to approximately 20 db. An additional advantage is that the differences in energy between adjacent filters become ratios and produce a degree of amplitude-independent feature abstraction. A common log-attenuator circuit was designed to avoid the difficulties which would result in matching 19 such attenuator circuits over a large dynamic range. The outputs of the full-wave rectifiers are converted by a multiplexer to a pulse train as the input to the log circuit. A second bank of synchronous switches converts the serial pulse train emerging from the log-attentuator back to individual samples which are then integrated prior to the initial levels of parallel processing.

From Figure 1, it may be seen that differences in energy between adjacent filters are then derived by 36 difference-taking circuits. With further processing, the envelope shape of the spectrum and its time variations can be obtained from the difference circuit outputs. Martin, Putzrath, and Talavage (1962) give a detailed description of the networks used to abstract local energy maxima, local minima, positive and negative local slopes, and their time variations.

Sounds Investigated and Methods of Analysis

Very little information is presented in the literature concerning the statistical distribution of speech parameters. Most of the early work on speech was concerned with vowel sounds, specifically the determination of the frequencies of the first and second formants. Figure 3

shows an idealized representation of the vowel sound in the word "bed."
On the assumption that no time variations exist, it is apparent that, in
addition to the formants F1, F2, F3, the vowel is typified by local
energy maxima, minima, and regions of positive and negative energy
slopes (dE/df). In actual context, the entire structure of a vowel is
modified by the preceding and following sounds.

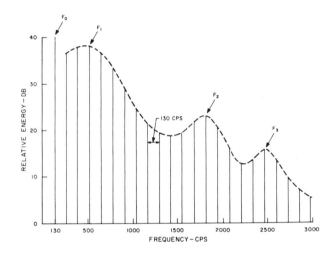

Fig. 3. Idealized characteristics of the vowel sound in the
word "bed."

Analysis of the spectral content of consonants requires an even
greater capability to perform complex spectral analysis. Many consonants have no steady-state representation, but are instead composed
of dynamic time variations throughout their duration. For these
sounds it is necessary to determine the time variations of the local
energy maxima, minima, and slopes.

In order to investigate the fricatives (as well as the other consonant
classes), CVC word lists were generated which placed these consonants
in initial position with each of 10 following vowels followed by the final
consonant /d/ for all words. The first step in the analysis and tabulation of data was to obtain oscillographic recordings of the primary
features consisting of the responses from the local maxima, minima,
positive and negative slope networks. The positive and negative slope
outputs indicate at any instant of time the regions of increasing and
decreasing spectral energy. Trained investigators familiar with the
characteristics of speech tabulated this initial data in order to deter-

mine the characteristics of the individual phonemes. Specific feature-abstraction networks were interconnected for each sound, and combinations of these specific networks were then used to develop the final recognition networks for each phoneme. Recordings were made for two repetitions of each word list by six male speakers.

After some initial experience was obtained, both with the networks and in the analysis of the primary data, it became apparent that the most reliable clues for machine recognition were contained in the positive and negative slope data. This results partly from the fact that a highly damped formant or nearly flat energy distribution will not be detected by even a very sensitive system capable of operating over a large dynamic range. If a formant should be missed in an analyzer abstracting only formants, all the information about that sound is completely lost in the region of the formant. It can be seen through observation of Figure 3 that, for the idealized vowel presented in this figure, the majority of the spectrum consists of regions of increasing and decreasing energy. A loss of any one of these channels will most likely occur at either the beginning or the ending channel representing the length along the frequency axis of the increasing or decreasing energy. As a result, more responses are produced by the slope networks, and a loss of any one of them is not as critical as the loss of a maximum response in an analyzer based on formant extraction only.

Another factor that limits the use of formant extraction, when spectrum analysis is performed by a fixed set of bandpass filters, is the possible location of the formant at the crossover points of adjacent filters. Should this occur, the difference of energy between the adjacent filters is zero, and again the formant will not be detected. In actual practice, in the region of the crossover points there exists a null zone in which the differences are too small to be detected. In the present system, this null zone is less than 10% of the individual filter bandwidth over the entire 60-db dynamic range. However, even with this large dynamic range, local energy maxima could not be abstracted as consistently as regions of increasing and decreasing energy. Because of these two factors (broadness of formants and possible formant location between adjacent filters), slope features were found to contain clues which are much more reliable for machine recognition of phonemes.

To state that the slope outputs were found to be much more reliable as recognition features is not to say that formant or pole-zero analyses are not meaningful from the standpoint of speech synthesis or speech recognition by humans. It says only that positive and negative slopes were found to be easier to abstract experimentally and were found to be more reliable as recognition cues for the individual phonemes, particularly consonants.

Because parallel processing is used throughout, an individual recognition unit can have four possible states in response to a speech stimulus. For example, consider a recognition unit interconnected to recognize phoneme "X. " This recognition unit can then either respond or not respond to phoneme "X," or can respond or not respond to all other phonemes. The errors are produced in two ways: lack of response to phoneme "X" and false responses to all other phonemes. Because of this, the recognition scores have been computed considering both the response and the rejection capabilities of the recognition units. The response accuracy is:

$$\text{Percentage of response accuracy} = \frac{\text{No. of responses to phoneme "X"}}{\text{No. of "X"s presented}} \times 100.$$

Accordingly, the rejection scores are:

Percentage of rejection score =

$$\frac{\text{No. of responses to all other phonemes}}{\text{No. of all other phonemes presented}} \times 100.$$

No attempt was made to compute the rejection scores of one class with respect to the other classes of sounds. The main effort was spent in separating accurately the very similar sounds within a given class, rather than the significantly easier task of separating quite dissimilar classes of sounds from one another.

Some typical examples of features utilized for the acoustic recognition of some of the fricatives will be presented next. A more complete analysis of these phonemes is given in Martin, Nelson, and Zadell (1964).

Fricatives

Fricative consonants are produced by the passage of air through the narrow openings in the vocal tract or over the edge of the teeth. As a result, their energy spectra usually exhibit broad noiselike frequency bands, with certain frequency regions accentuated. The fricatives may be sustained in duration, and may vary considerably in acoustic power, depending both on the fricative and the talker.

The fricatives that have been analyzed here are: /s/, /f/, /ʃ/, /h/, /v/ and /z/. Of these, /v/ and /z/ are voiced (that is, the vocal cords are in vibration at their fundamental frequency), and the remaining four are classified as unvoiced.

Gross Class Features. Five major classes of features have been derived from the speech energy spectra. These classes are local maxima, useful for locating the familiar frequency formants; local minima, positive slopes, (dE/dF); negative slopes (-dE/dF); and channel energy intensity (E). The most prominent features for identifying fricative consonants were found to be displayed by the positive slope, the negative slope, and the spectrum energy distribution data. Many of the unvoiced fricatives are characterized by complete absence of negative slopes, however, and the recognition decision depends entirely upon the positive slope and the spectrum energy distribution data.

In general, discrimination between voiced and unvoiced fricatives is performed on the basis of recognizing the presence or absence of negative slopes in the low-frequency channels. Since there is some variation in the magnitude and duration of these negative slopes for different talkers, several means of determining the presence of voicing are available. One method is to AND negative slope Channels 1 and 2; AND negative slope Channels 3 and 4; and then OR these combinations with an ATL element, using the output as a voicing indicator. A second method, useful for signals of short duration, is to integrate and add negative slope Channels 1 through 5. The resultant sum must overcome a fixed threshold prior to amplification and utilization as a voicing indicator. The combination of the above techniques has proven to be a very reliable voicing indicator, and has been used successfully for six talkers with nearly 100% accuracy.

Characteristic Features. The fricative consonants were first classified as voiced or voiceless, according to their articulatory processes. Then each phoneme was analyzed for invariant features and ATL decision networks were designed which respond to positive stimuli and reject all negative stimuli. Recognition accuracies were tabulated for several repetitions of the test words uttered by six male talkers.

a. Voiceless Fricatives. The spectra of unvoiced fricatives /s/ and /f/ are characterized by broad frequency noise, with a very strong energy component in the region above 7.6 kc. This characteristic agrees closely with data reported by Hughes and Halle (1956), and

Heinz and Stevens (1961). The continuity of the positive slopes and the initial onset suggests that the energy spectra begin at the uppermost frequency band and fall off sharply at the transition into the following vowel. No negative slopes were observed for these sounds. Considerable overlap in the positive slopes of /s/ and /f/ due to variations in talkers was noted; therefore, additional features were required to attain satisfactory separation of these two phonemes. Of particular interest in this regard was the nonexistence of spectral energy for /f/ in Channels 1 through 9. This condition can be utilized in separating /s/ from /f/ in the instances where /s/ exhibits a positive slope pattern similar to that of /f/. Also, a general weakening of the low-frequency positive slopes may be noted in the lower frequency channels. Thus, by subtracting the positive slopes below 2,500 cps from the positive slopes above 2,500 cps, an additional /f/ excitation feature is available for most of the talkers investigated.

In general, the /ʃ/ spectrum is characterized by high energy content above 500 cps, with a pole around 4,000 cps. This sound consistently exhibits continuous positive slopes in Channels 1 through 11 for all talkers investigated, but no negative slopes have been observed. Due to the lack of poles above 4,000 cps and to the absence of a continuous positive slope pattern in the upper frequency channels, /ʃ/ was easily distinguished from /s/ with practically no confusion. The response of the /ʃ/ decision network to /h/ was the most frequent error encountered. But the duration of the /ʃ/ stimuli was much greater than that of /h/, and this cue alone was sufficient for accurate /ʃ/ - /h/ discrimination.

The fricative /h/ was found to be very dependent on the following vowel, and no single feature with only one invariant set of acoustic parameters could be utilized in the perception of /h/. For this phoneme, an examination of the general trend of the spectral energy of several talkers proved useful. A large concentration of energy was noted in the region of the second formant for the vowels with low-frequency first formants, and concentrations of energy occur in the region of F1 and F2 in the vowels with low F1 and high F2; e.g., /æ/ and /e/. Consequently, /h/ was subclassified into four separate categories determined by grouping the most similar patterns. Feature-abstraction networks were developed for each of the four classes, and these in turn excite a single decision circuit, which responds to a stimulus from any of the four networks.

b.   Voiced Fricatives.   Spectra of voiced fricatives /z/ and /v/ contain a strong energy component below 500 cps or, more precisely, at Fl.   This factor has been utilized as the primary cue for distinguishing between the voiced and unvoiced fricatives.   In the region above 1,000 cps, the spectra of voiced fricatives do not differ markedly from the spectra of many voiceless fricatives, as was reported by Hughes and Halle (1956).

To separate /z/ from /v/, the positive slope data and energy data were found to contain the most useful features.   Since /z/ contains more energy in the frequency bands above 1,500 cps than /v/, this characteristic was utilized as the primary cue in distinguishing between /z/ and /v/ in the instances where the positive slopes of /v/ resembled those of /z/.   An additional feature depended upon the successful recognition of /z/, which was performed solely through utilizing the frictional positive slope features of /z/, and inhibiting the /v/ decision with this response.

Recognition Scores

Recognition networks, utilizing analog-threshold-logic, were developed to abstract the features summarized in the preceding discussions. Since parallel processing has been used throughout, an individual recognition unit must be characterized both by its response to the phoneme to be recognized and by its rejection of all other phonemes. These two characteristics have been expressed as response accuracy and rejection score, as previously described.   The scores obtained for the fricatives in combination with ten following vowels for six male speakers are presented in Table 1.

Discussion

Results up to the present time indicate that acoustic recognition by machine can be achieved with a high degree of accuracy for isolated speech.   The speech features that have been abstracted by the experimental networks for the recognition of the individual phonemes correspond quite closely to the results from previous speech-analysis and speech-synthesis studies.   A significant deviation, however, between the present work and past investigations has been the type of features utilized for the recognition of the individual phonemes.   In previous investigations, the location in the spectrum of the formants and their movements with time have been considered to be the primary

Table 1. Summary of Response Accuracy and Rejection Score.

Phoneme	Percentage of response accuracy	Percentage of rejection score
/f/	96.0	1.83
/h/	99.2	1.67
/s/	96.7	1.83
/ʃ/	93.5	0.50
/v/	86.0	1.50
/z/	97.5	0.17

features of speech. The results of the present study, however, indicate that the spectral regions of increasing and decreasing energy (positive and negative slopes) are also highly significant clues for recognition. A striking example of the invariance of the slope features is the fact that a single onset transition of slope features was sufficient for the recognition of a semivowel in combination with ten following vowels for all six male speakers used in the investigation. The formants, on the other hand, undergo wide ranges of movement within the spectrum for the ten following vowels. The invariance of slope features and the ease with which they could be implemented for machine recognition are two of the most significant findings of the present study.

Only the fricative sounds have been reported on in this paper; however, present data indicate that the vowel-like consonants, the plosives, the liquids and nasals, and the vowels, can be brought to the level of the recognition scores obtained for the fricatives.

The next goal in this program is to apply these techniques to the recognition of continuous speech through the inclusion of such higher-level functions as linguistics and context.

Acknowledgment

This work was supported by the Air Force Avionics Laboratory, Research and Technology Division, Air Force Systems Command.

References

Heinz, J. M., and Stevens, K. N. On the properties of voiceless fricative consonants. J. acoust. Soc. Amer., 1961, 33, 589-596.

Hughes, G. W., and Halle, M. Spectral properties of fricative consonants. J. acoust. Soc. Amer., 1956, 28, 303-310.

Martin, T. B., Nelson, A. L., and Zadell, H. J. Speech recognition by feature-abstraction techniques. Avionics Lab., Res. and Tech. Div., AFSC, USAF, Tech. Doc. Rep. No. AL-TDR-64-176, Aug. 1964. (AD604526)

Martin, T. B., Putzrath, F. L., and Talavage, J. J. Speech-pattern recognition by simulated neural networks. Electromag. Warfare and Comm. Lab., Aeronautical Systems Div., AFSC, USAF, Tech. Doc. Rep. No. ASD-TDR-62-511; Pt. I, July 1962, Pt. II, Dec. 1962. (AD277200)

A FEATURE BASED COMPUTER RECOGNITION PROGRAM FOR THE MODELING OF VOWEL PERCEPTION

John F. Hemdal [1] **and George W. Hughes**
School of Electrical Engineering
Purdue University
Lafayette, Indiana

Introduction

Several approaches to the solutions of problems of automatic speech recognition have been studied which differ in their theoretical constructs and by reason of their intended purpose. These recognition procedures may be broadly described as (a) pattern or template matching and (b) pattern or feature recognition. The pattern matching method, whether utilizing stored templates or adaptive procedures for automatically classifying speech patterns, yields results where the internal recognition behavior is usually not accessible for investigation. Thus, standard correlation techniques, while achieving recognition success, offer little insight into the information bearing attributes of the acoustic signal. Feature tracking, on the other hand, relies upon hypothesizing certain acoustic parameters of recognition and a direct relationship exists between these parameters and the results of human or mechanical recognition attempts. The feature approach provides a means of modeling human speech perception since the pertinence of the recognition details may be tested by a perturbation of the recognition functions and subsequent comparison of the results with the response of listeners for the same stimuli. In particular, a feature

---

[1] Now at the center for Research on Language and Language Behavior, University of Michigan, Ann Arbor, Michigan.

recognition model of speech perception may be evaluated by comparison with human performance under the adverse conditions in speech
communications created by the addition of noise, filtering, and time or
frequency compression or expansion. If a close correlation between
human and machine responses can be demonstrated for natural speech,
as well as when such adverse conditions are in effect, then the hypothesis under study will serve as a model of human speech recognition.

    With this viewpoint in mind, a computer recognition program was
devised to extract the physical correlates of the distinctive features
proposed by Jakobson, Fant, and Halle (1952) and Jakobson (1962).
This program provides for the recognition of ten cardinal vowels, nine
diphthongs and most of the consonants, insofar as the consonantal context was required for correct vowel recognition. Differentiation between the environmental effects of surrounding consonants and the
characteristics of diphthong variation is accomplished by invoking
simple linguistic constraints.

    The decision logic described has as its goal the accomplishment of
primary recognition alone, that is, recognition based solely on the
sound shapes of the acoustic signal without the benefit of knowledge of
the meaning of the utterance, the rules of grammar of the language or
the interpretive faculty of the listener. Thus attention is focused on
acoustic parameters of importance to recognition. In order that a
valid comparison be made between the computer results and the listening tests, it is necessary to ensure that the speech utterances used as
test data admit of only primary recognition. It is for this reason that
the computer recognition studies undertaken for this experiment dealt
with simple nonsense forms.

    It has been pointed out by Fant (1956) that the physical properties of
each distinctive feature may be relative for each speaker and that
proper normalization must be performed on the speech data in order to
track adequately the features. It is reasonable to expect that a mechanical device would be required to perform automatically a similar
normalization in order to handle the diversities of several speakers.
A useful degree of normalization has not been determined. It was
proposed that by adjusting a recognition scheme to individual speakers
in turn, the minimum changes required for optimal accuracy would
lead to the proper normalization.

    The speech data, introduced into an IBM 7090 computer in spectral
form, were obtained by sampling, at 60 times a second, the rectified

and smoothed outputs of 35 bandpass filters whose center frequencies
spanned the range of interest. Each sample from each filter output
was quantized into one of 1,024 possible levels by a Datrac analog-to-
digital converter and punched on data-processing cards. The recognition program was written to perform measurements and decisions
on the data in this form.

The initial portion of this study involved the analysis of 227/həˈ/ CVC
nonsense syllables which were recorded on magnetic tape using a con-
denser microphone. These recordings were made under normal conversational conditions and no particular attempt was made to obtain an
ideal acoustic environment. Occasional background noises were evident but at no time was the noise found to be of sufficient amplitude
to affect the results. The nonsense syllables were augmented by 50
short monosyllabic common words and samples of continuous speech.

The Vowels Examined, their Binary Features and Physical Correlates

Ten cardinal vowels were chosen for investigation; six tense vowels
/i/, /æ/, /a/, /ɔ/, /u/, /ɚ/ and four lax vowels /ɪ/, /ɛ/, /ʌ/, /ʊ/.
The complex sounds /o/ and /e/ were treated as the diphthongs /ʌu/
and /ɛɪ/ in addition to /aɪ/, /aɚ/, /au/, /ɛɚ/, /ɪɚ/, /uɚ/, and /ɔɪ/.
It will be noticed that each of these complex vowel sounds is considered
as a combination of two of the ten cardinal vowels. These 19 categories
of vowel sounds allow nearly complete transcription of General
American English.

The complex vowel sounds are considered to be characterized by a
shift of one or more formant frequencies and a consequent change in
one or more features. Four binary features, then, are sufficient to
characterize all diphthongs as well as the ten cardinal vowels.

The four binary feature-pairs found to distinguish among the vowels
are grave/acute, compact/diffuse, tense/lax and flat/plain.

As described in the "Preliminaries to Speech Analysis" (Jakobson,
Fant, and Halle, 1952), the grave phonemes have a larger concentration of energy in the lower portion of the spectrum as opposed to their
acute counterparts. For the vowels, a second formant closer to the
third than the first indicates an acute phoneme. A possible functional
relationship may be the ratio of the difference of the first and second
formants to the difference of the second and third formant frequencies.
A ratio less than approximately one would indicate a grave vowel. A
comparison of the ratio

$$\frac{F2 - F1}{F3 - F2}$$

has been made based on average formant frequencies given by Peterson
and Barney (1952) as follows:

/i/	2.80	/u/	.416
/ɪ/	2.86	/ʊ/	.475
/ɛ/	2.05	/a/	.267
/æ/	1.54	/ɔ/	.172
/ɚ/	2.53	/ʌ/	.458

It will be noticed that the value of this ratio for /ɚ/ definitely pre-
scribes an acute vowel due to its low third formant although this fact
is obscured by the position of /ə/ when plotted as a function of F1 and
F2 alone. It is sufficient, however, to consider the grave/acute
boundary as a line of constant second formant frequency (at approximately 1,500 cps for the data examined) with /ɚ/ handled as a special
case.

The frequency of the first formant has been suggested (Jakobson,
Fant, and Halle, 1952) as the characteristic index of the compact/
diffuse feature. With the manner of handling the complex vowels as
indicated, there is no necessity of introducing a noncompact or nondiffuse distinction in order to differentiate among the ten cardinal
vowels. A compact/diffuse F1 threshold set at approximately 500 cps
has been found to provide accurate results.

The flat/plain feature is characterized by a downward/upward shift
of a set of formants or all formants in the spectrum. The physical
correlate of this feature appears to be a function of the sum of the first
two or three formants.

The measure of the feature tense/lax is perhaps the least well
known of the vowel features. However, according to Fant (1959) one
should expect to see a lengthening of a tense vowel and a shift of the
formant frequencies away from a neutral position. Figures 1 and 2
show this tendency for two different speakers. The vowels /a/ and
/ɚ/ are excluded from the tense/lax comparison since they differ from
any lax vowel by at least two features, whereas the remaining vowels
occur in pairs with the only distinction being the tense/lax one. For
most speakers, there exists considerable overlap in the formant positions of tense/lax pairs. Much of this ambiguity can be resolved by
taking into consideration the duration of the vowel and the effect of the

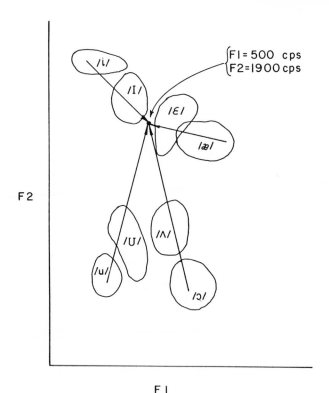

/i/

/I/

/ε/

/æ/

$\begin{cases} F1 = 500 \ cps \\ F2 = 1900 \ cps \end{cases}$

F2

/U/

/ʌ/

/u/

/ɔ/

F 1

Fig. 1.   Formant regions showing tense/lax tendency (Speaker GWH).

consonantal context upon the vowel duration.   Thus, the detection of the tense/lax feature in the consonant following the vowel under considera-tion, allows the tense/lax duration threshold to be altered in accordance with the observed duration changes in natural speech.

A decision tree for the ten vowels is shown in Figure 3.   Figure 4 is an idealized F1 - F2 plane with vowel regions shown along with the first three feature boundaries.   The inclusion of vowel duration infor-mation yields a parameter space on the order of that shown in Figure 5.   The vertical axis primarily represents vowel duration and con-sequently the upper (tense vowel) surface slopes toward the more dif-fuse vowels as indicated by House (1961).

General Description of the Computer Program

The decisions to be performed on the acoustic data may be con-sidered to fall into two categories: those which may be performed by

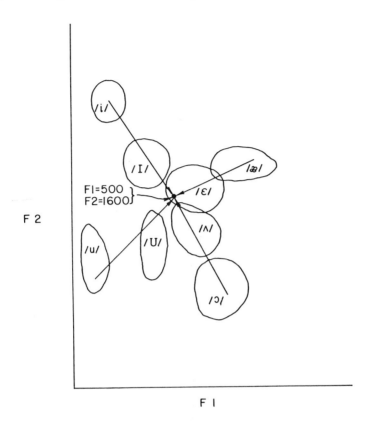

Fig. 2. Formant regions showing tense-lax tendency (Speaker JFH).

examining properties found in a single sample or time segment and those which require the examination of the combined characteristics of several segments or depend upon previous decisions performed on several surrounding time segments. The former group was performed initially on each time segment in sequence while the latter often required several passes on the data.

The first decision sequentially classifies each time segment as belonging to the speech utterance or to a silence by detecting a significant amount of energy above the noise level of the system. Each time segment not classified as silence is then labeled as belonging to either a sonorant or nonsonorant phoneme. This is done, as shown in the block diagram of Figure 6, by first eliminating segments belonging to stop, fricative, and affricate classes of phonemes. Thus, if any time segment exhibits one or more of the following properties, it will be classified as belonging to a nonsonorant phoneme:

ALL VOWELS

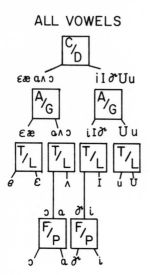

Fig. 3. Decision tree for
vowels.

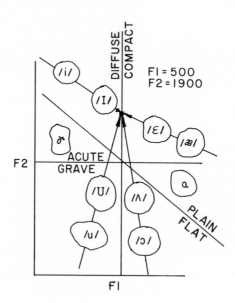

Fig. 4. Idealized formant locations for vowels.

1. A lack of voicing (as measured by the absence of energy below
    350 cps).

2. The presence of indications of turbulence (as measured by the
    presence of frequency components above 4,000 cps).

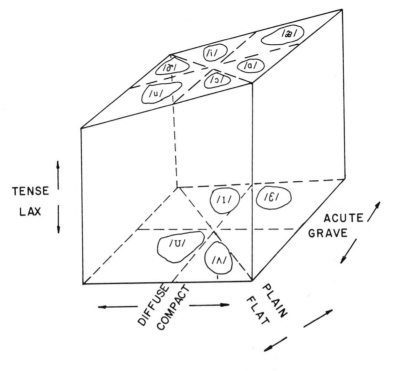

Fig. 5. Location of vowel regions.

3. The presence of silence with or without voicing which precedes
    the segment under consideration.

Separating the nonsonorant time samples in this manner results in
categorizing the stops, fricatives, and affricates into four groups as
shown in the four blocks in the upper right of Figure 6. Thus, property
(1) may be considered as the physical correlate of the feature tense/
lax (for consonants) and properties (2) and (3) are to be associated
with the feature continuant/interrupted.

The time segments labeled sonorant are further classified as belonging to either consonantal or nonconsonantal phonemes. This classification, dividing the vowel segments from the nasals, liquids, and
glides is based on the property that the nonvowel sonorants are weaker
sounds than the neighboring vowels due to a more complete closure of
the vocal tract.

After determining that a given segment belongs to a vowel, the computer program enters a routine which determines the approximate
formant frequencies by locating the spectral peaks (P1, P2, and P3) in
each of the first three formant regions. Typical results of the peak-

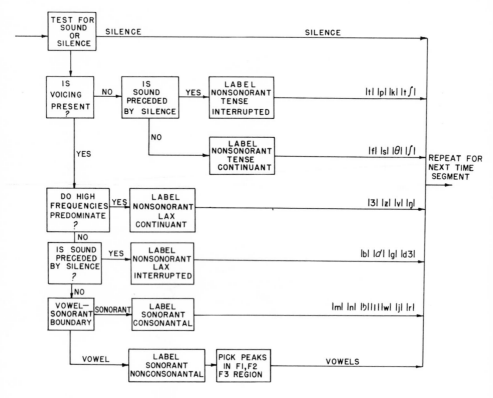

Fig. 6.   Independent time segmentation classification.

picking routine are shown as white dots superimposed on the standard
sound spectrogram of Figure 7.

Based upon the determined formant peaks and the duration of the
vowel in which the segment is embedded, each vowel time sample
is classified as one of the ten cardinal vowels in accordance with
the distinctive features tracked.   For example, a given segment
has spectral peaks located at 450 cps, 1,430 cps, and 1,930 cps.   The
decision logic determines that P1 < 500 cps and the segment is labeled
diffuse; 2. 38 P1 + P2 < 2,830 and the segment is labeled flat; P2 > 1,170
cps and the segment is labeled tense; P2 < 1,500 but P3 < 2,100 cps so
the segment is labeled acute.   This segment is then labeled /ɚ/, the
only acute, diffuse, tense, flat vowel.

In nearly all normally pronounced vowels, the formant frequencies
change throughout the duration of the vowel as a result of the consonantal influence.   In addition, there are formant frequency changes which
characterize the complex vowel sounds or diphthongs.   Since each time

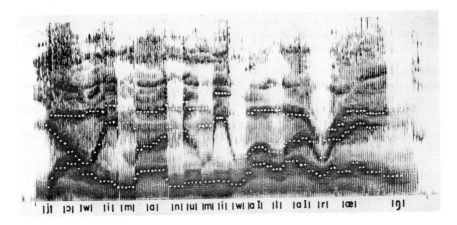

ıji   ıɔı ıwı   ıiı ımı   ıɑı   ınıuı ımı ıiı ıwı ıɑ Iı   ıɪı   ıɑ Iı ırı   ıœı   ıŋı

Fig. 7.   Example of results of the peak-picking routine.

segment, at this point in the program, is labeled independently from the
rest, a changing series of vowel labels occurs as the time samples
progress along the vowel.   It is necessary to have the machine distinguish between formant transitions for diphthongs and those which
arise as a result of the consonantal influence.   This distinction may
be accomplished by utilizing information at the physical level which
characterizes each type of formant transition and by knowing the context in which the vowel appears.   For example, it is noted that diphthongs are usually a merger of a given vowel with a more diffuse
vowel following (i.e., a lowering of F1 usually occurs during the progress of the diphthong) while the adjacent nonsonorants most often
affect only the second formant which may either rise or fall depending
upon whether the consonant is grave or acute.   Logic rules may be
formulated from the foregoing knowledge which will dictate when a
given sequence of vowel classifications may result in a vowel output
symbol:

1. A lax vowel must be at least 100 msec in duration.
2. A tense vowel must be at least 133 msec in duration.
3. The output symbol must agree with the maximum or minimum
    second formant frequency if such an extremum exists.
4. The only pairs of output symbols allowed are /aɪ/, /ʌ u/, /ɛɪ /,
    /aɚ /, /aʊ /, /ɛɚ /, /ɪɚ/, /uɚ/, and /ɔɪ /.
5. If no symbol has previously been assigned the output corresponds
    to the majority of time segments.

6. Classifications of two or more symbols will be reduced to one or
    two if such multiple classification can be inferred from the con-
    sonantal context.

As an example of the application of these rules consider 18 vowel
segments which have been independently classified as: /ɪ/ 67 msec,
/u/ 133 msec, and /ɪ/ 100 msec. The consonant following this vowel
is known to be a /t/. The computer would ignore because of insufficient length, the first /ɪ/ and would tentatively select /u/ and /ɪ/ as
the output as a result of Rules (1) and (2). The second /ɪ/ classification would be deleted either by Rule (4) as unallowed or by Rule (6)
since it may be inferred from the /t/ that the vowel second formant
will increase resulting in a change from /u/ to /ɪ/.

Experimental Results

Speech utterances consisting of 227 nonsense /hə'/ CVC words
spoken in isolation by the first talker were processed by the system
and operated on by the recognition program. There were 21 vowel
samples which produced a computer output different than the intent of
the speaker for a recognition accuracy of 92%. Apparently because
of the greater length, there were fewer errors among the tense vowels
(four out of 137 samples in all possible consonantal contexts). There
were 17 errors in 90 samples of the lax vowels and this error rate
was almost entirely due to the failure of the second formant to reach
its target position.

A list of 50 additional words containing some diphthongs and many
consonant clusters was processed by the recognition program. Of the
30 cardinal vowels, 24 were classified correctly and 5 of the 6 errors
were /ε/ - /æ/ reversals – a problem also prevalent in the nonsense
word list. Of the 20 diphthongs present in the additional word list,
14 were classified correctly. All but two samples had at least an
element of the diphthong classified correctly.

Evaluation of the recognition results was obtained by comparing with
the responses of a panel of 25 partially trained listeners who were
presented with 100 of the original 227 nonsense words. The words used
for these tests were dubbed directly from the tapes providing the input for the data system. Each listener was asked to listen to each
word twice and to transcribe what he heard.

Considering their responses for vowels only, one notes that at least
20 of the 25 listeners agreed on 85% of the vowels. Eight vowels pro-

duced confusion with not more than 60% of the listeners in agreement. The most common of these eight confusions were /ʌ/ - /ʊ/ which accounted for six. (Compare with the most common confusions, /ɛ/ - /æ/, for the computer.) Four words caused confusion among listeners and an error from the computer. Two of these four resulted in the same response from listeners and machine but differed from the intent of the speaker.

The word list of /hə'/ CVC words used in this study was constructed in an artificial manner in order to ensure that all CV and VC combinations would occur. It was expected then that some of the words on the list would be identical to meaningful English words. Of the list of 100 of these words presented to the panel of listeners, 22 had possible meaning; for example, p̲i̲n̲g̲, c̲h̲e̲c̲k̲, B̲e̲r̲t̲, b̲u̲t̲, b̲a̲t̲, s̲u̲b̲, b̲o̲u̲g̲h̲t̲, b̲e̲t̲, b̲i̲n̲, p̲i̲t̲, j̲e̲t̲, s̲a̲w̲e̲d̲, h̲e̲e̲d̲, f̲u̲l̲l̲, c̲a̲d̲, j̲o̲t̲, c̲u̲r̲b̲, d̲o̲o̲m̲, f̲i̲l̲l̲, r̲e̲e̲t̲, y̲e̲s̲, and t̲h̲u̲d̲. Of these 22 words, o̲n̲l̲y̲ o̲n̲e̲ (f̲u̲l̲l̲) was missed by more than five listeners. Furthermore, the most common error in four other words was the substitution of the correct word by a wrong but meaningful English word. For example, /fut/ → /fʊt/, /bʊŋ/ → /bʌŋ/, /dʊn/ → /dʌn/, and /sʊm/ → /sʌm/. The results suggest that listeners make use of meaning at the word level (or familiarities at the syllable level?) even if the words are spoken in isolation and the listeners expect nonsense words. The computer recognition results for these 26 special words were slightly lower than the over-all average.

Conclusions and Summary

This experiment indicated that a feature based vowel recognition method compared favorably with the capabilities of a panel of partially trained listeners. Depending upon the confidence level chosen, (60% or 80% in agreement) the listeners achieved a recognition accuracy of 96% or 88% with regard to the intent of the speaker. The recognition accuracy of the computer was 92%.

At the present time only primary recognition is performed by the computer. Consequently, in comparing the results with the behavior of a panel of listeners it is necessary to ensure that the human subjects may perform o̲n̲l̲y̲ p̲r̲i̲m̲a̲r̲y̲ r̲e̲c̲o̲g̲n̲i̲t̲i̲o̲n̲. Their ability apparently to make use of meaning even at the isolated word level may make it difficult to provide a fair comparison and simultaneously avoid completely trivial input stimuli.

Examination of speech data from two other speakers has substantiated the same form for the decision logic in tracking the distinctive features. However, it was found necessary to vary the threshold boundaries significantly from speaker to speaker to maintain the recognition accuracy. The tense/lax feature was most affected by interspeaker variability. The physical correlate of the tense/lax feature chosen for this recognition program (including a tense/lax oval and focus) suggests a hypothetical "ideal neutral vowel" which, if it could be clearly defined, may be of value in determining interspeaker normalization.

The tense/lax boundary established for carefully spoken isolated monosyllables, again fails for continuous speech. In two samples of short sentences introduced into the recognition program, many tense vowels were labeled as their lax counterparts. Both a shortening of duration and a neutralizing of formant positions are evident with increases in tempo, suggesting that the tense/lax oval boundary may be considered as shrinking with increases of tempo, or decrease in stress or duration (Lindblom, 1963; Stetson, 1951; Tiffany, 1959).

Extensions of the experiment of testing the feature approach are evident:

1. Adjustment of decision boundaries to increase the correlation in behavior between the computer and the listeners.
2. Degradation of the acoustic signal by the addition of noise, filtering, etc., and a study of comparison and contrast between computer and listener.
3. Provisions for the recognition of consonants and consonant clusters.
4. Introduction of a larger class of input stimuli to the comparison including continuous speech.

Acknowledgment

This research was supported by the Air Force Cambridge Research Laboratories, Office of Aerospace Research, Bedford, Massachusetts under the Contract Number AF19(628)-305.

References

Fant, G. On the predictability of formant levels and spectrum envelopes from formant frequencies. In M. Halle (Ed.), For Roman Jakobson. 's-Gravenhage: Mouton, 1956. Pp. 109-121.

Fant, G. Acoustic analysis and synthesis of speech with applications to Swedish. Ericsson Technics, 1959, 1, 3-108.

House, A. S. On vowel duration in English. J. acoust. Soc. Amer.,
1961, 33, 1174-1178.

Jakobson, R. Selected writings, 's-Gravenhage: Mouton, 1962.

Jakobson, R. , Fant, G. , and Halle, M. Preliminaries to speech
analysis. Acoust. Lab., Mass. Inst. Tech., tech. Rep., 1952,
No. 13. [Cambridge: M. I. T. Press, 1963].

Lindblom, B. Spectrographic study of vowel reduction. J. acoust.
Soc. Amer., 1963, 35, 1773-1781.

Peterson, G. E., and Barney, H. L. Control methods used in a study
of the vowels. J. acoust. Soc. Amer., 1952, 24, 175-184.

Stetson, R. H. Motor phonetics. Amsterdam: North-Holland, 1951.

Tiffany, W. R. Nonrandom sources of variation in vowel quality.
J. Spch. Hrng. Res., 1959, 2, 305-317.

A STATISTICAL ANALOG OF PERCEPTION

S. J. Campanella and D. C. Coulter
Research Division
Melpar, Incorporated
Falls Church, Virginia

Statistical recognition techniques have been applied to the recognition
of human utterances and the talkers who spoke them. The technique,
which is briefly described here, classifies events by computing distribution functions of patterns that are assumed by various parametric
measures of the events. In the application described here, facsimile
speech signals are first translated into digitized formant trace patterns
that represent a shorthand encapsulation of information pertinent to the
identification of the utterance and the talker; then probability distributions of the patterns for classes of utterances and talkers are developed by using samples taken from a group of talkers uttering a list
of words. The individual classes that have been examined are the
utterances of all of the spoken letters of the alphabet and of the ten
talkers who produced the utterances. Distributions for these classes
have been determined by digital data processing and these distributions
have then been used to recognize automatically any utterance and talker
taken from the original samples. In the method that has been developed,
the generation of distribution functions from samples is referred to as
the "learning" process. The "recognition" process consists of the
identification of an unkown by assigning it to the learned distribution

with which it is associated with maximum probability. A statistical
pattern matching in which an entire formant trace pattern is matched
against a set of possible patterns is employed. The set of possible
patterns is generated during the learning process by computing both
the mean formant pattern and dispersion of the patterns about the
mean for each class of events that is to be recognized. This constitutes
a formant trace pattern memory. Recognition of an unkown formant
trace pattern does not require an identical correspondence with a
pattern in the memory but only a maximum in the probability that the
formant trace pattern is associated with one of the classes in the
memory.

In its mathematical formulation, the method employs the expression
of an entire pattern as a single n-dimensional vector. Each vector
component represents a sample on one of the parameter values at a
given time. The dimensionality of the n-space is determined by the
product of the number of parameters sampled and the number of
observation epochs.

A computer program processes these data in two steps. In the first
step, the "learning" program, separate statistical categories are
established by the computation of the mean vector and covariance
matrix describing a normal distribution function for the set of vectors
that define each category. In the second step, the "recognition" program, an unkown is recognized by computing the statistical distance to
all possible categories and selecting the category for which this distance is a minimum.

It is rather difficult to visualize the distribution functions that define
the categories in the multidimensional space, since everyday experience
extends only to three dimensions. However, it is possible to visualize
the entire process of "learning" and "recognition" without loss of
rigor by considering the probability density distributions of two categories plotted versus a single parametric measure. Such a plot for
two categories against a parametric measure Y is shown in Figure 1,
where $p_1(y)$ and $p_2(y)$ represent Gaussian approximations to a posteriori distributions for Events 1 and 2, respectively. These distributions are developed in the "learning" process. Ignore for the moment
the a priori probabilities q_1 and q_2 and the costs of assignment C_{12} and
C_{21} by assuming that $q_1 = q_2$ and $C_{12} = C_{21}$. Consider only the a
posteriori distributions and that a new event, having a parametric
measure $y = Y$, is to be recognized as a member of either Category 1

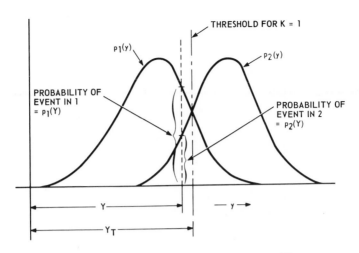

Fig. 1. Decision process for two categories. (K = $q_1 C_{21}/q_2 C_{12}$ and K = 1 for the maximum likelihood decision process. The value of y_T is determined by setting $S_{12} = 0$ in the equation $S_{12} = \log p_2(y) - \log p_1(y) - \log K$.)

or 2. The recognition is then achieved by assigning the event to that category for which the intersection of y = Y with the probability density distribution function is a maximum. Hence, for the example shown in the figure the unkown event would be assigned to Category 1 since $p_1(Y) > p_2(Y)$. This process can be reduced to a simple threshold decision by determining a threshold Y_T such that $p_1(Y_T) = p_2(Y_T)$ and assigning Y to Category 1 if $Y < Y_T$ and Category 2 if $Y > Y_T$. If the a priori probabilities and decision costs are not equal then the threshold is modified as indicated in the figure.

For N categories and hence N probability density functions, $p_L(U)$, L = 1, 2 ... N in n-dimensional space, the same decision process is extended with only minor change. Assuming that all events are equally likely and that all assignment costs are equal, one can simply compute the probability density intersect of the n-dimensional parameter vector $\bar{U} = u_i, u_2 \cdots u_n$ with each of the distribution functions and assign the event to that category for which the probability density $p_L(U)$ is a maximum. In the analysis conducted here $u_1, u_2 \cdots u_n$ are measures of three formant frequency values, F1, F2, F3/FF,[1] taken at 20 uniformly spaced epochs along with the duration of the event and epochs

---

[1] FF indicates a "fricative formant." Information about this formant is multiplexed onto the F3 channel during unvoiced intervals.

Table 1. Recognition of the Utterance "A" among a Group of 10 Talkers.

CATEGORIES	A	B	C	D	E	F	G	H	I	J
UNKNOWNS					DISTANCES					
DCC	-2.0190E 01	-7.3752E 00	4.2486E 01	3.2280E 00	2.0498E 02	1.7977E 03	8.5366E 01	1.2263E 02	1.4883E 02	6.1471E 01
PE	-2.0190E 01	-7.9485E 00	4.2110E 01	1.3808E 00	5.8546E 01	1.5526E 03	2.9543E 01	1.0326E 02	2.0754E 02	6.9664E 01
SJC	-2.0191E 01	-7.2343E 00	5.0938E 01	-9.9002E 00	1.0316E 02	1.0745E 03	5.2236E 01	1.4612E 02	2.7898E 02	8.3352E 01
TEW	-2.0191E 01	5.3370E 00	5.2761E 01	2.5234E 00	9.1867E 01	1.1748E 03	4.5616E 01	1.4238E 02	2.7573E 02	9.7155E 01
LB	-2.0191E 01	-4.1210E 00	3.4846E 01	-1.1973E 00	7.7298E 01	1.5416E 03	2.6608E 01	1.0921E 02	1.3599E 02	4.9180E 01
EB	-2.0190E 01	-4.6348E 01	6.6377E 01	-2.6712E 00	1.2406E 02	1.4623E 03	6.9913E 01	9.7924E 01	2.0476E 02	1.3350E 02
RI	-2.0190E 01	-7.8410E-01	4.7814E 01	5.5702E 00	9.2107E 01	1.6520E 03	1.2484E 02	1.3760E 02	1.9656E 02	5.5803E 01
DE	-2.0195E 01	-7.7043E 00	4.3643E 01	-6.4678E 00	1.2015E 02	1.8090E 03	5.5014E 01	1.2930E 02	1.5549E 02	4.7850E 01
HDC	-2.0191E 01	2.7945E 01	2.7408E 01	2.0476E 01	5.6787E 01	1.5525E 03	-3.3742E 00	1.1031E 02	8.8284E 01	3.7703E 01
ER	-2.0190E 01	-6.0300E 00	6.1583E 01	-1.6291E 01	4.7290E 01	7.6271E 02	2.0094E 02	1.6417E 02	4.4617E 02	1.2653E 02

Table 2. Recognitions of Utterance Means

CATEGORIES	DISTANCES									
UNKNOWNS	A	B	C	D	E	F	G	H	I	J
A	-7.2924E 00	-4.1483E 00	2.4389E 01	-6.3345E-01	3.5182E 00	5.4363E 02	5.4155E 00	1.4909E 01	2.9147E 01	2.1459E 01
B	-3.9687E 00	-6.4495E 00	2.2991E 01	-3.9111E 00	-2.7179E 00	5.2571E 02	4.5565E 00	1.6216E 01	3.1858E 01	2.4488E 01
C	2.4646E 02	3.3131E 02	9.8454E-01	1.9773E 02	2.5718E 02	6.2106E 02	1.8415E 01	3.5274E 01	2.6213E 02	1.2918E 02
D	6.4614E-01	-4.3726E 00	2.1251E 01	-5.4052E 00	-3.5734E 00	4.5907E 02	4.5056E 00	1.7031E 01	3.8902E 01	3.1269E 01
E	1.4790E 00	-4.2484E 00	2.2508E 01	-2.6509E 00	-6.3867E 00	5.3814E 02	4.5251E 00	1.8251E 01	3.2210E 01	3.1334E 01
F	1.7029E 03	7.2895E 02	6.1290E 01	2.4887E 02	5.5437E 02	-1.9433E 00	6.5745E 01	7.1164E 01	1.2245E 03	1.0103E 03
G	1.6609E 01	3.6168E 01	1.8656E 01	2.2841E 01	1.7089E 01	4.9562E 02	2.0625E-01	1.7169E 01	4.9912E 01	3.8507E 00
H	1.2379E 02	8.5624E 01	3.4504E 01	8.8719E 01	2.1967E 02	6.1877E 02	1.9775E 01	8.0802E-01	1.6109E 02	2.0619E 02
I	3.5567E 01	5.5801E 01	2.1570E 01	1.4800E 01	5.6130E 01	5.6524E 02	6.5702E 00	1.3910E 01	-7.5983E 00	1.6099E 01
J	2.7496E 01	8.3871E 01	1.9310E 01	4.5487E 01	5.2470E 01	5.6378E 02	2.8182E 00	1.4919E 01	2.4871E 01	-7.2711E 00

of up to three significant excitation mode changes.   Results were produced for ten male talkers uttering all of the letters of the alphabet.
Shown in Table 1 are the results for the recognition of the utterance
"A" as uttered by each of ten talkers for learning on the same ten
talkers.   Each probability density intersect is printed as a distance
$D = K - \log p_L(U)$.   Hence, for small values of $p_L(U)$, D is a large positive number and for large values of $p_L(U)$, D is a large negative number.   An unkown event is assigned to the column category for which D
is a minimum.   For estimating confusions among categories, the matrix
of probability intersects at utterance means is computed.   Categories
that are well separated possess significant minima along the major
diagonal.   Typical data are shown in Table 2.

A DETECTION THEORY APPROACH TO THE STUDY OF SPEECH PERCEPTION

Frank R. Clarke
Sensory Sciences Research Center
Stanford Research Institute
Menlo Park, California

We wish to outline an approach to the problem of identifying the information-bearing aspects of speech waveforms utilized by the human being in
recognition and discrimination tasks.   This approach is based on two sup-
positions: First, we suggest that in the performance of a task which requires a discrimination between the members of a pair of specified messages the human observer demonstrates his greatest capacity to make use
of the information contained in transmitted waveforms.   Second, we suggest that the receiver operating characteristic provides a powerful tool
for the development of physical measures of speech waveforms which may
be used to predict human performance in speech discrimination tasks.

The development of such measures will provide an important advance
in our basic knowledge of speech perception and will have ready application
in the refinement of physical measures suitable for the evaluation of speech
transmission systems and of the human auditory system.

With respect to the first supposition we would comment that human
performance in complex recognition tasks is affected by many variables
and a complete mathematical model of human recognition performance
awaits the solution of basic problems in memory, learning, motivation,

and other areas. However, we know of no reason to believe that the human observer attends to a more extensive class of information-bearing elements of the stimulus in recognition experiments than he does in discrimination experiments. If anything, the opposite is probably true. Consequently, the study of simple discrimination tasks should provide us with the necessary information to develop a detailed understanding of the human's ability to utilize information contained in speech waveforms. Furthermore, several important methodological advantages are to be realized by the study of discrimination tasks. Extrastimulus variables such as relative word frequency, context, degree of training of observer, and many others play a much larger role in recognition experiments than they do in discrimination experiments. The latter type of investigation should, therefore, reduce the role of extraneous factors which contribute both systematic and random error to results and complicate the problem of inferring the role that stimulus variables play in human performance. Also, discrimination experiments allow us to use the receiver operating characteristic as a tool in the development and evaluation of physical measures of the waveforms designed to predict human performance in speech perception. The remainder of this paper will be devoted to a discussion of this technique.

We wish to predict the scores that human observers will obtain when attempting to discriminate between two signals transmitted over a noisy channel. Clearly such scores will depend on the properties of the speech sounds involved, the communication channel, and the observers themselves. Let us consider the properties of the speech signals and of the communication channel as they affect some particular individual's performance.

We intend to take obtained ROC curves as our basic response data. Here we are dealing with the Type I ROC curve – a plot of the probability that the observer responds "A" given that word A was, in fact, transmitted as a function of the probability that the observer responds "A" when in fact word B was transmitted. At least with simpler stimuli such curves have been demonstrated to be a useful description of the human observer's ability to distinguish between two possible inputs. This function is generated by causing the criterion of the observer to change from test to test. Consequently, instructional or criterial variables do not affect the function itself, only the location of a point on the function. The concepts underlying such ROC curves have been shown to be consistent with a wide variety of experiment results.

Consider an individual's receiver operating characteristic for some specified pair of words. In this one-dimensional case it appears "as though" the human observer were testing statistical hypotheses. That is, when S_1 and S_2 are the two speech sounds, human performance in discriminating between them is consistent with the notion that there is an underlying decision variable, x, with associated conditional probability density functions $f(x|S_1)$ and $f(x|S_2)$. The ROC curves provide data to allow us to infer approximate distributions $f(x|S_i)$ and $f(x|S_j)$ for a large number of pairs of messages transmitted over varying types of degrading channels. We may then seek a physical measure of the input to the observer such that it is a monotonic transformation of the inferred decision variable, x. The net result of such a measure would be that if we were to apply a simple decision process to this measure we would obtain the same ROC curve as given by the human observer. We should then be in a position to conclude that the human observer was behaving in a manner consistent with the hypothesis that he was utilizing those features of the signal which went into the calculation of the physical measure.

The fact that we are attempting to predict human discrimination performance for particular pairs of words provides us with an additional methodoligical advantage for deriving a successful physical measure of the input. Traditional approaches to the study of human performance in speech communication tasks typically involve averaging over a number of speech sounds as in obtaining an intelligibility score or articulation index. This results in an irretrievable loss of detailed information about those features of the waveforms which the observer is using in distinguishing among the signals. In the present approach we will be able to start with some measure of promise, M_1, and using this measure, construct predicted ROC curves for each of a number of pairs of input messages. The obtained ROC curves will bear some relation to these curves calculated on the basis of M_1. If, for example, all predicted curves are lower than all obtained curves we know immediately the measure M_1 is too gross, i.e., it is discarding information which the human is using. If all predicted curves are too high we know that our measure M_1 incorporates information not used by the human. If some curves are too high and some too low we can look at the potential distinguishing features associated with the various pairs and begin to identify those aspects of the signals for which our measure M_1 is too gross and those aspects of the signals for which our measure is too fine. Such comparisons should lead us to generate a new and more adequate measure M_2 for predicting human performance. Reiterative refinement of our measure in this manner may enable us fairly quickly to converge on a reasonable representation of the manner in which the human auditory system processes input information. At the very least, we shall be in a strong position insofar as rejecting incorrect hypotheses about information processing of auditory inputs.

The foregoing approach is applicable regardless of the properties of the initially chosen measure M. However the ultimate success of the endeavor to identify those aspects of the signal utilized by the human observer is dependent upon this choice. The degree to which two signals may be distinguished is clearly related to differences in the way power is distributed over time and frequency; consequently we shall be interested in some measure of the difference in power of some frequency component at some instant in time, integrated over the frequencies important for speech and the duration of words. Initial efforts on this problem will be directed toward selecting an appropriate measure of power, appropriate frequency bands, time constants, and weighting factors for arriving at a useful measure of difference. As a starting point we shall use values suggested in the literature.

In summary we suggest that discrimination studies are the most effective means of determining the information bearing aspects of the speech waveform which are utilized by the human observer in speech perception. We suggest further that comparison of ROC curves generated by a physical measure with those obtained by the human observer provides a powerful technique for the evaluation and modification of a measure which purports to predict human performance.

NAME INDEX

Abplanalp. P. , 297, 303
Abramson, A. S. , 75, 85
Alpern, M. , 163, 169
Anderson, N. S. , 220, 223
Andrews, D. P. , 262, 268, 270, 271
Applegate, J. , 95, 102
Argyle, M. , 333, 337
Armstrong, L. E. , 315, 319
Arnold, J. , 80, 86
Arnoult, M. D. , 363, 379
Aronson, M. , 2, 3
Ashby, W. R. , 403, 407
Attneave, F. , 56, 64, 66, 108, 200,
        201, 363, 379
Averbach, E. E. , 157, 169, 171, 173,
        174, 178, 179

Bailey, P. , 359, 361
Ball, G. H. , 405, 407
Barlow, H. B. , 33, 42, 45, 55, 128,
        134, 159, 169, 384, 387
Barney, H. L. , 443, 453
Bartlett, F. C. , 246, 250
Bastian, J. , 78, 79, 80, 85, 86, 87
Battersby, W. S. , 163, 169
Baxt, N. , 177, 179
Békésy, G. von, 13, 24
Bell, A. M. , 90, 102
Bell, C. 314, 319
Bever, T. G. , 329, 335, 336, 338
Bhartrhari, 6
Biddulph, R. , 340, 343
Biernson, G. , 306
Biersdorf, W. R. , 167, 169
Birdsall, T. G. , 333, 338
Birukow, G. , 130, 135
Bishop, P. W. , 129, 134, 135
Bitterman, M. E. , 363, 379
Blackwell, D. , 414, 417
Blackwell, H. R. , 163, 169
Blaschke, W. , 401, 402
Bledsoe, W. W. , 389, 397
Blum, H. , 44, 62, 362, 379
Bomba, J. S. , 394
Boring, E. G. , 60, 66, 180, 181, 184
Borst, J. M. , 418, 427
Bossom, J. , 262, 271
Boycott, B. B. , 130, 135
Boynton, R. M. , 168, 169
Bradt, R. N. , 415, 417
Braverman, D. , 413, 417
Brecher, G. , 140, 141, 153
Breen, M. , 211
Broadbent, D. E. , 80, 85, 103, 106,
        107, 110, 127, 135, 247, 250,
        333, 334, 336, 338, 339, 345,
        353
Brown, P. K. , 128, 135
Brown, R. 159, 162, 169
Brown, R. W. , 108, 110
Browning, I. , 389, 397
Burnett, E. D. , 342, 343
Butsch, L. M. , Jr. , 404, 407

Cahn, L. , 363, 380
Campanella, S. J. , 453
Capranica, R. , 244, 245, 246
Carterette, E. C. , 247, 250, 418, 421,
        427
Casey, T. , 186
Chaney, R. B. , Jr. , 1, 246
Chang, S. -H. , 413, 417
Charnwood, J. R. B. , 180, 184
Cherry, C. , 321, 325, 334, 338
Chistovich, L. A. , 82, 85, 111, 113, 115,
        116, 117, 124
Chomsky, N. , 325, 331, 333, 338
Chow, C. K. , 413, 417
Chow, K. L. , 218, 219
Clark, W. A. , Jr. , 17, 24
Clarke, F. R. , 332, 333, 337, 338, 458
Clayden, D. O. , 397
Clowes, M. B. , 388, 391, 397
Coffey, J. L. , 73, 85
Cohen, A. , 320, 323, 325
Colwell, R. N. , 405, 408
Conrad, R. , 107, 110
Cooper, F. S. , 2, 68, 70, 73, 74, 75,
        78, 85, 86, 87, 101, 102, 103,
        110, 111, 121, 125, 322, 325, 413,
        418, 427
Coriell, A. S. , 173, 174, 179
Corliss, E. L. R. , 339, 340, 343
Coulter, D. C. , 453
Curtis, J. F. , 247, 251

Daniel, P. M. , 129, 135
Darwin, C. , 314, 319
David, E. E. , Jr. , 413, 417
Davis, H. , 13, 24
De Cordemoy, G. , 88
Delattre, P. , 70, 74, 75, 76, 85, 86,
        87, 418, 427
Denes, P. B. , 309, 334, 338
Deutsch, J. A. , 363, 380
DeValois, R. L. , 129, 135
Ditchburn, R. W. , 401, 402
Dobelle, W. H. , 128, 135
Dodwell, P. , 180, 184, 258, 262, 381
Doyle, W. , 187, 201
Draper, M. , 79, 86
Dusser de Barenne, J. G. , 359

Efstathiou, A. , 297, 303
Egan, J. P. , 247, 250
Eimas, P. , 75, 78, 79, 85, 87
Engel, R. , 180, 184
Epstein, W. , 301, 303
Eriksen, C. W. , 163, 169, 203, 211
Essigman, M. W. 413, 417
Ettlinger, G. , 185, 186, 234, 238
Evans, E. F. , 33, 42
Exner, S., 140

Falter, J. W. , 428

462

SUBJECT INDEX